PRENTICE HALL
WRITING AND GRAMMAR

Grammar Exercise Workbook

Teacher's Edition

Grade Six

Boston, Massachusetts,
Upper Saddle River, New Jersey

Copyright © by Pearson Education, Inc., publishing as Pearson Prentice Hall, Boston, Massachusetts, 02116. All rights reserved. Printed in the United States of America. This publication is protected by copyright, and permission should be obtained from the publisher prior to any prohibited reproduction, storage in a retrieval system, or transmission in any form or by any means, electronic, mechanical, photocopying, recording, or likewise. The publisher hereby grants permission to reproduce these pages, in part or in whole, for classroom use only, the number not to exceed the number of students in each class. Notice of copyright must appear on all copies. For information regarding permission(s), write to: Rights and Permissions Department, One Lake Street, Upper Saddle River, New Jersey 07458.

Pearson Prentice Hall™ is a trademark of Pearson Education, Inc.
Pearson® is a registered trademark of Pearson plc.
Prentice Hall® is a registered trademark of Pearson Education, Inc.

ISBN 0-13-361649-5

3 4 5 6 7 8 9 10   10 09 08

Contents

Note: This workbook supports Chapters 14–27 (Part 2: Grammar, Usage, and Mechanics) of Prentice Hall *Writing and Grammar.*

14.1 The Noun • Practice 1

A noun is the name of a person, place, or thing.

People	Places	Things
Dr. Linsley	Treasure Island	ship
Jim Hawkins	island	barrel
pirate	mountain	plot
crew	cave	robbery

Exercise 1   **Recognizing Nouns.**   Underline each noun in the sentences below.

EXAMPLE: Mrs. Nelson has postponed the test until Monday.

1. Several reporters arrived at the scene to interview the survivors.
2. Many young children are afraid of the dark.
3. Our neighbors spent their vacation in the mountains.
4. Jason found his missing sneaker under the couch.
5. Amanda wants to see that movie, too.
6. Without Nancy, our team will surely lose.
7. That tree hasn't lost a single leaf yet.
8. The architect planned for a fountain in the lobby.
9. Phil told only his parents about this fear.
10. Marc cannot see much without his glasses.

Exercise 2   **Adding Nouns to Sentences.**   Fill in each blank in the following sentences with an appropriate noun.

EXAMPLE: _____Alison_____ ordered a _____sandwich_____ with mustard.

1. The _____ I found had _____ inside.
2. A(n) _____ stopped the _____ at the corner.
3. We asked the _____ to bring us some _____.
4. _____ promised me a(n) _____.
5. The last _____ was a(n) _____.
6. A large _____ grows beside the _____.
7. _____ works at the _____.
8. Some _____ enjoy _____.
9. _____ makes delicious _____.
10. The _____ took a trip to _____.

14.1 The Noun • Practice 2

▶ **Exercise 1** **Identifying Nouns.** Underline the nouns in each sentence below.

EXAMPLE: My favorite <u>author</u> is <u>James Ullman</u>.

1. James Ullman wrote many books and stories.
2. Ullman was born in America, but also lived in the mountains of Tibet.
3. This experienced adventurer loved to climb mountains.
4. Ullman joined an expedition to climb Mount Everest.
5. The climb is described in a novel.
6. Another story by Ullman unfolds in the Amazon.
7. People enjoy the adventures described in his books.
8. Readers admire his knowledge and his daring.
9. Ullman traveled throughout the world as a reporter.
10. This famous man was a traveler, a writer, and a fascinating person.
11. I also like to read the works of Jack London.
12. Many of his stories also have snowy settings and interesting characters.
13. This author once went to Alaska to look for gold.
14. When he was fourteen years old, London had to leave school and go to work.
15. After many different jobs and adventures, London began a career as a writer.

▶ **Exercise 2** **More Work With Nouns.** Follow the directions for Exercise 1.

1. The proper ingredients for making bread are flour, water, milk, butter, and yeast.
2. First, dissolve the yeast in warm water.
3. Add sugar and flour and let the mixture rise in a bowl.
4. Add warm milk and more flour and knead the dough on a wooden board.
5. Again, let the dough rise, punch it down, shape it, and bake each loaf for thirty minutes.
6. Remove loaves from the oven and let them cool in their pans for a short while.
7. Then, take the bread out of the loaf pans and place each loaf on a cooling rack.
8. Keep your cats away from the kitchen while the bread is cooling.
9. Curious cats will sometimes try to sample your food.
10. With dinner, you might want to dip chunks of the bread in olive oil.

▶ **Writing Application** **Using Nouns to Describe a Room.** List ten nouns that name things you can see in your classroom or in a room in your home. Then, use the nouns to write a paragraph describing the room. Underline the ten nouns.

_____

_____

_____

_____

_____

_____

14.1 Compound Nouns • Practice 1

A compound noun is one noun made by joining two or more words. Compound nouns are written in three different ways: as single words, as hyphenated words, and as separate words.

COMPOUND NOUNS		
Single Words	**Hyphenated Words**	**Separate Words**
plaything	jack-in-the-box	teddy bear
grandmother	bird-watcher	day care
classmate	fund-raiser	high school

▶ **Exercise 1** **Recognizing Compound Nouns.** Circle each compound noun in the sentences below.

EXAMPLE: Mom made some ⟨hard sauce⟩ to serve with the ⟨gingerbread⟩.

1. Morning glories climb up the lamppost.

2. That paperback became a bestseller almost immediately.

3. After a number of successful dramatic plays, the playwright is now working on a musical comedy.

4. Kevin Parker is studying political science.

5. A passerby must have found my wallet on the sidewalk.

6. The reporter rushed to get the story to the city desk before deadline.

7. Paul had his bathing suit and towel in his backpack.

8. The caretaker has a skeleton key that opens all the doors.

9. Do not unfasten your seat belt until the airplane has come to a complete stop at the gate.

10. I had trouble using chopsticks to eat my chow mein.

▶ **Exercise 2** **More Work With Compound Nouns.** Follow the directions for Exercise 1.

1. My grandmother recites nursery rhymes to my little cousin.

2. How do you write seventy-seven in Roman numerals?

3. My brother's roommate was first runner-up in the contest.

4. The footnote contained a cross-reference to another book.

5. My cousin lost a contact lens on the shag rug in the bedroom.

6. The folk singer has recorded a song based on the hero of a tall tale.

7. The stage manager will supervise the final run-through of the play.

8. The follow-up showed that the treatment had lowered the patient's blood pressure.

9. Kneepads are good safety devices for people who use skateboards.

10. A bookkeeper must have legible handwriting.

14.1 # Compound Nouns • Practice 2

▶ **Exercise 1**   **Finding Compound Nouns.**   Underline the compound nouns in the following sentences.

EXAMPLE: The <u>Golden Gate Bridge</u> shone in the <u>sunlight</u>.

1. The salesclerk sold me a goldfish.
2. My sister-in-law has a wheelbarrow filled with potatoes.
3. Like clockwork, each day she turns on the soap opera.
4. The left-hander threw a fastball.
5. Take your backpack and your snowshoes on the expedition.
6. Is any member of your family a sleepwalker?
7. The short story was about a cowboy and a farmhand.
8. Will you watch basketball or football this weekend?
9. My girlfriend owns a sheep dog and a Siamese cat.
10. I know a folk tale about people in the Russian countryside.
11. After playing handball, Eddie had a milkshake.
12. The lawyer played the tape recording in the courtroom.
13. Put a bookmark in the book and return it to the bookcase.
14. I brought my armchair closer to the fireplace.
15. An eyewitness told the policeman what she had seen.
16. The mail carrier left greeting cards in my mailbox.
17. An attorney-at-law is the chairperson of our committee.
18. I need eyeglasses to see the handwriting on the blackboard.
19. The housekeeper answered the doorbell and smiled.
20. Do you prefer applesauce or rice pudding for dessert?
21. From the control tower, we could see the aircraft make its approach.
22. We followed the child's footsteps in the sand and found only his teddy bear.
23. In the city-state of ancient Sparta, do you think they had a city hall?
24. The fool's gold sparkled along the riverbed.
25. No spaceship has ever traveled even one light-year.

▶ **Writing Application**   **Writing Sentences With Compound Nouns.**   Below, write five sentences describing a vacation. Include one of the following compound nouns in each sentence: *classmates, wristwatch, roller coaster, amusement park,* and *football.* Underline these compound nouns.

1. _____
2. _____
3. _____
4. _____
5. _____

14.1 Common and Proper Nouns • Practice 1

A common noun names any one of a group of people, places, or things. A proper noun names a specific person, place, or thing. The important words in proper nouns are always capitalized.

Common Nouns		Proper Nouns	
planet	language	Uranus	Russian
street	day	Market Place	New Year's Day
horse	train	Flicka	the Silver Meteor
woman	story	Mrs. Bailey	"A Day's Wait"

▶ **Exercise 1** **Recognizing Proper Nouns.** Write the proper noun in each sentence below on the line after the sentence. Use capital letters correctly.

EXAMPLE: Our former neighbors now live on maple street. ___*Maple Street*___

1. Fireworks are traditional on the fourth of july. _____
2. The new principal is mrs. jacobson. _____
3. Every year my aunt takes her children to see santa claus. _____
4. We play our last game against the lancers. _____
5. The beach boys will perform at the festival. _____
6. We have a family reunion every august. _____
7. That poem was written by henry wadsworth longfellow. _____
8. The box on the hall table came from uncle albert. _____
9. That bestseller has just been translated into japanese. _____
10. Did you take the stairs to the top of the washington monument? _____

▶ **Exercise 2** **Distinguishing Between Common and Proper Nouns.** Write each noun from the box in its proper column. Write a related noun in the other column to complete the chart. The first two are done for you.

1. book	3. building	5. comic strip	7. Sitting Bull	9. school
2. Broadway	4. capital	6. Yankee Stadium	8. Eleanor Roosevelt	10. South America

COMMON NOUNS   PROPER NOUNS

1. *book* _____   *The Time Machine* _____
2. *street* _____   *Broadway* _____
3. _____   _____
4. _____   _____
5. _____   _____
6. _____   _____
7. _____   _____
8. _____   _____
9. _____   _____
10. _____   _____

14.1 Common and Proper Nouns • Practice 2

▷ Exercise 1 **Identifying Common and Proper Nouns.** Below are two columns labeled Common Nouns and Proper Nouns. Write each noun listed below in the correct column. Then, for each common noun, write a related proper noun. For each proper noun, write a related common noun.

EXAMPLE: **Common Nouns** **Proper Nouns**
car Model-T

1. singer   5. Poland   8. girl
2. Lake Superior   6. football team   9. Einstein
3. computer   7. university   10. Franklin D. Roosevelt
4. neighbor

COMMON NOUNS   **PROPER NOUNS**

1. _____   _____
2. _____   _____
3. _____   _____
4. _____   _____
5. _____   _____
6. _____   _____
7. _____   _____
8. _____   _____
9. _____   _____
10. _____   _____

▷ Exercise 2 **More Work With Common and Proper Nouns.** Follow the directions for Exercise 1.

1. China   5. Spanish   8. friend
2. Wrigley Field   6. George Washington   9. San Diego
3. school   7. gulf   10. canal
4. Civil War

COMMON NOUNS   **PROPER NOUNS**

1. _____   _____
2. _____   _____
3. _____   _____
4. _____   _____
5. _____   _____
6. _____   _____
7. _____   _____
8. _____   _____
9. _____   _____
10. _____   _____

Name _____ Date _____

14.2 The Pronoun • Practice 1

A pronoun takes the place of a noun. The noun that is replaced by a pronoun is called the antecedent.

PRONOUNS AND ANTECEDENTS	
Person	ANT PRON The *forecaster* revised *her* weather forecast.
Place	ANT PRON When we got to the *amusement park*, we found that *it* was closed.
Thing	ANT PRON All those *umbrellas* have holes in *them*.

▶ **Exercise 1**   **Recognizing Pronouns and Antecedents.**   Circle the pronoun in each sentence below. Underline its antecedent.

EXAMPLE: The <u>campers</u> had a variety of food in (their) backpacks.

1. Alison forgot to give her mother the telephone message.

2. Someone let the parakeets out of their cage.

3. Iowa is famous for its corn and beef.

4. Several students forgot their homework assignments.

5. Mr. Wilson will retire next year. He has worked at First Bank for forty years.

6. Whenever Angie visits, she wants to play Trivial Pursuit.

7. The members of the committee will reveal their plans next week.

8. Mom is visiting Uncle Bert in Oklahoma. Dad will join her next week.

9. The Mississippi River has its origin at Lake Itaska in Minnesota.

10. Some identical twins enjoy fooling their friends and acquaintances.

▶ **Exercise 2**   **Using Pronouns in Sentences.**   Write an appropriate pronoun in each blank below to complete the sentence.

EXAMPLE: The Haywards are spending the weekend at _____*their*_____ cabin at Loon Lake.

1. Did David bring _____ camera along?

2. Chipmunks make _____ homes in underground tunnels.

3. The children rebelled because _____ summer schedules were too busy.

4. Luke complained of pains in _____ ankle.

5. The lion had a thorn in _____ paw.

6. The house will look better when _____ has a fresh coat of paint.

7. Rachel has kept every story _____ has written since first grade.

8. The neighbors complained that _____ couldn't sleep because of the noise.

9. The O'Shaughnesseys showed slides of _____ trip to Ireland.

10. The sauce has just a hint of garlic in _____ .

14.2 The Pronoun • Practice 2

▶ **Exercise 1**   **Recognizing Pronouns and Antecedents.**   Each sentence below contains one pronoun. Underline the pronoun and its antecedent. Then, draw an arrow from the pronoun to its antecedent.

EXAMPLE: The settlers grew corn and ate it often.

The settlers grew corn and ate it often.

1. The colonists worked hard when they first came to America.

2. Farmers spent their time working the land.

3. A woman invented a machine she could use to grind corn.

4. Sybilla Masters sold her cornmeal in Philadelphia.

5. The people enjoyed their evenings.

6. The colonists enjoyed tall tales and told them often.

7. A child would listen to a bird and imitate its call.

8. A girl who owned a doll could dress it in fancy clothes.

9. A settler wrote that he was glad to live in America.

10. If a boy had free time, he might play ball.

▶ **Exercise 2**   **More Work With Pronouns and Antecedents.**   Follow the directions for Exercise 1.

1. Every seashell has its own look.

2. There are 70,000 varieties, and they are all different.

3. An interesting fact about shells is that they have no backbones.

4. Shells with skeletons have them on the outside.

5. The animals that live in shells are affected by their surroundings.

14.2 **Personal Pronouns • Practice 1**

Personal pronouns refer to (1) the person speaking or writing, (2) the person listening or reading, or (3) the topic (person, place, or thing) being discussed or written about.

	PERSONAL PRONOUNS	
	Singular	**Plural**
First Person	I, me, my, mine	we, us, our, ours
Second Person	you, your, yours	you, your, yours
Third Person	he, him, his, she, her, hers, it, its	they, them, their, theirs

▶ **Exercise 1** **Recognizing Personal Pronouns.** Underline the personal pronoun in each of the following sentences. On the lines after each sentence, write *1st*, *2nd*, or *3rd* for person and *S* or *P* for singular or plural.

EXAMPLE: Pete and Aaron have their parents' permission to go. ____*3rd*____ ____*P*____

1. Class, open your test booklets. _____ _____

2. Last summer I took tennis lessons. _____ _____

3. The house with the pale blue shutters is ours. _____ _____

4. Dana was surprised that she won first prize. _____ _____

5. Have you finished with the paper, Frank? _____ _____

6. Both Phil and Steve lost their library cards. _____ _____

7. The kitten has black markings around its eyes. _____ _____

8. Dad has scheduled his vacation for the last week in July. _____ _____

9. Please tell us how to get to Jefferson Park. _____ _____

10. That orange sweatshirt is mine. _____ _____

▶ **Exercise 2** **Adding Personal Pronouns to Sentences.** Fill in the blank with an appropriate personal pronoun to complete each sentence.

EXAMPLE: Did you remember to bring your lunch with ____*you*____ ?

1. Both Tim and I enjoyed _____ trip to the United Nations.

2. The Barkers are moving into _____ new house next week.

3. I wish someone would explain that magic trick to _____ .

4. Louisa wrote in _____ diary every night.

5. Did you and Ben bring _____ swimming trunks?

6. Mr. Sawyer told us where to find the key to _____ desk.

7. That company gives _____ employees excellent benefits.

8. Justin was sorry that _____ had been so rude.

9. Mrs. Hawkins is very popular with all of _____ students.

10. We arrived at the game after _____ had started.

14.2 Personal Pronouns • Practice 2

▶ **Exercise 1**   **Recognizing Personal Pronouns.**   Underline the personal pronoun in each sentence below. Then, label it as first person, second person, or third person.

EXAMPLE: Marlene and I examined the building. ____*first person*____

1. Have you ever heard of a rock scraper? _____

2. It could be called an underground skyscraper. _____

3. The designer says he believes in space above ground. _____

4. His prediction is for more underground buildings. _____

5. We may have buildings more than 110 feet underground. _____

6. People may not realize how far down they are. _____

7. My concern is whether there will be enough light. _____

8. I read that lenses could beam light downward. _____

9. A worker said that the amount of light inside surprised him. _____

10. A woman said that she liked the constant temperature
    underground. _____

11. Sandra brought her little brother into a rock scraper. _____

12. The two of them enjoyed the experience. _____

13. Your sister might also like to go. _____

14. Living in a rock scraper is not an ambition of mine. _____

15. We should go see what the rock scraper is like. _____

▶ **Exercise 2**   **More Work With Personal Pronouns.**   Follow the directions for Exercise 1.

1. Was your summer vacation pleasant? _____

2. I spent the summer traveling in Mexico. _____

3. The entire family went with me. _____

4. There are five of us in all. _____

5. Henry brought along his camera and took pictures. _____

6. Andrea brought her sketch pad and charcoals. _____

7. Of course, our journals were packed. _____

8. Sometimes, Andrea spent her time in the park. _____

9. Other times, they went to the museum. _____

10. In the evenings, we all got together for dinner. _____

11. It's good that Henry brought a camera because mine was left at
    home. _____

12. This photo is very good—is it yours? _____

13. Marcie takes good pictures, so that photo might be hers. _____

14. Please have them take pictures of the flowers. _____

15. Seeing slides of their vacation is always so boring. _____

14.2 # Demonstrative Pronouns • Practice 1

A demonstrative pronoun points out a person, place, or thing.

	DEMONSTRATIVE PRONOUNS	
	Singular	**Plural**
Nearby	this	these
Farther	that	those

▷ **Exercise 1** **Recognizing Demonstrative Pronouns.** Underline the demonstrative pronoun in each sentence below. Then, circle the noun to which it refers.

EXAMPLE: <u>This</u> must be the (book) you ordered.

1. That was a loud firecracker.

2. All the pastries look good, but I think I'll try one of these.

3. These are tomatoes from our garden.

4. Isn't this the sweater I loaned you?

5. Those were the best meatballs I've ever eaten.

6. That is the woman I was telling you about.

7. These are the curtains my grandmother made.

8. Doesn't this stew smell good?

9. That was a terrific movie we saw last night!

10. The best pictures I've ever taken are those of my baby cousin.

▷ **Exercise 2** **Using Demonstrative Pronouns in Sentences.** Fill in each blank below with an appropriate demonstrative pronoun to complete the sentence.

EXAMPLE: Those slacks are a great color, but _____*these*_____ are more practical.

1. _____ is the first eclipse I have ever seen.

2. _____ was a thrilling experience.

3. The tomatoes on the windowsill are ripe, but _____ on the vines are still green.

4. Bob refused to believe the warnings, and _____ was his first mistake.

5. All of Mrs. Parker's meals are good, but _____ is outstanding.

6. Of all his paintings, _____ that he did in his youth are the most realistic.

7. That fabric looks good on the couch, but _____ is a better color.

8. If you think these roses are beautiful, you should see _____ in the back yard!

9. Miss Walters said that of all my essays, _____ is the best one.

10. Those cookies on the trays are still hot, but _____ on the plate are ready to eat.

14.2 Demonstrative Pronouns • Practice 2

▶ **Exercise 1** **Recognizing Demonstrative Pronouns.** Underline the demonstrative pronoun in each sentence below. Then, circle the noun to which it refers.

EXAMPLE: This is a new (magazine) .

1. These are paintings by Charles Willson Peale.

2. This is a portrait of George Washington.

3. Do you know if those are also paintings by Peale?

4. Peale set up a gallery of paintings for the public. This was the first in America.

5. He created a portable bathtub. That was quite useful.

6. He kept live birds. These are admired by friends.

7. This was a household full of artists.

8. That was the studio Thomas Jefferson praised.

9. Yes, these are pictures by Peale's brother.

10. I think those are letters Peale wrote.

▶ **Exercise 2** **More Work With Demonstrative Pronouns.** Follow the directions for Exercise 1.

1. This is the street where I live.

2. That is our house.

3. Those are the bushes I planted.

4. Of all my coins, that is the one I value most.

5. This is a coin from Africa.

6. My pennies come from different places. These were minted in San Francisco.

7. Those are French francs.

8. This is a buffalo-head nickel.

9. Yes, this is money from Italy.

10. These are some coins for you.

▶ **Writing Application** **Using Demonstrative Pronouns.** Write a paragraph in which you point out interesting things in your school to a visitor. Use all four demonstrative pronouns. Underline the demonstrative pronouns.

_____

_____

_____

_____

_____

_____

15.1 The Verb • Practice 1

A verb expresses the action or condition of a person, place, or thing.

VERBS	
Action	**Condition**
amuse	was
inspected	seems
remember	become
begins	am
discovered	appear

> **Exercise 1** **Recognizing Verbs.**   Underline the verb in each sentence below. In the blank, indicate whether the verb expresses *action* or *condition*.

EXAMPLE: Marlene memorized her speech in half an hour.   ___action___

1. Judd offered a reward for the lost wallet. _____

2. This stew tastes too salty. _____

3. Shannon always wears funny hats. _____

4. At the age of five, Larry gave his first recital. _____

5. Even after the argument, Gary remained loyal to his old friend. _____

6. We felt refreshed after a shower and a cold drink. _____

7. Linda played shortstop during the last half of the season. _____

8. That pitcher is famous for his curve ball. _____

9. Laura seems upset about something. _____

10. We carefully planned every detail of the party. _____

> **Exercise 2** **Adding Verbs to Sentences.**   Complete each sentence below with a verb of the kind indicated in parentheses.

EXAMPLE: Lauren ___practices___ the piano two hours every day. (action)

1. Marc _____ soccer better than basketball. (action)

2. The nurse _____ the patient's temperature. (action)

3. We _____ disappointed in the outcome of the game. (condition)

4. Paula _____ good in that shade of blue. (condition)

5. Kevin _____ the experiment several times. (action)

6. The child's endless questions _____ her parents. (action)

7. Yesterday, a record number of fans _____ the game. (action)

8. Those leaves _____ orange in autumn. (condition)

9. That song _____ better on the piano than on the guitar. (condition)

10. Gerry _____ her lesson the hard way. (action)

15.1 The Verb • Practice 2

▶ **Exercise 1** **Recognizing Verbs.** Underline the verb in each sentence below.

EXAMPLE: Mrs. Bethune <u>received</u> donations from the school.

1. Mary McLeod Bethune dreamed of a school for black children.
2. She explored different locations.
3. Daytona, Florida, was her choice.
4. She felt sure of herself and her idea.
5. Five students paid fifty cents a week as tuition.
6. Mrs. Bethune taught her pupils useful skills.
7. The school grew larger each year.
8. In the evening, adults studied there.
9. The students worked very hard.
10. Mrs. Bethune became a famous educator.

▶ **Exercise 2** **More Work With Verbs.** Underline the verb in each sentence below.

1. My friend Mark enjoys skiing.
2. Last year his family spent two weeks in Vail, Colorado.
3. He and his brother Paul tried the beginner slopes.
4. Soon they felt confident.
5. Mark and Paul attended some classes in skiing.
6. They seemed excited about the sport.
7. Several days later, the boys attempted a steeper slope.
8. This attempt was successful.
9. Mark skillfully raced past a group of people.
10. Now he is an experienced skier.

▶ **Writing Application** **Using Verbs in Sentences.** Write a paragraph of five or more sentences explaining how to do or make something. Underline the verbs in your sentences.

_____

_____

_____

_____

_____

_____

_____

_____

_____

Name _____ Date _____

 Action Verbs • Practice 1

An action verb indicates the action of a person or thing. The action can be visible or mental.

ACTION VERBS	
Visible Actions	**Mental Actions**
blow	wonder
follow	forget
run	annoy
write	pretend
stir	consider

▶ **Exercise 1**   **Identifying Action Verbs.**   Underline the verb in each sentence below.

EXAMPLE: The bloodhound <u>lost</u> the scent at the edge of the creek.

1. The teacher explained the directions again.
2. We planted four kinds of lettuce in our garden.
3. Lana teased her brother about his socks.
4. Steve borrowed lunch money from me again today.
5. Despite a number of fielding errors, the home team won.
6. Grandma promised all of us rewards for our report cards.
7. Dad estimated the distance fairly accurately.
8. Sherman's army left a trail of destruction behind it.
9. The auctioneer started the bidding at fifty dollars.
10. At least three students failed the math test.

▶ **Exercise 2**   **Adding Action Verbs to Sentences.**   Complete each sentence below with an action verb of the kind indicated in parentheses.

EXAMPLE: The committee ____considered____ the choices carefully. (mental)

1. Too late, Julie _____ the right answer. (mental)
2. Anthony _____ butter on his potato. (mental)
3. Waiting for news, Dennis _____ back and forth in the hallway. (visible)
4. That puzzle _____ everyone. (mental)
5. The prince and princess _____ hands with everyone at the party. (visible)
6. We _____ everywhere for Mom's missing keys. (visible)
7. Mr. Salvin _____ his students to work hard. (mental)
8. Phil _____ the ball down the court. (visible)
9. The announcer _____ the winning ticket from the barrel. (visible)
10. Marci _____ her ticket to the flight attendant. (visible)

15.2 Action Verbs • Practice 2

▶ **Exercise 1** **Identifying Action Verbs.** Underline the action verb in each sentence below.

EXAMPLE: The audience <u>applauded</u> the performers.

1. A glassblower built an unusual glass instrument.
2. The glass harmonica produces a loud, unforgettable sound.
3. People remember its unusual tones.
4. A player gently rubs the glass rims with his hands.
5. An electric motor twirls the glasses on this instrument.
6. Modern composers appreciate the sound of the harmonica.
7. They wonder about its future as a concert instrument.
8. Eighteenth-century composers wrote music for the harmonica.
9. Some people feared the strange music.
10. In fact, a few towns in Europe banned the instrument.

▶ **Exercise 2** **More Work With Action Verbs.** Follow the directions for Exercise 1.

1. I selected three mystery books for you.
2. The campers gathered together for a meeting.
3. Larry signaled to his friend across the room.
4. I understand the unusual nature of this case.
5. The judge awarded the prize to Alice's dog.
6. Suddenly, I realized my mistake.
7. Pedro recognized the bearded man immediately.
8. She heard incomprehensible sounds over the radio.
9. He adjusted the sound of the television.
10. After a few moments, the student chose a topic for her composition.

▶ **Writing Application** **Using Action Verbs to Tell What Is Happening.** Observe someone working or playing. Then, write ten sentences describing what the person did. Try to use exact, specific verbs. Underline the verbs you use.

1. _____
2. _____
3. _____
4. _____
5. _____
6. _____
7. _____
8. _____
9. _____
10. _____

15.2 # Linking Verbs • Practice 1

A linking verb joins a noun or pronoun at or near the beginning of a sentence with a word at or near the end. The word at the end identifies or describes the noun or pronoun.

LINKING VERBS					
Forms of *Be*				**Other Linking Verbs**	
am	am being	can be	have been	appear	seem
are	are being	could be	has been	become	smell
is	is being	may be	had been	feel	sound
was	was being	might be	could have been	grow	stay
were	were being	must be	may have been	look	taste
		shall be	might have been	remain	turn
		should be	must have been		
		will be	shall have been		
		would be	should have been		
			will have been		
			would have been		

▶ **Exercise 1**   **Recognizing Linking Verbs.**   Circle the linking verb in each sentence below. Then, underline the words that are linked by the verb.

EXAMPLE: Penny (grew) tall over the summer.

1. Beginning violinists usually sound terrible for the first few weeks.

2. Rail service in this area has been irregular recently.

3. With Steven away on vacation, I am bored.

4. The crowd became restless because of the long delay.

5. Many of Erica's classmates were jealous of her success.

6. Jerry feels listless much of the time recently.

7. Louisa should have been more careful about her facts.

8. Those cookies smell delicious.

9. Linus feels secure with his blanket.

10. Alicia remained calm throughout the blackout.

▶ **Exercise 2**   **Adding Linking Verbs to Sentences.**   Complete each sentence below with an appropriate linking verb. Then, underline the two words that are linked by the verb.

EXAMPLE: Jason _____*appeared*_____ nervous at the beginning of his speech.

1. Nancy _____ lucky at winning the drawing.

2. Some of the questions _____ hard to understand.

3. The order _____ too large for one shipment.

4. Dorothy _____ surprised to be back in Kansas.

5. The store _____ open even after the fire.

6. Phil _____ confused about the announcement.

7. The weather _____ cold during the night.

8. Luke _____ an actor in spite of his parents' objections.

9. Jennie _____ excited about her news.

10. M-m-m-m, something _____ good in here.

15.2 Linking Verbs • Practice 2

▶ **Exercise 1** **Recognizing Linking Verbs.** Underline the linking verb in each sentence below. Then, draw a double-headed arrow to connect the words that are linked by the verb.

EXAMPLE: Wolves are shy.

1. Rita is an artist.
2. The candidates seem confident.
3. Some trees grow tall.
4. The fresh bread smelled delicious.
5. My neighbor sounded frightened on the phone.
6. This new magazine looks interesting.
7. Mr. Davis was a farmer in the Midwest.
8. The old couple's store stayed open all week.
9. We remained partners for five years.
10. The inexperienced traveler felt tired.

▶ **Exercise 2** **More Work With Linking Verbs.** Follow the directions for Exercise 1.

1. The speaker appeared relaxed.
2. This new report sounds accurate.
3. I am a relative of the senator.
4. My sister remained calm during the emergency.
5. John became impatient after ten minutes.
6. Michelle turned red with embarrassment.
7. The small horses were Shetlands.
8. Every item looked new.
9. Ted seemed fit for the job.
10. This holiday dinner smells delicious.

▶ **Writing Application** **Using Linking Verbs in Sentences.** Write a paragraph about a stranger who has knocked at your door. Use all of the following linking verbs: *sound, seem, remain, appear, become, is, am, are, were,* and *look.*

_____
_____
_____
_____
_____
_____
_____
_____
_____
_____

15.3 Helping Verbs • Practice 1

A helping verb is a verb that comes before the main verb and adds to its meaning.

COMMON HELPING VERBS			
am	being	could	must
are	been	do	shall
is	have	does	should
was	has	did	will
were	had	may	would
be	can	might	

▶ **Exercise 1** **Identifying Helping Verbs.** Underline each helping verb in the sentences below. Circle the main verb in each sentence.

EXAMPLE: Carol has been (studying) French this summer.

1. The kitchen staff will be serving from 4:30 until 9:00.

2. The train should arrive any minute.

3. Dr. Young has examined our dog.

4. My little brother can be a real pest sometimes.

5. The secretary has ordered a new supply of erasers.

6. Perhaps Jake really did forget his boots.

7. Grandma may know the answer.

8. Judson has taken a job at the supermarket.

9. I am waiting for a phone call.

10. Elsa should have tried harder.

▶ **Exercise 2** **Adding Helping Verbs to Sentences.** Fill in each blank below with an appropriate helping verb.

EXAMPLE: Paul _____is_____ taking a computer course at summer school.

1. Surely everyone _____ be surprised to see us.

2. Someone _____ told Mandy about the surprise party.

3. Uncle Dave _____ working at the bank for twenty years.

4. Susan _____ visiting her grandparents.

5. I _____ seen that movie twice already.

6. The run of the play _____ extended for two more weeks.

7. Lou _____ need some help.

8. Patty _____ be sorry she said that.

9. I _____ studied harder for that test.

10. Quentin _____ painting the house all summer.

15.3 Helping Verbs • Practice 2

▶ **Exercise 1** **Identifying Helping Verbs.** Find the verb phrases (main verb plus helping verb) in each sentence below. Then, underline the helping verbs and circle the main verbs.

EXAMPLE: A snowflake is (created) from a fleck of dust.

1. No one can explain the exact formation of snowflakes.

2. A snowflake might begin as an uncomplicated shape.

3. Eventually, it will look like crystal.

4. Its growth could be caused by a slight push.

5. It will grow even more with a second push.

6. One scientist has been working on a theory.

7. This scientist might be solving the snowflake mystery.

8. A computer is being used in the scientist's work.

9. He has written many mathematical formulas.

10. The formulas have been fed into the computer.

▶ **Exercise 2** **More Work With Helping Verbs.** Follow the directions for Exercise 1.

1. Historians have written about Nathan Hale's bravery.

2. He was serving in the army during the American Revolution.

3. Later, he would become a spy.

4. He was captured by British soldiers and was sentenced to die.

5. We should remember him as a hero.

6. Hale had lived only twenty-one years.

7. Perhaps he should not have volunteered for the spy mission.

8. A slyer man could have done the job.

9. Nathan Hale might have been too open and honest.

10. His last words must have inspired the American soldiers.

▶ **Writing Application** **Writing Sentences With Helping Verbs.** Write five sentences explaining something you like to do at home or at school. Use helping verbs in each sentence.

1. _____

_____

2. _____

_____

3. _____

_____

4. _____

_____

5. _____

_____

The Adjective • Practice 1

An adjective is a word that describes something.

QUESTIONS ANSWERED BY ADJECTIVES	
What Kind?	A *huge* monster, *ugly* and *hairy*, arose from the sea.
	She is *talented* and *hard-working*.
Which One?	*That* bike belongs to me. I need *those* nails.
How Many? How Much?	*Few* tickets remain. *Some* cake is left.

▶ **Exercise 1** **Identifying Adjectives.** Underline the adjectives in the sentences below.

EXAMPLE: <u>Tired</u> and <u>hungry</u>, the campers found the camp a <u>welcome</u> sight.

1. That popular star has many enthusiastic and loyal fans.
2. The smallest building on that vast estate will be a guest house.
3. The two old maple trees are beautiful in the fall.
4. That large white house looks expensive.
5. Nervous and excited, I went up to accept the blue ribbon.
6. Only an expert fisherman could have caught an enormous fish like that one.
7. As the withered old woman approached the microphone, the audience became silent.
8. Fat shoelaces in neon colors were a brief but colorful fad.
9. Diligent and determined, Len soon became expert at tennis.
10. That feathery green fern looks beautiful in the front window.

▶ **Exercise 2** **Adding Adjectives to Sentences.** Fill in each blank below with an appropriate adjective. Circle the word it describes.

EXAMPLE: (Jenny) appeared ___*angry*___ about something.

1. Janice has a(n) _____ appetite for someone her size.
2. A(n) _____ snake crawled out from under a rock.
3. The view from the top of the mountain was _____.
4. Tanya seemed _____ for our friendship.
5. One _____ student stood off to one side watching the others.
6. The team, _____ and _____, left the field amid cheers.
7. Check carefully before riding your bike into _____ traffic.
8. The farmers hope for a(n) _____ harvest.
9. The police gave Tom a citation for his _____ rescue.
10. The _____ fish swam back and forth in the _____ tank.

16.1 The Adjective • Practice 2

▶ **Exercise 1** **Recognizing Adjectives.** Underline each adjective in the sentences below.

EXAMPLE: Dream houses often have large rooms.

1. I like to fish in clear, cold, deep lakes.
2. Old clothes are often comfortable.
3. Vera enjoys frisky, playful kittens.
4. Dad's new car uses less gas than his old one.
5. Red and white roses were everywhere.
6. Hot cocoa is my favorite beverage.
7. I like to watch old silent films.
8. Sunsets can be magnificent around here.
9. Blue, green, brown, and orange sweaters were on display.
10. Chocolate, vanilla, and strawberry ice cream was served in gleaming cups.
11. I know of two good and cheap restaurants nearby.
12. The long race left the runner exhausted.
13. Frightened and confused, the small children hugged their mothers.
14. My ideal home would have large rooms.
15. My older sister is both artistic and athletic.
16. Used cars can sometimes be good bargains.
17. Three small sunfish were all my brother caught.
18. Look at Don's fancy new sneakers!
19. Large wet flakes were falling in swirls of bitter wind.
20. Andy writes funny and interesting letters.

▶ **Writing Application** **Using Adjectives to Describe a Movie.** Write a paragraph in which you describe the characters, setting, and plot of a movie. Use one or more adjectives in each sentence.

_____

_____

_____

_____

_____

_____

_____

_____

_____

_____

16.1 Articles • Practice 1

The is the definite article. It points to a specific person, place, or thing. *A* and *an* are the indefinite articles. They point to any member of a group of similar people, places, or things.

ARTICLES		
Definite Article	**Indefinite Article Before Consonant Sounds**	**Indefinite Article Before Vowel Sounds**
the woman	a young woman	an old woman
the underbrush	a unique gift	an ugly episode
the operator	a one-sided argument	an only child

▶ **Exercise 1** **Identifying Articles.** Underline the articles in the sentences below. Above each one, write *D* if it is definite or *I* if it is indefinite.

              I   *D*

EXAMPLE: A robin built its nest in the tree outside my window.

1. Sharon is taking a writing course at summer school.

2. Allison has a book on reserve at the library.

3. Everyone at the party wore an unusual hat.

4. The coach has called an extra practice before the game on Saturday.

5. We had a good time on the camping trip.

6. The sentence on the second line needs a period at the end.

7. The child drew a picture of a visitor from another planet.

8. An unfortunate incident broke up the party early.

9. The principal made an announcement about the class trip.

10. We all made an effort to be polite to the newcomers.

▶ **Exercise 2** **Using Indefinite Articles.** Fill in each blank below with the correct indefinite article.

EXAMPLE: _____*an*_____ unsuccessful attempt

1. _____ unified paragraph
2. _____ exciting opportunity
3. _____ outstanding student
4. _____ colorful garden
5. _____ friendly discussion

6. _____ elegant restaurant
7. _____ willing worker
8. _____ perfect day
9. _____ playful cat
10. _____ early riser

16.1 Articles • Practice 2

▶ **Exercise 1**   **Using Indefinite Articles.**   Write an appropriate indefinite article on the line before each noun phrase.

EXAMPLE: ___a___ delicate instrument

1. _____ new film
2. _____ telephone directory
3. _____ successful deal
4. _____ evergreen tree
5. _____ uninterrupted game
6. _____ radio program
7. _____ foreign language
8. _____ additional feature
9. _____ idea
10. _____ unusual time
11. _____ one-time senator
12. _____ absent friend
13. _____ innocent mistake
14. _____ universal truth
15. _____ endless task
16. _____ cheerful child
17. _____ brilliant idea
18. _____ idle mind
19. _____ uniform to wear
20. _____ huge amount

21. _____ gold ring
22. _____ imaginary creature
23. _____ agreeable partner
24. _____ reasonable explanation
25. _____ early appointment
26. _____ friendly puppy
27. _____ impatient customer
28. _____ useful tool
29. _____ graceful leap
30. _____ tropical storm
31. _____ original painting
32. _____ obvious mistake
33. _____ telegram message
34. _____ panic attack
35. _____ unpleasant time
36. _____ humorous story
37. _____ unwilling person
38. _____ inside joke
39. _____ special report
40. _____ popular club

▶ **Writing Application**   **Using Articles in Sentences.**   Write a paragraph describing some of the presents you have received during your life. When you have finished writing, underline all the definite and indefinite articles.

_____
_____
_____
_____
_____
_____
_____
_____
_____
_____

16.1 Proper Adjectives • Practice 1

A proper adjective is (1) a proper noun used as an adjective or (2) an adjective formed from a proper noun.

PROPER ADJECTIVES	
Proper Nouns Used as Adjectives	**Proper Adjective Forms**
Philadelphia lawyer	Parisian restaurant
Franklin stove	Jeffersonian democracy
United States Army base	American citizens

▶ **Exercise 1** **Identifying Proper Adjectives.** Underline the proper adjective in each sentence below. Then, circle the noun it modifies.

EXAMPLE: My (uncle) is Chinese.

1. Scandinavian winters are long and cold.

2. We went down the river in an Eskimo kayak.

3. The class had a perfect June day for graduation.

4. Brazilian restaurants are becoming very popular.

5. The cruise will stop at several Caribbean ports.

6. Do you like Mel Gibson films?

7. The coffee was made from fresh-ground Colombian coffee beans.

8. Italian ice is a refreshing summertime dessert.

9. I am reading a collection of Greek myths.

10. Mom has always admired that Monet painting.

▶ **Exercise 2** **Using Proper Adjectives to Modify Nouns.** Rewrite each group of words below to include a proper adjective before the underlined noun.

EXAMPLE: a vacation in Europe _____a European vacation_____

1. a new video made by Michael Jackson _____

2. the soccer team from Australia _____

3. an opera written by an Italian _____

4. a diplomat from the Middle East _____

5. an island in the Mediterranean _____

6. the overture by Tchaikovsky _____

7. a spokesman in the White House _____

8. snowstorms in Alaska _____

9. the potato from Idaho _____

10. a representative from California _____

16.1 Proper Adjectives • Practice 2

▶ **Exercise 1**   **Identifying Proper Adjectives.**   Underline the proper adjective in each sentence below. Then, circle the noun it modifies.

EXAMPLE: My family dined at an Italian (restaurant) .

1. Georgia peaches are famous for their sweet taste.

2. Patricia prefers French dressing on her salad.

3. We have tickets to hear a Beethoven symphony.

4. Put the Swiss watch on the counter.

5. The actor wore a Panama hat and carried a cane.

6. A Parisian designer made this dress.

7. We read several examples of Spanish literature.

8. The Canadian team is well prepared.

9. March winds howled around us as we landed in Chicago.

10. Michelle wrote to the Venezuelan embassy for information.

▶ **Exercise 2**   **More Work With Proper Adjectives.**   Follow the directions for Exercise 1.

1. Last year we vacationed on a Hawaiian island.

2. A Chaplin movie is playing nearby.

3. Have you seen the Portuguese coins?

4. Susan wants to read the Carter memoirs.

5. My mother chose Mediterranean furniture.

6. Our club met during the Christmas vacation.

7. An Irish leprechaun is the team mascot.

8. The Swedish film has a good plot.

9. We decided to go to a Mexican restaurant.

10. I can play a Chopin waltz on the piano.

▶ **Writing Application**   **Writing Sentences With Proper Adjectives.**   Imagine that you took a trip around the world. Write five sentences about things you saw and did. Use a proper adjective, such as *French, Spanish, Mexican, Peruvian,* or *Greek,* in each sentence.

1. _____

2. _____

3. _____

4. _____

5. _____

16.1 Possessive Adjectives • Practice 1

A personal pronoun can be used as an adjective if it modifies a noun.

PERSONAL PRONOUNS USED AS POSSESSIVE ADJECTIVES	
Singular	**Plural**
I lost *my* sneakers.	He and I have had *our* differences.
You will need *your* boots, Ed.	Students, you may take out *your* books.
Alana enjoyed *her* trip.	Many students ride *their* bikes to school.
Ben lent me *his* notes	
The paper changed *its* format.	

▶ Exercise 1 **Recognizing Possessive Adjectives.** Underline the pronoun used as an adjective in each sentence below. Underline its antecedent twice, and circle the noun it modifies.

EXAMPLE: Andrew has chosen a biography for his (book report).

1. The orchestra played the *1812 Overture* for its finale.

2. Mandy went to Chicago with her family during spring break.

3. The record became a hit during its first week on the racks.

4. The stars have donated their services for the charity concert.

5. Gina, you should have proofread your work more carefully.

6. I wish I had brought my umbrella.

7. Rick brought his guitar to the party.

8. Betsy and I have always shared all our secrets with each other.

9. Many people brought their folding chairs to the fireworks.

10. Denise and Len are visiting their grandparents this weekend.

▶ Exercise 2 **Using Possessive Adjectives in Sentences.** Write an appropriate possessive pronoun in each blank below. Then, underline the noun it modifies.

EXAMPLE: Len and I enjoyed _____*our*_____ trip to the museum.

1. Tim and Janet have been using _____ computer for school work.

2. Mark carefully put _____ coin collection away.

3. Mom is famous all over town for _____ lemon meringue pie.

4. That magazine has doubled _____ circulation in two years.

5. Thomas Jefferson designed _____ own home at Monticello.

6. I cannot take very good pictures with _____ camera.

7. The network revised _____ program schedule because of the news conference.

8. Lily writes to _____ family every day while she is at camp.

9. Ramon takes _____ new puppy everywhere with him.

10. Have you started writing _____ report yet?

16.1 Possessive Adjectives • Practice 2

Exercise 1 **Recognizing Possessive Adjectives.** Underline the possessive adjective in each sentence below. Then, draw one arrow connecting the possessive adjective to its antecedent and another arrow connecting it to the noun it modifies.

EXAMPLE: Eric wrote his story on a microcomputer.

1. Andrea said that computers make her life easier.

2. Computers don't lose their patience.

3. Eric added, "My homework was done on a computer."

4. Juan spends his time designing programs.

5. A student who uses a computer will learn its uses.

6. Michael, has your school developed any software for science classes?

7. Mary will show her program to you.

8. "Donna, your program is saved on a diskette."

9. The boys have made revisions in their compositions.

10. Chris says his skills in word processing have improved.

Exercise 2 **More Work With Recognizing Possessive Adjectives.** Follow the directions for Exercise 1.

1. Dr. Alice Hamilton is known for her work in medicine.

2. She helped people in Chicago care for their children.

3. Dr. Hamilton received her degree in 1893.

4. The governor appointed the doctor to head one of his committees.

5. She studied workers' diseases and their causes.

Name _____   Date _____

 16.2 **The Adverb • Practice 1**

An adverb is a word that modifies a verb, an adjective, or another adverb.

WHAT ADVERBS TELL ABOUT THE WORDS THEY MODIFY	
Where?	Put the packages *there*.
	We held the party *outside*.
When?	I will meet you *later*.
	Grandma is coming *today*.
In What Way?	The elephant moved *awkwardly*.
	The shortstop runs *fast*.
To What Extent?	Janet was *completely* honest.
	Lucy seems *very* upset.

▶ **Exercise 1**   **Identifying Adverbs.**   Underline the adverb in each sentence below. On the line after the sentence, write the question the adverb answers.

EXAMPLE: The teacher carefully explained the experiment. _____*In what way?*_____

1. My best friend's family has moved away. _____

2. Jason was thoroughly disgusted by the display. _____

3. Tony always finishes all his work on time. _____

4. Roses will grow well in that location. _____

5. Kevin seemed unusually excited at the party. _____

6. Grandpa is sometimes shy about describing his adventures at sea. _____

7. Martha will be here by dinnertime. _____

8. Phil worked hard on his science project. _____

9. Mr. Murphy is a truly dedicated teacher. _____

10. My father can take us home after the movie. _____

▶ **Exercise 2**   **More Work With Adverbs.**   Underline the adverb(s) in each sentence below. Then, circle the word each adverb modifies.

EXAMPLE: Jeff was very (unhappy) about his lost puppy.

1. That new baby seldom cries.

2. Yesterday, I discovered a leak in the boat.

3. Our mail usually arrives in the afternoon.

4. Gary did extremely well at his first recital.

5. Lenore is sometimes careless.

6. We gradually solved the puzzle.

7. The club has two large parties annually.

8. The neighbors were quite annoyed by the loud noise.

9. The ice melted rapidly in the sun.

10. Paul practices his scales diligently.

16.2 The Adverb • Practice 2

▶ **Exercise 1** **Finding Adverbs.** Circle the adverb that modifies each underlined word below.

EXAMPLE: We (playfully) created a new symbol.

1. I often <u>think</u> about numbers.

2. Yesterday I <u>read</u> about large numbers.

3. A boy once <u>created</u> a new number word.

4. He jokingly <u>named</u> it a googol.

5. Carefully <u>write</u> 1 with one hundred 0's.

6. Mathematicians accepted the idea most <u>enthusiastically</u>.

7. Eventually he <u>created</u> another large number expression.

8. He very <u>quickly</u> named this one the googolplex.

9. I rarely hear about the Mega, another amazingly <u>large</u> number.

10. A scientist carefully <u>gave</u> it a serious name.

▶ **Exercise 2** **More Work With Adverbs.** For each sentence below, circle the adverb that modifies the underlined word.

1. All our relatives <u>gather</u> yearly.

2. Joyously, we <u>celebrate</u> our good fortunes.

3. We <u>hold</u> a barbecue outside.

4. I <u>received</u> my engraved invitation early.

5. This year we <u>celebrated</u> uptown.

6. A restaurant carefully <u>catered</u> the affair.

7. This change utterly <u>surprised</u> us.

8. Eagerly, the restaurant promised an unusually <u>favorable</u> rate.

9. They <u>guaranteed</u> everything fully.

10. I dine at that restaurant quite <u>often</u>.

▶ **Writing Application** **Using Adverbs in Sentences.** Write ten sentences, using an adverb in each sentence.

1. _____

2. _____

3. _____

4. _____

5. _____

6. _____

7. _____

8. _____

9. _____

10. _____

16.2 Adverb or Adjective? • Practice 1

If a noun or pronoun is modified by a word, that word is an adjective. If a verb, adjective, or adverb is modified by a word, that word is an adverb.

DISTINGUISHING BETWEEN ADJECTIVES AND ADVERBS	
Adjectives	**Adverbs**
We'd better have a *closer* look.	She works *hard* for her money.
That is a *weekly* magazine.	Ed moved *closer* to the stage.
That was a *hard* job.	The club meets *weekly*.

Exercise 1   **Distinguishing Between Adjectives and Adverbs.**   Write *adjective* or *adverb* to identify each underlined word below.

EXAMPLE: Turn left at the first intersection. _____*adverb*_____

1. I have never seen a faster horse than that one. _____
2. The nurse should have acted faster. _____
3. Joe made a sharp left turn just past the bridge. _____
4. The old man's stories always seem endless. _____
5. Marcia made a sudden move toward the water. _____
6. Wendy may have taken a later train. _____
7. The mother hummed quietly to the infant in her arms. _____
8. Do you think the watermelon is cold yet? _____
9. Harvey watched the parade go past. _____
10. The plane departed later than scheduled. _____

Exercise 2   **Writing Adjectives and Adverbs in Sentences.**   Write two sentences for each word in parentheses below. In the first sentence, use the word as an adjective; in the second, use it as an adverb.

EXAMPLE: (harder)   _____*That test was harder than I thought it would be.*_____
                        _____*Grace worked harder than ever on her math.*_____

1. (upside-down) _____

   _____

2. (backward) _____

   _____

3. (early) _____

   _____

4. (high) _____

   _____

5. (only) _____

   _____

16.2 Adverb or Adjective? • Practice 2

▶ **Exercise 1** **Recognizing Adverbs and Adjectives.** Write *adverb* or *adjective* for each underlined word below.

EXAMPLE: I bought an electric clock. _____*adjective*_____

1. She gazed at the far horizon. _____
2. He traveled far. _____
3. I know that you write well. _____
4. Sarah is well and so am I. _____
5. A daily flight leaves from here. _____
6. The flight leaves daily at 10 A.M. _____
7. The crowd pushed forward. _____
8. The forward movement pulled me along. _____
9. In order to see better, George moved near. _____
10. It was a near miss. _____

▶ **Exercise 2** **More Work With Adverbs and Adjectives.** Write *adverb* or *adjective* for each underlined word in the sentences below.

1. I heard a humorous story. _____
2. He spoke endlessly. _____
3. She gave a farewell speech. _____
4. My recent offer is a generous one. _____
5. The builder successfully completed the house. _____
6. They actively swap ideas. _____
7. He carefully recorded the music. _____
8. Have you seen the valuable jewel? _____
9. The giant tree amazed the hikers. _____
10. The group meets weekly. _____

▶ **Writing Application** **Using Adverbs and Adjectives in Sentences.** Watch a person doing something. Then, write ten sentences describing what the person is doing. Use an adverb or an adjective in each sentence, and underline it.

1. _____
2. _____
3. _____
4. _____
5. _____
6. _____
7. _____
8. _____
9. _____
10. _____

17 The Preposition • Practice 1

A preposition relates a noun or a pronoun to another word in the sentence.

PREPOSITIONS
We ordered pizza { with / without / instead of } meatballs.

▷ **Exercise 1** **Identifying Prepositions.** Circle the preposition(s) in each sentence below. The number in parentheses indicates the number of prepositions in the sentence.

EXAMPLE: Gerry left (without) a word (to) anyone. (2)

1. A new family has moved into the house next to ours. (2)

2. The club isn't much fun without Sharon. (1)

3. Among the three of us, we had just enough money for a pizza. (3)

4. Because of that incident, the families do not speak to each other. (2)

5. We watched the fireworks display from a spot across the river. (2)

6. Draw a line through any words that are not needed. (1)

7. The rake has been leaning against the garage since yesterday. (2)

8. A letter for Mike is on the table in the hall. (3)

9. You will be safe from the mosquitoes until dusk. (2)

10. No one except Judy's mother baked brownies. (1)

▷ **Exercise 2** **Using Prepositions in Sentences.** Fill in each blank below with a preposition to complete the sentence.

EXAMPLE: We agreed to meet _____before_____ dinner.

1. Carl has ridden his bike _____ the river.

2. I haven't seen Louise _____ a month.

3. We waited _____ six o'clock for the train to arrive.

4. A crowd of people pressed _____ the movie star.

5. I found my sneakers _____ the couch.

6. Many people became restless _____ the long delay.

7. I am reading a book _____ Judy Blume.

8. Basketball is my favorite sport _____ baseball.

9. The realtor took us _____ a number of houses.

10. Fred sits _____ me in math class.

17 The Preposition • Practice 2

▶ **Exercise 1** **Supplying Prepositions.** Fill in each blank below with a preposition to complete the sentence.

EXAMPLE: I will meet you _____*outside*_____ the store.

1. Put your briefcase _____ the table.
2. Tie the string _____ the package.
3. We have been waiting for a reply _____ yesterday.
4. The game will not be held _____ noon.
5. The restaurant is _____ a lake.
6. Draw a line _____ the paper.
7. I will search for the letter _____ my desk.
8. The covering was placed _____ the furniture.
9. Look _____ the telescope to see Saturn.
10. Call me any day _____ Tuesday.

▶ **Exercise 2** **More Work With Prepositions.** Follow the directions for Exercise 1.

1. Pull the chair out from _____ the table.
2. The liquid smells _____ perfume.
3. The plants reach _____ the light.
4. There is a garage _____ the grocery store.
5. I traveled _____ the town on a bicycle.
6. I voted _____ the changes suggested by the mayor.
7. The meat and vegetables were already _____ the table.
8. Wait _____ tomorrow for the results of the survey.
9. We looked for the pad _____ the pile of papers.
10. Please leave the newspaper _____ the front door.

▶ **Writing Application** **Using Prepositions in Sentences.** Using a preposition in each sentence, write ten sentences telling where a number of things in your home are located. Use as many different prepositions as you can.

1. _____
2. _____
3. _____
4. _____
5. _____
6. _____
7. _____
8. _____
9. _____
10. _____

Preposition or Adverb? • **Practice 1**

A preposition will always be part of a prepositional phrase. An adverb can stand alone.

DISTINGUISHING BETWEEN PREPOSITIONS AND ADVERBS	
Prepositions	**Adverbs**
We walked *along* the river.	We took the dog *along*.
A car raced *up* the hill.	Everyone stood *up*.
I will be there *before* seven.	I have never seen her *before*.

▶ **Exercise 1**   **Distinguishing Between Prepositions and Adverbs.**   Write *preposition* or *adverb* for the underlined words in the sentences below.

EXAMPLE: Sign your name on the line <u>below</u>.   *adverb*

1. We watched the clouds float <u>by</u>. _____
2. Turn left just <u>beyond</u> the apple orchard. _____
3. Did you bring the paper <u>in</u>? _____
4. A large crowd gathered <u>outside</u> the ticket office. _____
5. The skis are in the garage <u>behind</u> the sleds. _____
6. These belong in the cupboard <u>below</u> the kitchen sink. _____
7. The concert was planned <u>by</u> the performers themselves. _____
8. Remember to leave your rubbers <u>outside</u>. _____
9. Did you see the headline <u>in</u> tonight's paper? _____
10. We seem to have left Robbie <u>behind</u>. _____

▶ **Exercise 2**   **Writing Prepositions and Adverbs in Sentences.**   Write two sentences for each word in parentheses below. In the first sentence, use the word as a preposition; in the second, use it as an adverb.

EXAMPLE: (besides)   *Besides Alice, we should invite Mark and Kathy.*
                          We are very tired, and we are hungry besides.

1. (above) _____
   _____
2. (inside) _____
   _____
3. (off) _____
   _____
4. (near) _____
   _____
5. (underneath) _____
   _____

17 Preposition or Adverb? • Practice 2

▶ **Exercise 1** **Recognizing Prepositions and Adverbs.** Write *preposition* or *adverb* for the underlined word in each sentence below.

EXAMPLE: Mr. Elliot stopped <u>by</u>. ____*adverb*____

1. Marilyn sat <u>down</u>. _____
2. The plumber went <u>down</u> the stairs. _____
3. The runners stood <u>behind</u> the white line. _____
4. The runner fell <u>behind</u>. _____
5. I saw you leap <u>across</u> and run away. _____
6. Ben ran <u>across</u> the street. _____
7. I asked Jane to come <u>inside</u> for a chat. _____
8. Mary placed the casserole <u>inside</u> the oven. _____
9. I read <u>past</u> the second chapter. _____
10. The train roared <u>past</u>. _____

▶ **Exercise 2** **More Work With Recognizing Prepositions and Adverbs.** Follow the directions for Exercise 1.

1. The child came <u>out</u>. _____
2. Helen raced <u>out</u> the door. _____
3. Miriam has been waiting <u>since</u> last Tuesday. _____
4. No one has visited <u>since</u>. _____
5. We took the notice <u>off</u> the bulletin board. _____
6. After dinner, they took <u>off</u> for the movies. _____
7. Mark painted <u>on</u> the smooth surface. _____
8. After you brush your teeth, put your shoes <u>on</u>. _____
9. This chair spins <u>around</u>. _____
10. A new store opened <u>around</u> the corner. _____

▶ **Writing Application** **Using Prepositions and Adverbs in Sentences.** Write two sentences for each word in parentheses below. In the first sentence, use the word as a preposition; in the second, use it as an adverb.

1. (after) _____
   _____

2. (before) _____
   _____

3. (over) _____
   _____

4. (off) _____
   _____

5. (around) _____
   _____

18.1 The Conjunction • Practice 1

Conjunctions connect words, groups of words, and whole sentences.

USING COORDINATING CONJUNCTIONS	
Nouns	The stew needs more *onions* and *carrots*.
Pronouns	Give the message to *him* or *me*.
Verbs	He *would* not *eat* nor *sleep*.
Adjectives	The runner was *exhausted* but *victorious*.
Adverbs	Mark spoke *clearly* and *forcefully*.
Prepositional Phrases	The gardener works *with great care* yet *without pleasure*.
Sentences	*We held our breath,* for *the figure moved closer.*
	Sandy missed the bus, so *we took her home.*

▶ **Exercise 1** **Recognizing Coordinating Conjunctions.** Circle the coordinating conjunction in each sentence below. Then, underline the words or word groups it joins.

EXAMPLE: Throughout the stormy night (and) into the morning, rescuers searched the cove.

1. Should I use green or blue for the lettering?

2. The pianist performed with great accuracy but without much feeling.

3. Carol and Luke are finalists in the spelling bee.

4. We arrived early, so we could get good seats for the concert.

5. Jason or Madeline should be able to give you directions.

6. The crowd was somewhat noisy yet otherwise well-behaved.

7. The puppy would not sit nor stay before it went to obedience school.

8. We took the subway to the ballpark, for we knew traffic would be heavy.

9. The children worked busily but quietly on their projects.

10. A combination of luck and skill is needed to win that game.

▶ **Exercise 2** **Writing Sentences With Coordinating Conjunctions.** Follow the directions in each numbered item below to write a sentence of your own.

EXAMPLE: Use *for* to join two sentences.
    High waves tossed the small boat, for a storm had come up unexpectedly.

1. Use *and* to join two prepositional phrases.

_____

2. Use *but* to join two adjectives.

_____

3. Use *so* to join two sentences.

_____

4. Use *yet* to join two adverbs.

_____

5. Use *or* to join two pronouns.

_____

18.1 The Conjunction • Practice 2

Exercise 1 **Recognizing Coordinating Conjunctions.** Circle the coordinating conjunction in each sentence below. Then, underline the words or word groups it joins.

EXAMPLE: The first humans did not use <u>tools</u> (or) <u>fire</u>.

1. Today, I have tests in mathematics and social studies.

2. I went to the game, but I left early.

3. Cars were parked in the street and in the driveways.

4. Bob reads slowly and carefully.

5. Mary wanted to buy those jeans, so she saved her allowance money.

6. The book was long but enjoyable.

7. The runner stumbled and fell.

8. I did not like the movie, nor did she.

9. Are you going with us or with them?

10. Bill phoned all day, yet nobody answered.

Exercise 2 **More Work With Coordinating Conjunctions.** Follow the directions for Exercise 1.

1. Jill could not get tickets, nor could Ed.

2. Do you want lemonade or soda?

3. The weather was sunny but cool.

4. I'm excited, for today is my birthday.

5. Put your bicycle in the garage or in the basement.

6. Did they fly or drive to Kansas City?

7. The song was simple but beautiful.

8. The boat glided silently yet rapidly.

9. Please put lettuce and mayonnaise in my sandwich.

10. Either you or she will be asked to speak.

Writing Application **Using Coordinating Conjunctions in Sentences.** Write ten sentences telling about two people you know. Use a coordinating conjunction in each sentence.

1. _____

2. _____

3. _____

4. _____

5. _____

6. _____

7. _____

8. _____

9. _____

10. _____

18.1 Correlative Conjunctions • Practice 1

Correlative Conjunctions   Correlative conjunctions are pairs of conjunctions that connect words or word groups.

Words Joined	USING CORRELATIVE CONJUNCTIONS Examples
Nouns	At the party, Jen served [both] *hamburgers* [and] *hot dogs*.
Pronouns	Mom wants to know [whether] *you* [or] *I* will set the table.
Verbs	Danny [not only] *entered* [but also] *won* the marathon.
Adjectives	The house was [neither] *attractive* [nor] *affordable*.
Adverbs	He spoke [both] *rapidly* [and] *clearly*.
Prepositional Phrases	You will find the books you need [either] *on reserve* [or] *in the* *reference room.*
Sentences	[Not only] *did we bake the pies*, [but] *we* [also] *sold them.*

▶ **Exercise 1**   **Finding Correlative Conjunctions.**   Circle both parts of the correlative conjunction in each sentence below, and underline the words or word groups it connects.

EXAMPLE: I wonder (whether) it will <u>rain</u> (or) <u>snow</u> during the night.

1. Ellen usually either walks or rides her bike to school.
2. This pie crust is not only tender but also flaky.
3. Both Paul and his family are Tiger fans.
4. My new record was neither in its jacket nor on the turntable.
5. Do you know whether Shana or her sister took the message?
6. The dinner includes either salad or vegetable.
7. Ben not only set the table but also washed the dishes.
8. Either Fran will make the arrangements, or Mom will be angry.
9. My sneakers are neither in the closet nor under my bed.
10. I like both sausage and peppers in my sandwich.

▶ **Exercise 2**   **Writing Sentences With Correlative Conjunctions.**   Follow the directions in each numbered item below to write sentences of your own.

EXAMPLE: Use *either . . . or* to join two adjectives.

       Only someone who is either brave or crazy would take that job.

1. Use *neither . . . nor* to join two adverbs.

_____

2. Use *whether . . . or* to join two pronouns.

_____

3. Use *either . . . or* to join two sentences.

_____

4. Use *not only . . . but also* to join two prepositional phrases.

_____

5. Use *both . . . and* to join two verbs.

_____

18.1 Correlative Conjunctions • Practice 2

▶ **Exercise 1** **Finding Correlative Conjunctions.** Circle both parts of the correlative conjunction in each sentence below, and underline the words or word groups it connects.

EXAMPLE: Basketball players need (both) ability (and) spirit.

1. Neither the bat nor the ball belongs to me.

2. My sister reads both novels and plays.

3. Ralph could not decide whether to go or to stay at the party.

4. She neither agreed nor disagreed.

5. Your brother is both funny and intelligent.

6. The ball landed either in the lake or in that bush.

7. The food here is both inexpensive and tasty.

8. Not only did we go to the fair but we also won a prize.

9. The coach would not say whether Phil or Don would pitch.

10. On ice, you must drive both slowly and carefully.

11. Both Eric and Aaron play tennis.

12. They not only compete but also practice.

13. They feel neither nervous nor upset in a game.

14. Eric studies his opponent both before a game and during a game.

15. They both play either singles or doubles.

16. It is hard to say whether Eric or Aaron is the better player.

17. They select not only their equipment but also the courts where they will play.

18. Aaron plays either during the day or during the evening.

19. To play well, they should be neither tired nor angry.

20. Instead, they should feel both focused and calm.

▶ **Writing Application** **Using Correlative Conjunctions to Write About a Sport.** Write five sentences, using a correlative conjunction in each one. Tell about games and sports you have played.

1. _____

_____

2. _____

_____

3. _____

_____

4. _____

_____

5. _____

_____

18.2 # The Interjection • Practice 1

Interjections are words that express sudden excitement or strong feeling.

SOME INTERJECTIONS				
ah	fine	huh	oops	ugh
aha	golly	hurray	ouch	well
alas	gosh	my	psst	whew
boy	great	nonsense	sh	wonderful
darn	hey	oh	terrific	wow

▶ **Exercise 1** **Recognizing Interjections.** Underline the interjection in each sentence below.

EXAMPLE: <u>Brother</u>! It surely is hot in here.

1. Nonsense! Who would ever believe a story like that?

2. Gosh, I wish I had thought of that.

3. Terrific! What a great hit that was!

4. Ugh! What is that awful smell?

5. Sh, the baby is sleeping.

6. Oh, no! What a mess I made!

7. Whew, that was a close call.

8. Alas, I should have studied harder.

9. My, what an unkind thing that was to say!

10. Psst, listen to this.

▶ **Exercise 2** **Writing Interjections in Sentences.** Fill in each blank below with an appropriate interjection.

EXAMPLE: _____Hush_____, don't say anything now.

1. _____! How spectacular the fireworks were!

2. _____, that was a silly thing to say.

3. _____! I just banged my thumb.

4. _____, that jar slipped out of my hand.

5. _____! Danny wouldn't say such a thing!

6. _____! That was a wonderful movie.

7. _____! This is the book I have been looking for.

8. _____, wait for me!

9. _____! We won!

10. _____? I never heard that version before.

18.2 The Interjection • Practice 2

▷ **Exercise 1**   **Supplying Interjections.**   Write an interjection in each of the blanks below.

EXAMPLE: _Wow_ ! I'm so happy you were selected.

1. _____ ! It's 10:30 A.M. and he is not here yet.
2. _____ ! I just shut the door on my finger.
3. _____ ! Elizabeth and I can hardly believe the news.
4. _____ , I can't hear the music.
5. _____ ! My briefcase is missing.
6. _____ ! This new recipe I tried tastes awful.
7. _____ ! She could not have been in Baltimore.
8. _____ ! It's a dramatic discovery.
9. _____ ! We just made it in time for the next train.
10. _____ , don't forget the CD player.

▷ **Exercise 2**   **More Work With Supplying Interjections.**   Follow the directions for Exercise 1.

1. _____ , I didn't realize it was so late.
2. _____ ! We won the city championships.
3. _____ ! I almost missed my appointment.
4. _____ , you have an impressive coin collection.
5. _____ ! This idea is really great.
6. _____ , what an original painting.
7. _____ , what a long movie.
8. _____ ! I scraped my knee on the sidewalk.
9. _____ ! You dropped the stack of books.
10. _____ ! Have you heard about Melissa's new plan?

▷ **Writing Application**   **Using Interjections in Sentences.**   Using an interjection in each sentence, write ten sentences about exciting events you have experienced. Place a comma or an exclamation point after each interjection.

1. _____
2. _____
3. _____
4. _____
5. _____
6. _____
7. _____
8. _____
9. _____
10. _____

19.1 The Two Parts of a Sentence • Practice 1

Every complete sentence contains a subject and a predicate. The subject tells who or what the sentence is about. The predicate tells something about the subject. The simple subject is a noun or pronoun that answers the question *Who?* or *What?* about the sentence. The simple predicate is the verb that expresses the action done by or to the subject, or tells what the condition of the subject is. In the chart below, simple subjects are underlined once and simple predicates are underlined twice.

SIMPLE SUBJECTS AND SIMPLE PREDICATES
The owner of the land had never returned.
These flowers bloom late in the fall.
Several of the new inventions were very clever.

> **Exercise 1**   **Finding Simple Subjects and Simple Predicates.**   Underline the simple subject once and the simple predicate twice in each sentence below.

EXAMPLE: The rain stopped in the afternoon.

1. A beach ball rolled onto the baseball diamond.

2. Dachshunds were bred to hunt badgers.

3. A book about vampires was missing.

4. Several people reported the accident.

5. Len speaks with a slight Australian accent.

6. The sink was full of dirty dishes.

7. Inspector Low held the paper up to the light.

8. Mr. Bixby rarely assigns homework.

9. No one noticed the theft until morning.

10. The map was soiled and torn.

> **Exercise 2**   **Writing Subjects and Predicates.**   In the sentences below, supply a simple subject for each blank underlined once. Supply a simple predicate for each blank underlined twice.

EXAMPLE: The _____canary_____ refused to sing.

   Inspector Low _____solved_____ the mystery.

1. Chickens _____ from eggs.

2. The _____ gave the speeder a ticket.

3. Luis _____ a fine for the overdue book.

4. The _____ was a great surprise.

5. The burglar probably _____ through the window.

19.1 The Two Parts of a Sentence • Practice 2

▶ Exercise 1   **Finding Simple Subjects and Simple Predicates.**   For each sentence below, underline the simple subject once and the simple predicate twice.

EXAMPLE: Colonial <u>women</u> <u><u>cooked</u></u> in a fireplace.

1. English settlers arrived in Plymouth Colony in 1620 after a long voyage.
2. The governor called these settlers "pilgrims."
3. Some people came to Plymouth Colony for religious reasons.
4. Their ship was called the Mayflower.
5. The settlers wanted a better life.
6. The men worked in the fields.
7. Women, too, helped on the farm.
8. Even children were expected to work.
9. Most houses were small.
10. These homes pleased the settlers.

▶ Exercise 2   **More Work With Simple Subjects and Simple Predicates.**   For each sentence below, underline the simple subject once and the simple predicate twice.

1. Yesterday we moved the old furniture out of our house.
2. My Uncle Jonathan will sell it at his garage sale this weekend.
3. I remember how every scratch in the old table was made.
4. The wooden chair wobbles a bit.
5. Many letters were written at that table.
6. Robert often studied there.
7. We felt a little sentimental about losing it.
8. The new furniture looks modern.
9. The table holds more books and papers.
10. The padded seat swivels.

▶ Exercise 3   **Writing Subjects and Predicates.**   For each sentence below, supply the word indicated in parentheses.

EXAMPLE: _____*Albert*_____ enjoys fishing. (subject)

1. She _____ that the event was extraordinary. (predicate)
2. _____ became interested in photography. (subject)
3. Muriel _____ the conversation. (predicate)
4. You _____ the cabin near the lake. (predicate)
5. The _____ is located beside the basketball court. (subject)
6. Across the room _____ our cat. (predicate)
7. My _____ encouraged me to travel. (subject)
8. Nora _____ her science project. (predicate)
9. Keith _____ to find a quiet spot. (predicate)
10. Each _____ returned to the cruise ship. (subject)

19.2 # Complete Subjects and Predicates

• Practice 1

The complete subject of a sentence is the simple subject and the words related to it. The complete predicate is the verb and the words related to it. In the chart below, complete subjects and predicates are identified. Each simple subject is underlined once, and each simple predicate is underlined twice.

COMPLETE SUBJECTS AND COMPLETE PREDICATES
Complete Subject/Complete Predicate
The shipwrecked <u>sailors</u>/<u>lived</u> in a cave.
Several <u>students</u> in our class/<u>entered</u> the poster contest.
<u>Michelle</u>/<u>won</u> first prize.
An unidentified <u>aircraft</u>/<u>approached</u> the airport.

▶ **Exercise 1** **Recognizing Complete Subjects and Predicates.** Draw a vertical line between the complete subject and the complete predicate of each sentence below.

EXAMPLE: Animals in fables | act like human beings.

1. A shiny new bicycle stood outside the door.

2. The third problem is a little tricky.

3. The first Monday in September is Labor Day.

4. My older brother earns money doing odd jobs.

5. The first radio station in the United States was KDKA in Pittsburgh.

6. The waiter accepted the tip with a grateful smile.

7. A few water lilies floated on the pond.

8. Boats of every description joined in the rescue.

9. A friend from the old neighborhood was visiting Ellen.

10. This tow requires some assembly.

▶ **Exercise 2** **Identifying Complete and Simple Subjects and Predicates.** In the sentences below, draw a vertical line between the complete subject and the complete predicate. Underline the simple subject once and the simple predicate twice.

EXAMPLE: The <u>dog</u> in the manger | <u>kept</u> the cows away.

1. The tanker was slowly breaking into pieces on the rocks.

2. The youngest of the three brothers has the best voice.

3. The manager of the Otters argued angrily with the umpire.

4. A large crocodile snoozed in the mud near the shore.

5. The hedge in front of the house concealed the street.

6. The drawer of the teller's desk contained only a few travel folders.

7. That girl in the trench coat is a reporter.

8. A simple majority is needed for passage.

9. Few of the spectators stayed until the end of the game.

10. Her sincere apology satisfied everyone.

19.2 Complete Subjects and Predicates
• Practice 2

▶ **Exercise 1** **Complete Subjects and Predicates.** Draw a *vertical line* between the complete subject and the complete predicate of each sentence below. Underline the simple subject once and the simple predicate twice.

EXAMPLE: The <u>guests</u> in the drawing room | <u><u>looked</u></u> suspicious.

1. The elegant lady glanced nervously at the clock.
2. Old Dr. Wentworth walked up and down the room.
3. A man in a blue suit looked out the window.
4. The famous artist mumbled some words to herself.
5. The pianist, pleasant and handsome, spoke constantly.
6. The alert hostess tried to relieve the tension.
7. A young woman offered the guests cold drinks.
8. This thoughtful offer helped a bit.
9. All the guests welcomed the distraction.
10. The conversation returned to normal.

▶ **Exercise 2** **More Work With Complete Subjects and Predicates.** Follow the directions for Exercise 1.

1. My older cousin works on his car every weekend.
2. He checks the pressure in the tires.
3. Paul opens the hood to check the oil.
4. The oil must be at the proper level.
5. The old radiator needs more water.
6. Several quarts of water must be added.
7. A friend from school sometimes helps Paul with these chores.
8. The two boys clean the inside of the car.
9. Other boys from town wash the outside.
10. Waxing is the last chore.

▶ **Writing Application** **Using Complete Subjects and Predicates.** Write ten sentences about a mysterious, funny, or unusual event. Separate each complete subject and complete predicate with a vertical line. Underline the simple subject once and the simple predicate twice.

1. _____
2. _____
3. _____
4. _____
5. _____
6. _____
7. _____
8. _____
9. _____
10. _____

19.3 Compound Subjects and Predicates
• Practice 1

A compound subject is two or more simple subjects that are related to the same verb. A compound predicate is two or more verbs that are related to the same subject.

COMPOUND SUBJECTS AND PREDICATES	
Compound Subjects	**Compound Predicates**
Trolls and ogres are fairytale creatures.	The big dog lay down and rolled over.
Sheila or Paula will take the message.	Most students walk or ride bikes to school.

▶ **Exercise 1** **Recognizing Compound Subjects.** Underline the simple subjects in each compound subject below.

EXAMPLE: An apple or a banana makes a good snack.

1. Trucks and buses may not use the lefthand lane.

2. A teacher or a parent accompanied each group.

3. An encyclopedia or a dictionary should have that information.

4. The director and her assistant hold the tryouts.

5. Before moving here, Rachel and her sister lived in New York City.

6. Neither threats nor pleas could change Peter's mind.

7. Bottles and glass jars belong in this bin.

8. A judge, justice of the peace, or ship captain can marry a couple.

9. Salad and dessert are not included in the special.

10. A doctor or nurse is present at all times.

▶ **Exercise 2** **Recognizing Compound Predicates.** Underline twice the verbs in each compound predicate below.

EXAMPLE: The speedboat capsized and sank.

1. Trees swayed and bent in the high winds.

2. The spectators stood up and cheered.

3. Many employees jog or do exercises at lunchtime.

4. Beatrix Potter wrote and illustrated her stories.

5. Customers can now deposit or withdraw money by machine.

6. The company repairs or replaces all defective watches.

7. Jeff sanded the surface lightly and wiped it clean.

8. From four to five, campers rest or write letters.

9. Volunteers stuff, address, and stamp envelopes.

10. The audience booed and hissed the villain.

19.3 Compound Subjects and Predicates
• Practice 2

▶ **Exercise 1**   **Recognizing Compound Subjects and Predicates.**   Each sentence below has a compound subject or a compound predicate. Underline each compound subject and compound predicate. Circle the conjunction.

EXAMPLE: English (and) math are my favorite subjects.

1. In English class, we read and discuss literature.
2. Mark Twain and Edgar Allan Poe are authors we discuss.
3. Marilyn or Evan will lead a debate this week.
4. We re-read and corrected our papers.
5. My dog eats, sleeps, and plays all day.
6. Decimals and percents are taught in math class.
7. Ellen or Hal will lead the discussion today.
8. Jim and Jane saw that movie.
9. Pairs of students check and correct each other's work.
10. Julia added and divided to solve that problem.
11. In the nineteenth century, few boys and girls stayed in school for as many years as students do today.
12. Instead, they worked on farms or labored in factories.
13. A boy or girl from a rich family might have a tutor.
14. Sometimes parents hired a teacher and started school.
15. Books and supplies were sometimes scarce.
16. Horace Mann visited schools and taught about learning improvements.
17. He and Mary Mann were interested in education.
18. Horace Mann wrote and spoke about schooling.
19. Schools and books were regularly inspected.
20. Horace Mann taught, practiced law, and ran a college.

▶ **Writing Application**   **Writing Sentences With Compound Subjects and Predicates.**   Write ten sentences describing a classroom activity. Use a compound subject or a compound predicate in each sentence. Underline the compound subject or compound predicate. Circle the conjunction.

1. _____
2. _____
3. _____
4. _____
5. _____
6. _____
7. _____
8. _____
9. _____
10. _____

19.4 # Hard-to-Find Subjects • Practice 1

The subject of a command or request is understood to be the word *you*. In questions, the subject follows the verb or is located between a helping verb and the main verb. The words *there* and *here* are never subjects.

LOCATING HARD-TO-FIND SUBJECTS	
Commands or Requests	**How the Sentences Are Understood**
Listen!	You listen!
Turn to page 24.	You turn to page 24.
Mike, please fasten your seatbelt.	Mike, you please fasten your seatbelt.
Questions	**Questions Changed to Statements**
Is it bigger than a house?	It is bigger than a house.
Has the play started?	The play has started.
When are they leaving?	They are leaving when.
Sentences With There or Here	**Reworded With Subjects First**
There goes the champ.	The champ goes there.
Here are the tickets.	The tickets are here.
There is a fly in my soup.	A fly is in my soup.

▶ **Exercise 1** **Recognizing Hard-to-Find Subjects.** Underline the subject in each sentence below.

EXAMPLE: There are chickens in the trees.

1. Where are my binoculars?

2. Here is the place to turn.

3. There are two pairs of twins in my class.

4. Does a cat always land on its feet?

5. When does the baseball season start?

6. Are cameras allowed inside the museum?

7. There goes our last chance to win.

8. Are there more nails in that can?

9. Here is my most valuable stamp.

10. There is a letter for you on the table.

▶ **Exercise 2** **Identifying the Subject of a Command or Request.** Write the subject of each sentence below in the blank at the right. Put a caret (∧) where the subject belongs in the sentence.

EXAMPLE: Mark, ∧ please lend me your ruler. ____*(you)*____

1. Jill, hand me those photographs, please. _____

2. Now, open to the last page of your test booklet. _____

3. Do not stick a knife or fork into the toaster. _____

4. Wendy, watch the baby for a moment, please. _____

5. John and Aaron, stop that roughhousing this minute! _____

19.4 Hard-to-Find Subjects • Practice 2

▶ **Exercise 1** **Recognizing Commands or Requests.** Write the simple subject of each sentence below in the blank. Five of the sentences are commands or requests.

EXAMPLE: Jennifer, look for Australia on the map. _____(you)_____

1. Remind me to take a picture of a koala bear. _____

2. Australia is a large country. _____

3. The British settled in Australia almost 200 years ago. _____

4. Look at the Australian flag. _____

5. Arlene, find the location of the capital, Canberra, on this map. _____

6. Most people in Australia speak English. _____

7. Listen to them speak. _____

8. Some Australian words are different from American English words. _____

9. Sydney is the largest city in Australia. _____

10. Maria, take a picture of that kangaroo. _____

▶ **Exercise 2** **Finding the Subject of Sentences That Ask Questions.** Write the simple subject of each question below in the blank. Remember to change the question into a statement if you are not sure of the subject.

EXAMPLE: Why did Laura send us a letter? _____Laura_____

1. What is the capital of Greece? _____

2. Has Richie decided on a career? _____

3. How did you spend the afternoon? _____

4. Did June remember to bring her racket? _____

5. When will the show begin? _____

6. Where is the museum? _____

7. Are swimming lessons given today? _____

8. Is the Arctic Ocean the smallest ocean? _____

9. Have scientists studied this animal? _____

10. Were advertisements printed in the magazine and in the newspaper? _____

▶ **Exercise 3** **Recognizing Hard-to-Find Subjects.** Write the simple subject of each sentence below in the blank. Commands and requests, questions, and sentences beginning with *there* and *here* are all included.

EXAMPLE: Is a cat a mammal? _____cat_____

1. Is the whale the largest mammal? _____

2. There are some very large whales. _____

3. Would the class like to visit the zoo? _____

4. Rita, find out the zoo's opening and closing times. _____

5. Look at the seal asleep on the rock. _____

19.5 Direct Objects • Practice 1

A direct object is a noun or pronoun that appears with an action verb and receives the action of the verb.

```
SENTENCES WITH DIRECT OBJECTS
                                   DO
      The first baseman dropped the  ball .
                          DO         DO
      Sam collects  stamps  and  coins .
                                          DO
      The candidate gave a rousing  speech .
```

▶ **Exercise 1**   **Finding Direct Objects.**   Draw a box around the direct object in each sentence below. If there are two or more direct objects in a sentence, draw a box around each one.

EXAMPLE: The mechanic checked the brakes and oil .

1. The pianist played several encores.

2. An animal often warns other animals of danger.

3. Sanchez hit the ball over the right-field fence.

4. Mrs. Lewis greeted each guest at the door.

5. The magician passed his wand slowly over the box.

6. Mr. Kelly grows orchids as a hobby.

7. Buckling up in seatbelts saves lives.

8. Stephanie studied the blueprints and the directions.

9. The magazine publishes articles and a few stories.

10. The boy cut his foot on a sharp rock.

▶ **Exercise 2**   **Writing Sentences With Direct Objects.**   Add words to each sentence beginning below to make a complete sentence. Be sure that the complete sentence contains a direct object.

EXAMPLE: Jennifer borrowed _____*a book from the library.*_____

1. In science today, we studied _____.

2. We all enjoyed _____.

3. At first, the detective suspected _____.

4. For a snack, I like _____.

5. The teacher complimented _____.

6. The treasure-hunters discovered _____.

7. Have you ever read _____?

8. The lifeguard rescued _____.

9. The letter carrier delivered _____.

10. Before the game, a soprano sang _____.

19.5 Direct Objects • Practice 2

▶ Exercise 1   **Finding Direct Objects.**   Underline the direct objects in each sentence below.

EXAMPLE: Ivan often plays <u>football</u>.

1. The jeweler displayed the bracelet in his window.
2. Kathy sings the opening song at the concert tonight.
3. One lucky person won the lottery.
4. The boss told the truth.
5. Patty noticed the daisies and lilies that I planted in my yard.
6. In the gym, Randy performed acrobatics on the mat.
7. Justine practices piano each Tuesday afternoon.
8. Mr. Murray locks the door at 6:00 p.m.
9. The plumber fixed the faucet and the drain.
10. Dr. Travis examined my teeth yesterday and said I have no cavities.

▶ Exercise 2   **More Work With Direct Objects.**   Follow the directions for Exercise 1.

1. I put film in the camera.
2. Mr. Brown grows flowers and vegetables every summer.
3. His family built a house in the country.
4. My mother listed the ingredients to buy.
5. The gift delighted them.
6. The student toured England and France.
7. Our committee appointed Mrs. Percy.
8. The child placed the dishes on the table.
9. The speaker showed charts, pictures, and graphs.
10. An announcer reported the news of the day.

▶ Writing Application   **Using Direct Objects in Sentences.**   Write ten sentences about something that happened in school last year. Use a direct object in each sentence. Underline the direct object.

1. _____
2. _____
3. _____
4. _____
5. _____
6. _____
7. _____
8. _____
9. _____
10. _____

19.5 Indirect Objects • Practice 1

An indirect object is a noun or pronoun usually located between an action verb and a direct object. It identifies the person or thing something is given to or done for.

INDIRECT OBJECTS
IO DO Supporters <u>gave</u> the │candidate│ a warm │welcome│.
IO DO The judges <u>assigned</u> each │finalist│ a │number│.
IO DO The paramedic <u>gave</u> the exhausted │runner│ │first aid│.

▶ **Exercise 1** **Recognizing Indirect Objects.** Draw a box around each indirect object in the sentences below. If there are two or more indirect objects, draw a box around each one.

EXAMPLE: The owner offered │Carla│ a reward.

1. Heather built her rabbit a new hutch.

2. A police officer showed the tourists the way.

3. The owner of the cheese shop offered Clare and me a free sample.

4. The librarian brought us the old newspaper.

5. Gail wrote her aunt a thank-you note.

6. The judges awarded Alicia first prize.

7. The principal gave Tom and Alex a stern warning.

8. Henry brought his mother a bouquet of flowers.

9. Mr. Dithers promised Dagwood a raise.

10. The Bemarks sent us a postcard from Greece.

▶ **Exercise 2** **Writing Sentences With Indirect Objects.** Rewrite each sentence below, changing the underlined prepositional phrase into an indirect object.

EXAMPLE: We fed peanuts <u>to the elephant</u>.

_____ *We fed the elephant peanuts.* _____

1. The mayor gave a medal <u>to Nicole</u>.

_____

2. The class sent canned goods <u>to the charitable organization</u>.

_____

3. My uncle found a summer job <u>for me</u>.

_____

4. I wrote a letter <u>to the author of the book</u>.

_____

5. The letter carrier brought a letter <u>for me</u>.

_____

19.5 Indirect Objects • Practice 2

▶ **Exercise 1** **Recognizing Indirect Objects.** Underline the indirect object in each sentence below.

EXAMPLE: I owe Martin a letter.

1. Several students brought the teacher an apple.
2. Sandra, please give him this message.
3. The family lent the museum their paintings.
4. Our agency finds people beautiful apartments.
5. My aunt wrote me with news of the new baby.
6. The architect showed her the plans for the house.
7. The company offered writers and lawyers good jobs.
8. Senator Alexander Blackwell sent the committee his report.
9. Please teach Kenny and me a tongue twister.
10. My watch tells me the time and the date.

▶ **Exercise 2** **More Work With Indirect Objects.** Follow the directions for Exercise 1.

1. Brenda told her mother, father, and brother the story.
2. Will you show my cousin and me your stamp collection?
3. The celebrity granted our magazine an interview.
4. A clever remark landed him the job.
5. The man in the tan sweater told me a tall tale.
6. Ron baked the children some bread.
7. The shiny penny could bring me some luck.
8. The teacher promised the class a party.
9. Before leaving, give us your new address.
10. The owner of the horse offered Chris a ride.

▶ **Writing Application** **Using Indirect Objects in Sentences.** Write ten sentences about your activities last week. Include an indirect object in each sentence. Underline the indirect object.

1. _____
2. _____
3. _____
4. _____
5. _____
6. _____
7. _____
8. _____
9. _____
10. _____

19.6 # Predicate Nouns • Practice 1

A predicate noun is a noun that appears with a subject and a linking verb. It renames or identifies the subject.

PREDICATE NOUNS

                                    PN
Wendy became a │ star │ overnight.

                                        PN
The horse car was a │ forerunner │ of the streetcar.

                                PN   PN
The co-captains are │ Laura │ and │ Betsy │.

                                        PN
Julie will be our next │ president │.

▶ **Exercise 1** **Recognizing Predicate Nouns.** Underline the predicate noun in each sentence below.

EXAMPLE: The turtle is a <u>kind</u> of reptile.

1. Whales and porpoises are mammals.

2. My favorite vegetables are corn and spinach.

3. The unicorn is a mythical beast.

4. After years of study, Dana became a doctor.

5. The mascot of the Navy team is a goat.

6. The former rivals became good friends.

7. John will probably remain team captain.

8. The runners-up were Lisa and Mark.

9. Eventually, the liquid became ice cream.

10. Leslie has remained my best friend.

▶ **Exercise 2** **More Work With Predicate Nouns.** Underline the predicate noun(s) in each sentence below. On the line, write the word the predicate noun(s) renames or identifies.

EXAMPLE: Hurricanes are tropical <u>storms</u>. _____*hurricanes*_____

1. Today's speaker is a nationally known columnist. _____

2. Lewis and Clark were famous American explorers. _____

3. Maurice Sendak is an author and an illustrator. _____

4. Australia is a continent and a country. _____

5. The first female astronaut was Valentina V. Tereshkova. _____

6. The number with 100 zeros is a googol. _____

7. Computer programming is a fast-growing career. _____

8. After a close election, Mr. Ramos remains the mayor. _____

9. John F. Kennedy became president at the age of forty-three. _____

10. Soccer is David's favorite sport. _____

19.6 Predicate Nouns • Practice 2

▶ **Exercise 1** **Recognizing Predicate Nouns.** Underline the predicate noun in each sentence below.

EXAMPLE: Janet became a <u>reporter</u>.

1. These books are novels.
2. Sarah was the illustrator of that story.
3. The young man is a beginner.
4. Our neighbor Georgia became an astronomer.
5. The group remained friends for many years.
6. This computer should be the machine for you.
7. I am an amateur tennis player.
8. The animals here are dogs, cats, and birds.
9. Dr. Parker has been my dentist for five years.
10. Mrs. Gomez is the school nurse.
11. A raccoon is a mammal.
12. That tree might be a maple.
13. Eddie will remain class treasurer for another year.
14. The brave fireman is my uncle.
15. This green stone must be an emerald.
16. Phil could become a professional golfer.
17. This flower with three petals must be an orchid.
18. I was a volunteer in the city hospital.
19. Broccoli and spinach are green vegetables.
20. Balboa and Magellan were Spanish explorers.

▶ **Writing Application** **Using Predicate Nouns in Sentences.** Write ten sentences about characters from books, movies, or TV. Use a linking verb and a predicate noun in each sentence. Underline the predicate noun.

1. _____
2. _____
3. _____
4. _____
5. _____
6. _____
7. _____
8. _____
9. _____
10. _____

19.6 Predicate Adjectives • Practice 1

A predicate adjective is an adjective that appears with a subject and a linking verb. It describes or modifies the subject of the sentence.

PREDICATE ADJECTIVES

PA
The price seems high .

PA
The crowd in the theater remained calm .

PA   PA
The pages of the old book were faded and dusty .

PA
The footbridge looked unsafe .

Exercise 1 **Recognizing Predicate Adjectives.** Underline each predicate adjective in the sentences below. Then, circle the subject each one modifies.

EXAMPLE: The new (law) is unfair to dogs.

1. Norman's plan sounds impractical.

2. It grows dark rapidly in the forest.

3. Today's crossword puzzle looks quite hard.

4. The defendant's story sounded fishy.

5. Most of the runners looked weary at the finish line.

6. This milk smells sour.

7. Sugar maples turn yellow in the fall.

8. The water feels cold at first.

9. The bank teller became suspicious.

10. The day was hot and muggy.

Exercise 2 **Using Predicate Adjectives in Sentences.** Complete each sentence below by adding an appropriate predicate adjective.

EXAMPLE: Skateboarding can be _____dangerous._____

1. In the fall, the days grow _____.

2. This album is _____.

3. A good adventure movie is _____.

4. After exercise, a shower feels _____.

5. Metal buttons on a uniform should be _____.

6. Pretzels usually taste _____.

7. Some scenes in a horror movie will probably be _____.

8. After winning an important game, a player feels _____.

9. Popcorn smells _____.

10. Velvet feels _____.

19.6 Predicate Adjectives • Practice 2

> **Exercise 1** **Recognizing Predicate Adjectives.** Underline the predicate adjective in each sentence below. Then, draw an arrow connecting the predicate adjective to the subject it modifies. Compound predicate adjectives are included.

EXAMPLE: The audience grew silent.

1. This winter has been cold and damp.

2. The plans sound perfect to me.

3. We were ready before noon.

4. That marching music is lively.

5. My pet cat is intelligent but mischievous.

6. Your home cooking always tastes wonderful.

7. The room looks strange without furniture.

8. The house will be empty all summer.

9. I became impatient with the slow service.

10. The listeners remained quiet and attentive.

> **Exercise 2** **More Work With Predicate Adjectives.** Underline the predicate adjective in each sentence below.

1. Mike is interested in computers.

2. You must be mistaken about the time and place.

3. I remained awake and restless all night.

4. The path became narrow and steep.

5. My parents will be happy with this news.

6. This large sculpture is attractive but unsteady.

7. You seem healthy and rested after your vacation.

8. This new fabric feels smooth.

9. My aunt appeared tired after her trip.

10. We were nervous about the noise.

> **Writing Application** **Using Predicate Adjectives in Sentences.** Write five sentences advertising one or more "new" products. Use a predicate adjective in each sentence. Remember to use only linking verbs.

1. _____

2. _____

3. _____

4. _____

5. _____

20.1 # Adjective Phrases • Practice 1

An adjective phrase is a prepositional phrase that modifies a noun or pronoun.

ADJECTIVE PHRASES
The shops *in the mall* are still open. (modifies a noun)
The manager wants someone *with experience*. (modifies a pronoun)

▶ **Exercise 1** **Finding Adjective Phrases.** Underline the adjective phrase in each sentence below. Circle the noun or pronoun it modifies.

EXAMPLE: (Teams) in the junior baseball league have ten players.

1. The main character in the story is a young boy.

2. He is a visitor from another planet.

3. Part of the treasure map is missing.

4. The road along the coastline has the best views.

5. Several of the eggs are cracked.

6. The sign on the bench said "WET PAINT."

7. I'm reading a book about the Pony Express.

8. I would like a bike with ten speeds.

9. The gate to the playground is locked.

10. The notebook with the plaid cover is mine.

▶ **Exercise 2** **Using Adjective Phrases.** Write a sentence of your own using the prepositional phrase in parentheses as an adjective phrase. Circle the noun or pronoun that the phrase modifies in your sentence.

EXAMPLE: (with the closed shutters) The (house) with the closed shutters is spooky.

1. (in the meadow) _____

2. (through the woods) _____

3. (from another country) _____

4. (about computers) _____

5. (of stamps) _____

20.1 Adjective Phrases • Practice 2

▶ **Exercise 1** **Finding Adjective Phrases.** In the sentences below, underline each prepositional phrase used as an adjective. There can be more than one in a sentence. Then, draw an arrow connecting the phrase to the word it modifies.

EXAMPLE: The surface of Earth holds water.

1. The water near the bottom of this lake is cold.

2. The water in the ocean is not drinking water.

3. Many people from the city enjoy water sports.

4. Faucets in houses bring us a good supply of water.

5. Water from the ocean evaporates.

6. Later, the moisture in the atmosphere returns as rain.

7. Industries along rivers often use the available water.

8. A house beside a lake is well located.

9. The tap water in this village tastes wonderful.

10. The water behind the dam is being saved.

▶ **Exercise 2** **More Work With Adjective Phrases.** Follow the directions for Exercise 1.

1. The sound of the machinery made us shout.

2. I will share my ideas on the subject.

3. The field across the road is where we play softball.

4. The sign near the road was an advertisement.

5. Today is a good day for a picnic.

6. The seat with the cushion is comfortable.

7. The car behind us was a convertible.

8. Irene heard the noise of the carpenter repairing the house next door.

9. The ground outside the building is muddy.

10. You should follow the advice of this expert.

▶ **Writing Application** **Using Adjective Phrases in Sentences.** Write five sentences about some goals you have set for yourself. Use an adjective phrase in each sentence.

1. _____

2. _____

3. _____

4. _____

5. _____

Name _____ Date _____

 20.1 # Adverb Phrases • **Practice 1**

An adverb phrase is a prepositional phrase that modifies a verb, an adjective, or an adverb.

ADVERB PHRASES
Camera club meets *on Wednesdays*. (modifies a verb)
Paul was happy *about his home run*. (modifies an adjective)
He arrived too late *for dinner*. (modifies an adverb)

▶ **Exercise 1** **Recognizing Adverb Phrases.** Underline the adverb phrase in each sentence below. Circle the word the phrase modifies.

EXAMPLE: Cindy (borrowed) lunch money <u>from the office</u>.

1. The soldiers crossed the river in small boats.

2. The library closes early on Saturdays.

3. Michelle delivers papers after school.

4. Water boils at 100° Celsius.

5. The coat was too big for the little boy.

6. Kevin plays the trumpet in the school band.

7. The children were curious about the large package.

8. The trail led along the rim of the crayon.

9. Sam practices for an hour every day.

10. We started hiking early in the morning.

▶ **Exercise 2** **Using Adverb Phrases.** Write a sentence of your own using each of the prepositional phrases in parentheses as an adverb phrase. Circle the word the phrase modifies in your sentence.

EXAMPLE: (for his age)   Steve seems (tall) for his age.

1. (through the window) _____

2. (after the storm) _____

3. (into the fishbowl) _____

4. (to the speaker) _____

5. (by six points) _____

20.1 Adverb Phrases • Practice 2

▶ **Exercise 1**   **Recognizing Adverb Phrases.**   In the sentences below, underline each adverb phrase. Then, draw an arrow connecting the phrase with the word it modifies.

EXAMPLE: The boy took his toy boat to the pond.

1. She placed my umbrella beside my coat.

2. Jim plays softball after school.

3. The books fell with a loud bang.

4. On Sunday afternoon I read the sports section.

5. During the meeting Jean explained her ideas.

6. The housekeeper led the visitor to the study.

7. The entire class agrees with our plan.

8. He seems afraid of the dark.

9. We studied that question in the fall.

10. The old newspapers and magazines were piled evenly in stacks.

▶ **Exercise 2**   **More Work With Adverb Phrases.**   Underline the adverb phrase in each sentence below. Then, circle the word it modifies.

1. E. B. White first lived in Mount Vernon, New York.

2. He studied at Cornell University.

3. He later wrote for *The New Yorker* magazine.

4. His writing is famous for its clarity and simplicity.

5. His essays are graceful in style.

6. His children's books appeal to many adults.

7. In *Charlotte's Web*, he wrote about a spider.

8. In his books, readers find fascinating details.

9. His stories are often full of his own experiences.

10. His book *Stuart Little* describes in detail a mouse's adventures.

▶ **Writing Application**   **Writing Sentences With Adverb Phrases.**   Write five sentences about a day you will never forget. Use an adverb in each sentence. Underline the adverbs.

1. _____

2. _____

3. _____

4. _____

5. _____

20.1 Appositive Phrases • Practice 1

An appositive phrase renames, identifies, or explains the noun with which it appears.

APPOSITIVE PHRASES
The equator, <u>an imaginary line</u>, separates the Northern and Southern Hemispheres.
James Madison, <u>our fourth president</u>, was the first to live in the White House.
The Adventures of Huckleberry Finn, <u>Mark Twain's most famous novel</u>, was published in 1884.

▶ **Exercise 1**   **Finding Appositive Phrases.**   Underline the appositive phrase in each sentence below. Circle the noun or pronoun it identifies or explains.

EXAMPLE: (Alfred Nobel), <u>the inventor of dynamite</u>, invented the Nobel Prizes.

1. The eohippus, a small hoofed mammal, was the ancestor of the horse.

2. Dave, a strong swimmer, works as a lifeguard in the summers.

3. The damaged plane, a Boeing 727, landed safely.

4. The lighthouse, a landmark for sailors, is nearly two hundred years old.

5. Enrico Caruso, a famous opera tenor, had an amazing voice.

6. Ms. Geering, the next mayor, has promised many reforms.

7. The blue whale, the largest mammal on Earth, can weigh up to 115 tons.

8. Mr. Amati, our neighbor, makes violins as a hobby.

9. Either of two alphabets may be used in writing Serbo-Croatian, the language of Yugoslavia.

10. The wallet should be returned to me, the rightful owner.

▶ **Exercise 2**   **Using Appositive Phrases.**   Write five sentences of your own in which you use each phrase below as an appositive phrase. Circle the noun or pronoun that the appositive phrase identifies or explains.

EXAMPLE: (my favorite rock group)

(The Wrecking Crew), *my favorite rock group, will be at the Orpheum on Friday.*

1. (our next-door neighbor) _____

_____

2. (my favorite snack) _____

_____

3. (a famous rock singer) _____

_____

4. (the school principal) _____

_____

5. (our state capital) _____

_____

20.1 Appositive Phrases • Practice 2

▶ **Exercise 1**   **Finding Appositive Phrases.**   In the sentences below, underline each appositive phrase. Then, draw an arrow from the phrase to the noun it identifies or explains.

EXAMPLE: This book, a suspense novel, is very popular.

1. Jim Kelly, the star of our show, was on TV.

2. Gym, my favorite class, is scheduled for today.

3. This car, an inexpensive model, uses gas efficiently.

4. We considered two choices, a Mexican restaurant and a French restaurant.

5. This letter, a message from my mother, arrived today.

6. Aunt Clara, my mother's sister, lives in Tennessee.

7. This cabinet was made by Bill Webster, my great-uncle.

8. The music, jazz of the 1930's, was great.

9. My friend, a computer whiz, leads a busy life.

10. The home, an elegant mansion, is owned by a millionaire.

▶ **Exercise 2**   **More Work With Appositive Phrases.**   In the sentences below, underline each appositive phrase. Then, draw an arrow from the phrase to the noun it identifies or explains.

1. Atlanta, the capital of Georgia, is a busy city.

2. Main Street, a busy thoroughfare, was closed to traffic.

3. Lisa, my cousin from Maine, will visit us.

4. The movie, an unusually long show, was a documentary.

5. We joined the club, a group of serious chess players.

6. That oil painting, a portrait of an ancestor, has been in the family since 1875.

7. Paul Revere, a Revolutionary War patriot, was an expert silversmith.

8. It would be hard to pet a porcupine, an animal with sharp quills.

9. We will see our cousins, Randy Cruz and Roberta Montoya, on Friday.

10. I had to choose between two classes, computer studies and drama.

▶ **Writing Application**   **Using Appositive Phrases.**   Write five sentences about people, places, and events you know well. Use an appositive phrase in each sentence.

1. _____

2. _____

3. _____

4. _____

5. _____

20.2 Recognizing Independent Clauses
• Practice 1

A clause is a group of words that contains both a subject and a verb. An independent clause has a subject and a verb and can stand alone as a complete sentence. A subordinate clause has a subject and verb but cannot stand alone as a complete sentence.

CLAUSES	
Independent Clauses	**Subordinate Clauses**
The library has a new computer.	if the door is not closed
Last week, it rained every day.	after the bell rings

▷ **Exercise 1**   **Recognizing Independent Clauses.**   In the space provided, identify each clause below as *independent* or *subordinate*.

EXAMPLE: the last scene scared many viewers _____*independent*_____

1. the ancient Egyptians worshiped cats _____

2. who have some experience _____

3. after the concert has begun _____

4. some trains travel at 120 miles per hour _____

5. the map of Thailand is shaped like an elephant's head _____

6. until the last out has been made _____

7. although Jamie did not expect to win _____

8. before the runner could get to first base _____

9. Ms. Maloney teaches science _____

10. we were waiting for the bus _____

▷ **Exercise 2**   **Writing Independent Clauses.**   Write each independent clause from Exercise 1, adding a capital at the beginning and a period at the end.

EXAMPLE: _____*The last scene scared many viewers.*_____

1. _____

2. _____

3. _____

4. _____

5. _____

20.2 # Recognizing Independent Clauses
• Practice 2

▶ **Exercise 1**   **Recognizing Independent Clauses.**   In the space provided, identify each group of words below as an *independent clause* or a *subordinate clause*.

EXAMPLE: Harriet was almost trapped by a posse _____*independent clause*_____

1. Harriet Tubman was born a slave _____
2. when she was six years old _____
3. she heard about slave uprisings _____
4. although Harriet was still a child _____
5. while she worked in the fields _____
6. Harriet Tubman escaped from slavery _____
7. she decided to help other slaves escape _____
8. after one group escaped _____
9. the Underground Railroad became famous _____
10. this woman of courage led many people to freedom _____

▶ **Exercise 2**   **More Practice Recognizing Independent Clauses.**   Follow the directions for Exercise 1.

1. Jan got his chance _____
2. until the senator began to speak _____
3. during the time that she worked in the factory _____
4. he stood there and fumbled for words _____
5. although the enemy destroyed the city _____
6. the guest told jokes during dinner _____
7. since everyone agrees with the plan _____
8. when they had all gathered in the hall _____
9. our teacher showed us some slides _____
10. while we were waiting for the trolley _____

▶ **Writing Application**   **Writing Independent Clauses.**   Write ten independent clauses, adding a capital at the beginning and a period at the end. Each should describe someone you know. Make sure each has a subject and verb and is a complete sentence.

1. _____
2. _____
3. _____
4. _____
5. _____
6. _____
7. _____
8. _____
9. _____
10. _____

20.2 Forming Compound Sentences • Practice 1

A compound sentence is made up of two or more independent clauses. The clauses are usually joined by a comma and a coordinating conjunction (and, but, for, nor, or, so, or yet). The clauses of a compound sentence may also be joined with a semicolon (;).

COMPOUND SENTENCES
The sky cleared, and the rain stopped.
The food at Casey's is good, but the service is terrible.
Both doors must be shut, or the elevator will not operate.
Lou wasn't ready for the big test; he had not studied at all.

▶ **Exercise 1** **Identifying the Parts of Compound Sentences.** In each compound sentence below, underline the subjects of the clauses once. Underline the verbs of the clauses twice. Circle the coordinating conjunction or semicolon that joins the clauses.

EXAMPLE: The boy cried "Wolf!" (;) no one paid any attention.

1. The water looked inviting, but it was very cold.

2. Leaves were turning, and the geese were flying south.

3. The recipe calls for salt, but I don't use any.

4. We expected rain, for all of the forecasts had predicted it.

5. Sharon could not make a decision; so much depended on the outcome.

6. We must score six runs, or the Renegades will win.

7. No one walked unnoticed down Maple Lane, for Mrs. Lewis was always at her window.

8. The work was dangerous, but it paid well.

9. Scott didn't expect to win the broad jump, yet he still entered.

10. We have to pay for the soda anyway, so we might as well drink it.

▶ **Exercise 2** **Writing Compound Sentences.** Combine each pair of independent clauses below into a compound sentence. Use a comma and the coordinating conjunction shown in brackets.

EXAMPLE: The ship sank. The passengers were all safe. [but]
_____The ship sank, but the passengers were all safe._____

1. Cinderella married the prince. They lived happily ever after. [and]

   _____

2. The inventor had many disappointments. He didn't give up. [but]

   _____

3. Voters must register. They cannot vote. [or]

   _____

4. My sister wants to graduate early. She is going to summer school. [so]

   _____

5. We expected a storm. The barometer was falling rapidly. [for]

   _____

20.2 **Forming Compound Sentences • Practice 2**

▶ **Exercise 1**   **Writing Compound Sentences.**   Combine each pair of independent clauses below into one compound sentence. Use a comma and the coordinating conjunction shown in brackets.

EXAMPLE: The forecast is for rain.
                The sun is still shining. [but]

_____*The forecast is for rain, but the sun is still shining.*_____

1. Ted brought the rolls.
    Robin brought the orange juice. [and]

    _____

2. The fans cheered the players on.
    The team couldn't even the score. [but]

    _____

3. I want to sell my old bicycle.
    I have outgrown it. [for]

    _____

4. We can take a bus to the theater.
    We can leave early and walk there. [or]

    _____

5. Susan helped me with my math.
    I helped her with her English. [and]

    _____

6. I have long, straight hair.
    My sister has short, curly hair. [but]

    _____

7. Bowling is a very old game.
    Balls and pins have been found in Egyptian tombs. [for]

    _____

8. Dinosaurs were very large.
    Their brains were very small. yet]

    _____

9. In 1910 there were no electric washing machines.
    There were no electric toasters. [and]

    _____

10. Frisbees today are made of plastic.
    Earlier models were made of metal. [but]

    _____

▶ **Writing Application**   **Creating Compound Sentences.**   Write five compound sentences. In three of them, use a comma and a coordinating conjunction. In the other two, use a semicolon to join the independent clauses. Underline each simple subject once and each verb twice.

1. _____
2. _____
3. _____
4. _____
5. _____

21.1 Four Kinds of Sentences • Practice 1

There are four kinds of sentences: declarative, interrogative, imperative, and exclamatory.

FOUR KINDS OF SENTENCES	
Kinds of Sentences	**Examples**
Declarative	Whitcomb L. Judson invented the zipper.
Interrogative	Who invented the zipper?
Imperative	Lend me your book about inventors.
Exclamatory	What a lot of inventions there are!

▶ **Exercise 1** **Identifying the Four Kinds of Sentences.** Identify each sentence below as *declarative*, *interrogative*, *imperative*, or *exclamatory*.

EXAMPLE: Add the milk to the dry ingredients slowly. _____*imperative*_____

1. Who was the first female astronaut? _____

2. Buckle your seatbelt even for short trips. _____

3. Please put the stamped envelopes in this box. _____

4. You must be joking! _____

5. What a thrill that ride was! _____

6. In 1776, there were fifty-three newspapers in London. _____

7. Who were the first people to use paper money? _____

8. Insert the diskette in this slot. _____

9. Insects outnumber people by millions to one. _____

10. What an amazing story that is! _____

▶ **Exercise 2** **Choosing the Correct End Mark for the Sentence.** On the line provided, supply an appropriate end mark for each sentence below.

EXAMPLE: English has many interesting names of groups of animals ___.___

1. Give us some examples _____

2. Well, a group of lions is a pride _____

3. What is a group of leopards called _____

4. Have you ever heard of a leap of leopards _____

5. What a great name that is for those cats _____

6. A gam is a group of whales _____

7. Then, what is a pod _____

8. Look up both words in a dictionary, please _____

9. Either noun can be used for whales _____

10. One is just as weird as the other _____

21.1 Four Kinds of Sentences • Practice 2

▷ **Exercise 1** **Recognizing the Four Kinds of Sentences.** On the line provided, label each sentence below *declarative*, *interrogative*, *imperative*, or *exclamatory*. Then, show what punctuation is needed at the end of the sentence.

EXAMPLE: Have you ever been to New England ____*interrogative* ?____

1. Maine is a New England state _____
2. What is the population _____
3. Visit Acadia National Park _____
4. Why is Maine called the Pine Tree State _____
5. What a rocky coast this is _____
6. How thrilling it is to ski down these mountains _____
7. Maine has many small, white churches _____
8. Try a Maine lobster _____
9. Have you ever been to the Tate House in Portland _____
10. The winters in this Northeastern state are very cold and long _____

▷ **Exercise 2** **More Work With the Four Kinds of Sentences.** Follow the directions for Exercise 1.

1. Our neighbor bought a new computer _____
2. Look at the color monitor _____
3. The computer has a large memory _____
4. Try this new piece of software _____
5. Can you save this report on a disk _____
6. How fast it prints _____
7. Can you make color graphics _____
8. What a fabulous device this is _____
9. You can write your own programs _____
10. A computer may change the way you write _____

▷ **Writing Application** **Writing Four Kinds of Sentences.** Write ten sentences about early morning sights, sounds, and thoughts. Use all four kinds of sentences.

1. _____
2. _____
3. _____
4. _____
5. _____
6. _____
7. _____
8. _____
9. _____
10. _____

21.2 Sentence Combining • Practice 1

Combine two or three short, choppy sentences into one longer sentence.

WAYS OF COMBINING SENTENCES	
Short Sentences	**Combined Sentences**
Arthur is taking tennis lessons. Louise is taking tennis lessons.	Arthur and Louise are taking tennis lessons. (compound subject)
Paul sat in his room. Paul read a book.	Paul sat in his room and read a book. (compound predicate)
We waited. The bus never came.	We waited, but the bus never came. (compound sentence)
Our new car is very economical. It is a small, compact model.	Our new car, a small, compact model, is very economical. (appositive phrase)
We saw Jason last night. He was at the movie.	We saw Jason last night at the movie. (prepositional phrase)
Fluffy was dozing by the fire. She looked quite content.	Dozing by the fire, Fluffy looked quite content. (participial phrase)

▷ **Exercise 1** **Combining Sentences.** Using the methods shown above, rewrite each group of sentences below as a single sentence.

EXAMPLE: Maine moose have huge noses. They have big droopy mouths. They are funny-looking animals.

_____ *Maine moose, funny-looking animals, have huge noses and big droopy mouths.* _____

1. The weather may clear. We may go sailing after all.

   _____

2. Last night Marcia called. She invited me to spend the day.

   _____

3. My father is building us a playhouse. My grandfather is helping him.

   _____

4. Jennie went to the movies. Sue went, too. I went with them.

   _____

5. The cookies smelled delicious. They are baking in the oven.

   _____

▷ **Exercise 2** **More Work With Combining Sentences.** Follow the directions for Exercise 1.

1. We were able to assemble the bicycle ourselves. We followed the directions carefully.

   _____

2. The horse got out of the barn. It ran across the field. It went into the woods.

   _____

3. The concert tickets raised lots of money. The album made money, too.

   _____

4. Mr. Gordon demands the best from the players. He is the girls' basketball coach.

   _____

5. Jogging is good exercise. Swimming is good exercise. Biking is good, too.

   _____

21.2 Sentence Combining • Practice 2

▷ **Exercise 1** **Combining Sentences.** Using any of the sentence-combining techniques, combine the sentences in each of the following items.

EXAMPLE: We sat on the beach. We watched the sun rise.

_____ *Sitting on the beach, we watched the sun rise.* _____

1. Joe parked the car. He carried the groceries into the house.
_____

2. Janice and Terry ran indoors. They were drenched from the sudden rain shower.
_____

3. The exhibit was a success. The bake sale was a success, too.
_____

4. I usually arrive early at school. I enjoy walking in the morning.
_____

5. Marty had a pet snake. It lived in a glass tank in Marty's bedroom.
_____

6. Mr. Wilson paints landscapes. He sells them at the Community Art Center.
_____

7. The Rangers tasted victory. It was the first time this season.
_____

8. Two famous ball players were the surprise guests. They were guests at our awards banquet. The banquet was held Friday.
_____

9. The bank robber was disguised. She looked like a policeman. She escaped unnoticed into the crowd on the sidewalk.
_____

10. The walrus looks clumsy. It appears sluggish. It is quite agile in the water.
_____

▷ **Exercise 2** **More Work With Combining Sentences.** Follow the directions for Exercise 1.

1. Mother ordered flowers for the party. The flowers were delivered next door by mistake.
_____

2. The tool shed stays warm during the winter. It has good insulation.
_____

3. Thomas Jefferson was the third president of the United States. He helped to write the Declaration of Independence.
_____

4. Stephanie wants to buy a new stereo. She wants to get a personal computer. She needs a new bicycle first.
_____

5: The beaver slapped the water with its tail. It swam away. It swam down the river.
_____

21.3 # Adding Details to Sentences • **Practice 1**

Enrich short sentences by adding details to the subject, verb, or complement.

LENGTHENING SHORT SENTENCES BY ADDING DETAILS	
	Adding Details to the Subject
The kitten was terrified.	Trapped in the tree with the Doberman barking below, the kitten was terrified.
	Adding Details to the Verb
The gardener trimmed the shrubs.	The gardener carefully and lovingly trimmed the shrubs.
	Adding Details to the Complement
The explorers found a treasure.	The explorers found an old, moldy treasure chest with a pile of rocks inside it.

▶ **Exercise 1**　**Adding Details to Short Sentences.**　Rewrite each sentence below by adding the details in parentheses where they fit best.

EXAMPLE: The ship flew a flag. (pirate; with a skull and crossbones)

　　　　　The pirate ship flew a flag with a skull and crossbones.

1. The students are making plans. (high-school, elaborate, for the prom)

_____

2. Fish swam in the tank. (colorful, tropical; large salt-water)

_____

3. The restaurant was full. (new Mexican; of happy, chattering customers)

_____

4. Judy decided to enter the race. (in spite of her trainer's advice, annual long-distance)

_____

5. The house is on a beautiful lot. (old colonial; wooded, with many pine trees)

_____

▶ **Exercise 2**　**More Work With Short Sentences.**　Rewrite each sentence below by adding at least two details of your own.

EXAMPLE: The politician attracted many supporters.

　　　　　The dynamic young politician attracted many supporters among various cultural groups.

1. The movie scared the child.

_____

2. We enjoyed the meal.

_____

3. Flowers cover the fence.

_____

4. Tim hated camp.

_____

5. Kelly's story had good details.

_____

21.3 Adding Details to Sentences • Practice 2

▶ **Exercise 1**　**Adding Details to Short Sentences.**　Rewrite each of the following sentences by adding the details in parentheses. Place them where they fit best and where they seem most clear.

EXAMPLE: The sun blazed down. (summer, onto the beach)

　　　　　　<u>The summer sun blazed down onto the beach.</u>

1. We ate a picnic lunch. (under the trees, of sandwiches and sodas)
   _____

2. The tree swayed in the wind. (its leaves rustling, outside my window)
   _____

3. They studied hard. (every night, afraid of failing their math test)
   _____

4. Birds perched in a cage. (large gilded, enormous multicolored)
   _____

5. We jumped and ran. (hearing a loud crash, afraid that the roof would cave in)
   _____

6. We roasted marshmallows. (gathered around the campfire, after dinner)
   _____

7. Ellen set the table. (with our best china and silverware, before the guests arrived)
   _____

8. Les made a mistake. (hurrying to finish the project in time, serious)
   _____

9. We had spaghetti. (with clam sauce, after an exciting day at the beach)
   _____

10. Phil took a hike. (on a beautiful spring day, along the rugged trail leading to the waterfall)
    _____

▶ **Exercise 2**　**More Work With Short Sentences.**　Rewrite each of the following sentences by adding at least two details.

1. Our kite soared._____

2. We painted my room._____

3. Pam spoke to my father._____

4. Eileen and I rode our bicycles._____

5. George saw a shape._____

21.3 # Shortening Rambling Sentences • Practice 1

Separate a rambling compound sentence into two or more shorter sentences.

Rambling Sentences	Revised Sentences
We had planned a family reunion and everyone was going to bring something, but my cousins got sick, so my aunt and uncle couldn't come, and we postponed the whole thing for a month.	We had planned a family reunion, and everyone was going to bring something. However, my cousins got sick, so my aunt and uncle couldn't come. We postponed the reunion for a month.
The batter stepped up to the plate and took a few practice swings, and the pitcher took the set position, but the batter stepped out of the box, and after a few more repeats of this, the fans began to boo.	The batter stepped up to the plate and took a few practice swings. Then the pitcher took the set position, but the batter stepped out of the box. After a few more repeats of this, the fans began to boo.

▶ **Exercise 1** **Shortening Rambling Sentences.** Rewrite the rambling sentence below to make two or more shorter ones.

EXAMPLE: I heard the doorbell ring, so I put down my book and went to answer it, but when I got there, I didn't see anyone, so I went back to my book, and once again the bell rang, but this time when I got there I found a beautiful basket of flowers.

I heard the doorbell ring, so I put down my book and went to answer it. When I got there and didn't see anyone, I went back to my book. Once again the bell rang. This time when I got there I found a beautiful basket of flowers.

Audrey is always very careful about getting assignments down clearly, so she was the best person to call with my question, but she wasn't home, so I tried Angie, but she wasn't home either, and by the time I could reach anyone the library was closed, so I couldn't do the work anyway.

_____

_____

_____

_____

_____

▶ **Exercise 2** **More Work With Shortening Rambling Sentences.** Follow the directions for Exercise 1.

We walked for miles through the woods, and we finally found a campsite that we liked, so we pitched our tent beside the stream, and Dad went off to fill the water buckets while we gathered sticks for kindling, and when we came back to camp, the tent was on the ground, and a raccoon was eating our bread and graham crackers.

_____

_____

_____

_____

_____

21.3 Shortening Rambling Sentences • Practice 2

▶ **Exercise 1** **Shortening Rambling Sentences.** Rewrite each rambling sentence below to make two or three shorter ones.

EXAMPLE: The cat stood up, and she jumped off the shelf, and she knocked over a vase.

_____*The cat stood up. She jumped off the shelf and knocked over the vase.*_____

1. My sister wanted to ride the roller coaster, but it was raining, so we couldn't, so we saw a movie instead, and on the way home we stopped for ice cream.

   _____

   _____

   _____

2. Uncle Henry bought a new car, and it looked sturdy, but it soon developed problems, and so he had to sell it.

   _____

   _____

   _____

3. Mix three eggs in a bowl and add half a cup of milk, and beat the ingredients, and dip slices of bread into mixture, and then fry the bread on a griddle.

   _____

   _____

   _____

4. Connie's aunt sent her some money, so Connie decided to buy some clothes, so she took the bus downtown, and she bought a new ski jacket and boots.

   _____

   _____

   _____

5. Bill closed his eyes and swung the bat, and it connected with a crack, and he started running, and he just made it to second base a second before the throw.

   _____

   _____

   _____

▶ **Writing Application** **Rewriting Rambling Sentences.** Rewrite the following passage by shortening rambling sentences.

   I thought drive-in movies were a thing of the past, but we found one near our summer cottage, so naturally we asked Dad to take us, and he did, but none of us remembers what movie was playing, because first Monica made friends with the girls in the next car, and then Skip and I explored the grounds, especially between the car and the refreshment stand, where we also made some new friends, and Dad spent his time cleaning out the trunk of the car, and we all accomplished a lot that night.

   _____

   _____

   _____

   _____

   _____

21.4 Recognizing Fragments • Practice 1

A fragment is a group of words that does not express a complete thought.

Fragments	What Is Missing
The damaged moving van.	a verb
Waited for an answer.	a subject
Guests strolling on the beach.	a complete verb
On the deck.	a subject and a verb
If it stops raining.	an independent clause

▶ **Exercise 1**   **Recognizing Fragments.**   Identify each group of words below as *fragment* or *sentence.*

EXAMPLE: In the middle of a quiet conversation.   _____*fragment*_____

1. Who always arrives at school half an hour early. _____

2. Several customers still waiting to be seated. _____

3. The principal asked me to step into his office. _____

4. In some bushes near the bike rack on the playground. _____

5. If it rains tomorrow, the picnic will be indoors. _____

6. The pants shrank. _____

7. Depended on the success of the mission. _____

8. A mysterious black limousine with smoked windows. _____

9. The bus finally got to the village. _____

10. A few customers complained loudly. _____

▶ **Exercise 2**   **Identifying What Is Missing From Fragments.**   For each fragment you found in Exercise 1, write down its item number and indicate what is missing: *a verb,* *a subject,* *a complete verb,* a *subject and a verb,* or *an independent clause.*

EXAMPLE: In the middle of a quiet conversation.   _____*a subject and a verb*_____

_____

_____

_____

_____

_____

21.4 Recognizing Fragments • Practice 2

▶ **Exercise 1** **Recognizing Fragments.** Write *sentence* or *fragment* for each group of words below.

EXAMPLE: The package on the steps. _____*fragment*_____

1. The day was dark and gray. _____
2. After we ate dinner. _____
3. On our street. _____
4. A bunch of flowers in her hand. _____
5. My brother and I explored the rooms in the vast, ancient castle. _____
6. Yelled back at us in a loud voice. _____
7. I didn't realize how cold it was. _____
8. In the middle of a big commotion. _____
9. My cousin chased me up the stairs. _____
10. A sharp turn into the driveway. _____

▶ **Exercise 2** **More Work With Fragments.** Follow the directions for Exercise 1.

1. My neighbors went on an African safari. _____
2. We saw some bighorn sheep. _____
3. Jumped out from behind the door. _____
4. Watching for the arrival of the plane. _____
5. When I was living in Columbus, Ohio, with my grandparents. _____
6. A few of us waited outside. _____
7. Every Saturday before practice. _____
8. Should have guessed immediately. _____
9. After the first week at camp. _____
10. The conductor checked the tickets. _____

▶ **Writing Application** **Writing About Fragments and Sentences.** Make up an example of a complete sentence and an example of a sentence fragment. Then, write a paragraph explaining the difference between the two groups of words.

_____
_____
_____
_____
_____
_____
_____
_____

21.4 Correcting Fragments • Practice 1

To correct a fragment, use one of these methods: (1) Connect the fragment to a nearby sentence. (2) Add the necessary words to change the fragments into a sentence.

CORRECTING FRAGMENTS

Connecting Fragments to Nearby Sentences
A few customers stood at the door. Waiting to be seated. (fragment)
A few customers stood at the door waiting to be seated. (joined to sentence)
Although the work was dangerous. The pay was good. (fragment)
Although the work was dangerous, the pay was good. (joined to sentence)

Adding Necessary Words to Fragments
During the scariest part of the movie. (fragment)
I closed my eyes during the scariest part of the movie. (sentence)
Depended on the success of the mission. (fragment)
Victory depended on the success of the mission. (sentence)

▶ **Exercise 1** **Connecting Fragments to Nearby Sentences.** Correct each fragment below by connecting it to a nearby sentence. Write only the sentence containing the corrected fragment.

EXAMPLE: She vanished. In a moment. No one ever saw her again.

_____ *She vanished in a moment.* _____

1. A ship sailed into the harbor. Flying a strange flag. Everyone was curious.

   _____

2. You may use my binoculars. If you are careful with them. Otherwise, you can't.

   _____

3. We got off the boat. With a few seconds to spare. Then, it went down.

   _____

4. The magician found the card. Right in my pocket! It was amazing.

   _____

5. We finished our set. Then, we took a swim. While you finished your set.

   _____

▶ **Exercise 2** **Adding Necessary Words to Change Fragments to Sentences.** Change the following fragments into complete sentences by adding the necessary words.

EXAMPLE: A crowd of curious passersby.

_____ *A crowd of curious passersby gathered to watch the artist.* _____

1. A parking space too small for our car.

   _____

2. A few minutes before midnight.

   _____

3. Carrying one important passenger.

   _____

4. People hoping to get a letter.

   _____

5. Elected unanimously.

   _____

21.4 **Correcting Fragments • Practice 2**

▶ **Exercise 1**   **Changing Fragments Into Sentences.**   Change the following fragments into complete sentences by adding the necessary words.

EXAMPLE: at the station

_____*I can meet you at the station tomorrow morning.*_____

1. Before the dance.

   _____

2. While we worked on the experiment.

   _____

3. Once the baseball season begins.

   _____

4. Ahead of me.

   _____

5. After the summer vacation.

   _____

6. Without a pen or pencil.

   _____

7. Opposite the park.

   _____

8. When she began to speak.

   _____

9. Even though the temperature was warm.

   _____

10. From my seat.

   _____

▶ **Exercise 2**   **More Work With Fragments and Sentences.**   Follow the directions for Exercise 1.

1. Next to the library.

   _____

2. How the rumor spread.

   _____

3. On top of my dresser.

   _____

4. Past the principal's office.

   _____

5. When they are found.

   _____

21.4 # Recognizing Run-ons • **Practice 1**

A run-on sentence is two or more sentences written as though they were one sentence.

RUN-ON SENTENCES
Large rain forests are located in South America and central Africa, rain falls there every day. (Only a comma separates two independent clauses.) It's hard to choose clothes there are so many things I like. (No punctuation mark separates the two independent clauses.)

▷ **Exercise 1** **Recognizing Run-Ons.** Identify each word group below as *sentence* or *run-on*.

EXAMPLE: The Wright brothers made the first successful powered flight, it lasted 12 seconds.   *run-on*

1. The governor was a fine speaker she gave a rousing keynote speech. _____

2. Students objected to the plan, and the teachers didn't like it either. _____

3. The soldiers were tired, they had marched all day. _____

4. Charles locked the windows and doors, then he turned out the lights. _____

5. The new vaccine seems promising, but it has not yet been fully tested. _____

6. The job paid less than John had hoped, yet he decided to take it. _____

7. The boys had no ticket stubs, they were asked to leave. _____

8. Cathy is the new president, and Mark is the treasurer. _____

9. Do not cook the stew too long, or the meat will get stringy. _____

10. The sign was unnecessary, no one went near the haunted house. _____

▷ **Exercise 2** **Analyzing Run-On Sentences.** Copy the run-on sentences you found in Exercise 1, including the number of each. Then, circle the place where the two sentences are incorrectly joined.

EXAMPLE: The Wright brothers made the first successful powered flight(,) it lasted 12 seconds.

_____

_____

_____

_____

21.4 Recognizing Run-ons • Practice 2

▶ **Exercise 1** **Recognizing Run-ons.** Write *run-on* or *sentence* for each group of words below.

EXAMPLE: The human brain is very complicated, it receives information from other parts of the body.
_____*run-on*_____

1. The size of your brain does not determine how smart you are, a genius may have an average-sized brain, a large brain, or a small brain. _____

2. Until you are about 15 years old, your brain will continue to grow. _____

3. Scientists study the brain they have many unanswered questions. _____

4. The brain of a human adult weighs about three pounds the brain of an elephant weighs about 11 pounds. _____

5. Different parts of your brain control different activities. _____

6. I want to go to Spain, I have been studying Spanish for two years and want to test my knowledge of it in real life. _____

7. The capital of Colombia is Bogotá it is located in the Andes Mountains. _____

8. Brazil is the largest country in South America most of the people live along the Atlantic coast. _____

9. The bark of some birch trees peels off in layers like sheets of paper. _____

10. Because they are thin, many birch trees are bent over but not destroyed during storms that do great damage to other kinds of trees. _____

11. A tree's roots absorb water and minerals from the soil, roots also help hold a tree in place. _____

12. Like other plants, trees have roots, stems, and leaves, but trees are much larger. _____

13. Some trees have one main root called a taproot, it grows straight down in the soil. _____

14. Other trees have fibrous roots, a system of roots that spread out in the soil. _____

15. The hard, woody stem of a tree is called the trunk, the trunk is made up of several layers including the tough outside layer, which is called the bark. _____

▶ **Writing Application** **Avoiding Run-ons.** Write a paragraph about the advantages or disadvantages of watching television. Check to see that none of your sentences are run-ons.

_____

_____

_____

_____

_____

_____

_____

21.4 Correcting Run-ons • Practice 1

Use one of the following methods to correct run-ons.

END MARK
The crowd was amazed they had never seen anything like it. (run-on) The crowd was amazed. They had never seen anything like it. (corrected)

COMMA AND COORDINATING CONJUNCTION
We built a big fire, the rescue party saw the smoke. (run-on) We built a big fire, and the rescue party saw the smoke. (corrected)

SEMICOLON
Water makes temperatures even, it neither heats nor cools as fast as land. (run-on) Water makes temperatures even; it neither heats nor cools as fast as land. (corrected)

ONE COMPLEX SENTENCE
We tried the plan, it was risky. (run-on) We tried the plan even though it was risky. (corrected)

▶ **Exercise 1**   **Preparing to Correct Run-ons.**   If a word group below is a run-on, insert a caret (∧) between the two sentences or independent clauses. If a sentence is correct, write *C* after it.

EXAMPLE: At the equator the sun's rays are direct, (∧) they are strong and hot. _____

1. Rain-forest people live in villages, and their houses are small and dim. _____

2. Alligators lay their eggs in the mud the sun hatches them. _____

3. Cooking is easy, a cookbook is all you need. _____

4. Many people collect baseball cards; some cards are very valuable. _____

5. The first playing cards came from China they were used to tell fortunes. _____

6. Most tourists view the canyon from the rim, but a few travel to its floor on donkeys. _____

7. Yellowstone Park is our oldest National Park it opened in 1872. _____

8. Regular mail takes several days, but express mail arrives the next day. _____

9. Tomatoes are expensive to ship, for they bruise easily. _____

10. The bus driver refused to drive so the passengers got off angrily. _____

▶ **Exercise 2**   **Correcting Run-ons.**   Rewrite five run-on sentences from Exercise 1. Use each method of rewriting noted in the chart at least once.

EXAMPLE: At the equator the sun's rays are direct; they are strong and hot.

1. _____

2. _____

3. _____

4. _____

5. _____

21.4 Correcting Run-ons • Practice 2

▶ **Exercise 1** **Correcting Run-ons.** Correct the following run-ons by using the methods given in this section.

EXAMPLE: My dog can do tricks, he can shake hands.

   My dog can do tricks. He can shake hands.

1. The smallest dog is the Chihuahua, the tallest dog is the Irish wolfhound.

_____

2. A husky can pull a sled through snow, a collie can herd sheep.

_____

3. A St. Bernard is the heaviest dog some St. Bernards weigh over 200 pounds.

_____

4. A person can see better than a dog, a dog can hear better than a person.

_____

5. Do wild dogs still exist I heard that there were some living in India.

_____

6. Dogs are not only used as pets some dogs are used as guide dogs for the blind.

_____

7. The dog was probably the first mammal to be tamed people had dogs as pets 12,000 years ago.

_____

8. In some ways, dogs exhibit a great deal of variety they vary in size, shape, and color.

_____

9. In many ways, dogs are alike they have sharp teeth and cold, wet noses.

_____

10. The jackal is a type of wild dog it is found mainly in Africa and Asia.

_____

▶ **Exercise 2** **More Work With Run-ons.** Follow the directions for Exercise 1.

1. What sites did you see in Boston, we saw Faneuil Hall.

_____

2. Last night we had a snowstorm the accumulation was over a foot.

_____

3. George visited the historic city of Williamsburg, a blacksmith there explained his work.

_____

4. The farm produces several kinds of fresh vegetables, most of them sold locally.

_____

5. Timothy's desk is made of oak Martha's desk is made of mahogany.

_____

21.4 Avoiding Double Negatives • Practice 1

Only one negative word is needed to give a sentence a negative meeting. Putting in more than one is a sentence error called a double negative.

NEGATIVE WORDS				
never	nobody	no one	not	nowhere
no	none	nor	nothing	n't

To correct a double negative, remove one of the negative words or change one to a positive.

CORRECTING DOUBLE NEGATIVES	
Double Negative	**Corrected Sentence**
We can't let nobody know about it.	We can't let anybody know about it.
	We can let nobody know about it.
I can't find the cat nowhere.	I can't find the cat anywhere.
	I can find the cat nowhere.

▶ **Exercise 1** **Correcting Double Negatives.**   Circle the word in parentheses that makes each sentence below negative without creating a double negative.

EXAMPLE: I wouldn't have (none, (any)) of the spinach.

1. Our family never does (nothing, anything) on the weekends.

2. The manager (can, can't) seem to keep nobody working for him.

3. I wouldn't have (no, any) part in playing that trick on Rod.

4. Those books (are, aren't) none of mine.

5. I never go (nowhere, anywhere) without buckling my seatbelt.

▶ **Exercise 2**   **More Work Correcting Sentences With Double Negatives.**   Correct each sentence below by eliminating the double negative in two ways.

EXAMPLE: I haven't never heard of that brand of ice cream.
> *I haven't ever heard of that brand of ice cream.*
> *I have never heard of that brand of ice cream.*

1. Max shouldn't never have tried to fix it himself.

   _____

   _____

2. We haven't heard nothing about your trip to Canada.

   _____

   _____

3. Your keys weren't nowhere that I could see.

   _____

   _____

4. My father says I never hear nothing that he says.

   _____

   _____

5. I didn't want help from nobody.

   _____

   _____

21.4 Avoiding Double Negatives • Practice 2

▶ **Exercise 1** **Correcting Sentences With Double Negatives.** Rewrite each sentence below to correct the double negative.

EXAMPLE: We haven't tried none of these programs.
We haven't tried any of these programs.

1. We hadn't never realized that Theodore wrote so well.
_____

2. I can't never remember that incident.
_____

3. Ann hasn't said nothing about her new job.
_____

4. This ice cream isn't sold nowhere else.
_____

5. There isn't room nowhere for this table.
_____

6. They aren't taking none of these rumors seriously.
_____

7. I wouldn't never make that journey alone.
_____

8. The court hasn't heard no testimony yet.
_____

9. The storyteller didn't tell none of the old legends.
_____

10. I haven't told nobody about your discovery.
_____

▶ **Exercise 2** **More Practice Correcting Double Negatives.** Follow the directions for Exercise 1.

1. The visitors don't want no publicity.
_____

2. The end isn't nowhere in sight.
_____

3. Our newspaper hasn't printed nothing about the event.
_____

4. We can't agree on no location for the meeting.
_____

5. The committee didn't select nobody as chairperson.
_____

22.1 # Regular Verbs • Practice 1

Regular verbs form the tenses following a regular, consistent pattern. The four parts used to form the tenses are the present, present participle, past, and past participle.

PRINCIPAL PARTS OF REGULAR VERBS			
Present	**Present Participle**	**Past**	**Past Participle**
laugh	(am) laughing	laughed	(have) laughed
offer	(am) offering	offered	(have) offered
fade	(is) fading	faded	(has) faded

▶ **Exercise 1**   **Using Regular Verbs.**   Look at the tense of the regular verb underlined in each sentence below. If it is correct, write *C* in the blank provided. If it is not correct, write the correct tense in the blank.

EXAMPLE: Yesterday, I am wishing for a bike.   *wished*

1. Last week, I have painted the fence. _____
2. The artist will donate a watercolor. _____
3. The group is lacked money for its next project. _____
4. I will present the awards last night. _____
5. We are watching a baseball game right now. _____
6. Yesterday, the band will practice for three hours. _____
7. In a moment, the horse jump over a hurdle. _____
8. After dinner, I will taste the chocolate cake. _____
9. After the job was done, we will divide the profits. _____
10. I love chocolate chip cookies. _____

▶ **Exercise 2**   **More Work With Regular Verbs.**   In each blank below, write the correct form of the verb in parentheses.

EXAMPLE: We ____*raced*____ down the street just now. (race)

1. Liz is _____ her hair. (brush)
2. Early in his career, Jim Carrey _____ famous people. (imitate)
3. He has _____ the tank with gasoline. (fill)
4. When I was little, I _____ spinach. (hate)
5. My mother is _____ the performance. (attend)
6. The school has _____ the library for the day. (close)
7. He will _____ us some magic tricks. (show)
8. We have _____ lots of card games. (play)
9. The gardener has _____ the lawn for weeds. (spray)
10. I am _____ the flag. (salute)

22.1 Regular Verbs • Practice 2

▶ **Exercise 1**   **Using Regular Verbs.**   In each blank below, write the correct form of the verb in parentheses.

EXAMPLE: I ___finished___ reading that book last week. (finish)

1. A few weeks ago, my friend _____ a book to me. (recommend)
2. While I was on vacation, I _____ to read it. (start)
3. It tells of a family that is _____ in Connecticut. (live)
4. They will _____ the start of the American Revolution. (witness)
5. One son has joined the army, but the rest of the family has _____ at home. (stay)
6. The parents have _____ loyal to England. (remain)
7. Everywhere, patriots are _____ about the British. (complain)
8. Many patriots have even _____ committees. (create)
9. I have _____ some history from this book. (learn)
10. I will _____ this novel to another friend. (suggest)

▶ **Exercise 2**   **More Work With Regular Verbs.**   Follow the directions for Exercise 1.

1. Scientists have _____ many underground caves and caverns. (explore)
2. They have _____ numerous interesting rock formations. (photograph)
3. Rock formations resembling flowers have _____ . (develop)
4. I am _____ about these fabulous interiors. (learn)
5. I have already _____ about how caves are formed. (learn)
6. Some caves in Italy have been _____ for thousands of years. (inhabit)
7. More than 17,000 caves have _____ in the United States. (discover)
8. I am _____ about cave exploration. (read)
9. Water dripped onto the cave floor and _____ minerals, forming spires. (deposit)
10. Interesting columns have _____ where spires of limestone join. (form)

▶ **Writing Application**   **Using Regular Verbs in Sentences.**   Write ten sentences telling about the activities of one of your friends. Use some form of each of the following verbs: *start, wait, call, act, help, joke, like, share, walk,* and *play.*

1. _____
2. _____
3. _____
4. _____
5. _____
6. _____
7. _____
8. _____
9. _____
10. _____

22.1 Irregular Verbs • Practice 1

A small group of verbs are called irregular verbs. These verbs differ from regular verbs in the way they form the tenses. Irregular verbs do not form the participle by adding -ed or -d to the present.

IRREGULAR VERBS WITH THE SAME PAST AND PAST PARTICIPLE			
Present	**Present Participle**	**Past**	**Past Participle**
shoot	(am) shooting	shot	(have) shot
wind	(am) winding	wound	(have) wound
feel	(am) feeling	felt	(have) felt

▶ **Exercise 1** **Using Irregular Verbs.** If the irregular verb underlined in each sentence is correct, write *C* in the blank. If the irregular verb is incorrect, write the correct verb tense in the blank.

EXAMPLE: I leaded the group on the hike. ____*led*____

1. Today, we are bought a new car. _____

2. The mosquitos are stinging us constantly. _____

3. The car spun out of control. _____

4. I shot at the target tomorrow. _____

5. I will hold your ice cream for you. _____

6. Yesterday, Mike has got some good fish. _____

7. In the past, I have even more baseball cards. _____

8. Nick is having second thoughts. _____

9. Last night, I am catching a fly ball. _____

10. Yesterday morning, I learn about the Civil War. _____

▶ **Exercise 2** **More Work With Irregular Verbs.** In each blank below, write the correct verb tense for the irregular verb in parentheses.

EXAMPLE: The company has ____*built*____ many homes in the area. (build)

1. Last year, they _____ a cake for his birthday. (buy)

2. My father is _____ his hair. (lose)

3. Our guests have _____ their vacation pictures. (bring)

4. Are you _____ what you need? (get)

5. We are _____ the crowds tiresome. (find)

6. Have you _____ the bill? (pay)

7. Last week, the police _____ the suspect. (catch)

8. I _____ the monkey while my picture was taken. (hold)

9. Yesterday, I _____ and missed. (swing)

10. Last year, we _____ to the original agreement. (stick)

22.1 Irregular Verbs • Practice 2

Exercise 1 **Using Irregular Verbs.** In each blank below, write the past or past participle for the verb in parentheses.

EXAMPLE: Last week, Michelle ___*bought*___ a new jacket. (buy)

1. Andrew had _____ enough trout to feed our entire family. (catch)
2. Have you _____ the postcard I sent you from Florida? (get)
3. Rita _____ the way and Paula followed. (lead)
4. Now that I have _____ for this tape, I can give it to you. (pay)
5. The storyteller _____ a tale of romance and adventure. (spin)
6. I _____ the ticket. (lose)
7. José _____ the bat, hit the ball, and ran to first base. (swing)
8. Mrs. Scott has _____ a new coat. (buy)
9. Eddie _____ good news waiting for him when he got home. (have)
10. My father _____ a guest home to dinner. (bring)
11. The club members _____ for the costumes. (pay)
12. Our team won the first game and _____ the second. (lose)
13. Have you _____ your guitar? (bring)
14. It seems that you have _____ a cold. (catch)
15. Dan has _____ three model airplanes this year. (build)
16. Last summer a bee _____ me on the thumb. (sting)
17. Dina has _____ this brand of toothpaste before. (buy)
18. Phil _____ in the orchestra during the first part of the performance. (sit)
19. The nurse had _____ out the instruments for the doctor. (lay)
20. Has the gate _____ shut? (swing)

Writing Application **Using Irregular Verbs.** Write an advertisement for a "new" cereal. Include some form of at least five of the following verbs: *buy, get, say, pay, have, build, lay,* and *sit.*

_____

_____

_____

_____

_____

_____

_____

_____

_____

_____

22.1 More Irregular Verbs • Practice 1

For one group of irregular verbs, the present, the past, and the past participle are the same.

IRREGULAR VERBS WITH THE SAME PRESENT, PAST, AND PAST PARTICIPLE			
Present	Present Participle	Past	Past Participle
cost	(is) costing	cost	(has) cost
let	(are) letting	let	(have) let
rid	(am) ridding	rid	(have) rid

▶ **Exercise 1** **Using Irregular Verbs.** Select an irregular verb from the list below to complete each sentence. Be sure to use the correct form.

EXAMPLE: Dad is _____*putting*_____ away the dishes.

bid	cost	hurt	read
burst	cut	let	rid
cast	hit	put	set

1. The drama teacher has _____ me to play the villain.

2. I am _____ the cheese into slices right now.

3. The child cried in disappointment when his balloon _____.

4. Right now, we are _____ the second chapter.

5. The high jumper _____ his back on the last jump.

6. We have already _____ up the stage.

7. We are _____ John act as the team captain.

8. The Forestry Service has _____ the area of rattle snakes.

9. Is the skateboard _____ you much money?

10. A reckless driver has _____ a parked car.

▶ **Exercise 2** **More Work With Irregular Verbs.** Complete the sentences below with a form of the underlined verb.

EXAMPLE: Are you <u>cutting</u> the grass as I asked?
      I already _____*cut*_____ the grass.

1. Is this house <u>rid</u> of fleas?
   Yes, our company guarantees it. This house is _____ of fleas!

2. Does your throat <u>hurt</u> anymore?
   It _____ yesterday, but not today.

3. Are you _____ up the chess pieces?
   I have already <u>set</u> them up.

4. I am _____ up the vegetables for the salad.
   Would you <u>cut</u> some of them for me?

5. I <u>let</u> you use the car yesterday.
   Why am I _____ you use it again today?

22.1 More Irregular Verbs • Practice 2

▶ **Exercise 1**   **Using Irregular Verbs Correctly.**   Complete the answer to each question below by using a form of the underlined verb.

EXAMPLE: Are you <u>setting</u> the table for dinner?

No, I ____set____ it an hour ago.

1. Are you <u>cutting</u> any more trees in this area?

   No, I _____ enough trees here.

2. Did your mother <u>let</u> you stay up for the second half of the program?

   She _____ me, but I fell asleep.

3. Are you <u>putting</u> more paper in the machine?

   No, I have _____ in enough.

4. Does your arm still <u>hurt</u>?

   No, it isn't _____ me anymore.

5. Is the collar <u>ridding</u> the dog of fleas?

   Yes, it has _____ him of most of them already.

6. Are you <u>reading</u> the magazine on the table?

   No, I have already _____ it.

7. Has the director <u>cast</u> the parts for the play?

   No, he is _____ them tomorrow.

8. Do you think that your balloon will <u>burst</u>?

   No, my balloon _____ yesterday.

9. Do oranges <u>cost</u> less this week?

   No, they _____ about the same as last week and the week before.

10. Are you <u>bidding</u> twenty-five dollars for the velvet-covered chair?

    Yes, I have already _____ fifteen dollars, but I will offer more.

▶ **Writing Application**   **Using Irregular Verbs in a Summary.**   Write a paragraph summarizing the things you did yesterday. Use some form of each of the following verbs: *cost, read, put, let, cut,* or any other irregular verbs.

_____

_____

_____

_____

_____

_____

_____

_____

_____

_____

22.1 Other Irregular Verbs • Practice 1

Some irregular verbs make many changes in spelling as they form the tenses. In some cases, all the principal parts of the verb undergo vowel or consonant changes. The chart below shows several of these irregular verbs. If you are ever confused about an irregular verb, check the dictionary.

IRREGULAR VERBS THAT CHANGE IN A VARIETY OF WAYS			
Present	**Present Participle**	**Past**	**Past Participle**
be	(am) being	was	(have) been
choose	(am) choosing	chose	(have) chosen
ring	(am) ringing	rang	(have) rung
write	(am) writing	wrote	(have) written

▶ **Exercise 1**   **Completing the Principal Parts of Irregular Verbs.**   Write the missing parts for the following irregular verbs. Try not to look back at the chart in the text.

EXAMPLE: sing   (am) ___singing___   sang   (have) ___sung___

1. eat   (am) _____   _____   (have) eaten
2. _____   (am) throwing   threw   (have) _____
3. speak   (am) speaking   _____   (have) _____
4. begin   (am) _____   began   (have) _____
5. _____   (am) _____   did   (have) done
6. know   (am) _____   _____   (have) known
7. _____   (am) being   _____   (have) been
8. drink   (am) drinking   _____   (have) _____
9. _____   (am) _____   tore   (have) torn
10. _____   (am) lying   lay   (have) _____

▶ **Exercise 2**   **Selecting the Correct Forms of Irregular Verbs.**   Circle the correct form of the verbs given in parentheses in order to complete the sentences below.

EXAMPLE: I (drinked, (drank)) too much pool water.

1. You just (tore, tear) your shirt.

2. The choir (sung, sang) the national anthem for us.

3. Are you (thrown, throwing) good curve balls consistently now?

4. Yesterday, we (lie, lay) in the sun for a couple of hours.

5. Our family has (driven, drove) across the country on vacation.

6. My brother (swam, swum) underwater for three pool lengths.

7. The manager has (began, begun) to give me more responsibility.

8. I am (doing, done) a report on the Aztec Indians.

9. The fishermen have (rose, risen) early every morning.

10. The winners of the contest are (flying, flew) to the Bahamas.

22.1 Other Irregular Verbs • Practice 2

▶ **Exercise 1** **Selecting the Correct Forms of Irregular Verbs.** Underline the correct verb from the choices given in parentheses below.

EXAMPLE: Sandra has (began, begun) to speak.

1. My brother (drove, drived) to Canada during the summer.
2. Have you (flown, flew) on a 747?
3. The late bell had already (rang, rung) when I arrived.
4. Jim and Eric (swam, swum) ten laps in the pool.
5. Today, I must (choose, chose) a partner in science class.
6. Ellen has (tore, torn) up the scrap paper.
7. He caught the ball and (threw, throwed) it to the pitcher.
8. The class had (knew, known) about the picnic for a week.
9. The balloon (rose, rised) high over our heads.
10. We (began, begun) our campaign for class president.
11. The student (did, done) a report on John Paul Jones.
12. Our class has (wrote, written) to our state senator.
13. The performers danced and (sang, sung) for us.
14. In the past, he (be, was) captain of the team.
15. Have you (gave, given) your suggestions to Miriam?
16. The principal has (spoken, spoke) to us about safety.
17. We (ate, eat) first and then went to the theater.
18. Cindy and Dan have (took, taken) a photography course.
19. Earlier in the afternoon, Sara (lay, lain) down to rest.
20. I have (drank, drunk) the apple juice.

▶ **Writing Application** **Using Irregular Verbs in Sentences.** Write ten sentences telling about some of the ways you have changed since last year. Use some form of each of the following verbs: *speak, know, write, eat, begin, choose, take, do, throw,* and *give.*

1. _____
2. _____
3. _____
4. _____
5. _____
6. _____
7. _____
8. _____
9. _____
10. _____

22.2 The Present, Past, and Future Tenses
• Practice 1

Verbs do not only describe actions. They can also tell when those actions occur. They do this by changing their form or tense. All the tenses are formed using the four principal parts of a verb.

PRINCIPAL PARTS OF A REGULAR AND IRREGULAR VERB			
Present	**Present Participle**	**Past**	**Past Participle**
live	(am) living	lived	(have) lived
speak	(am) speaking	spoke	(have) spoken

When these parts are combined with different pronouns, we can see all of the forms that a verb can take in a particular tense. This is a verb conjugation.

CONJUGATION OF THE PRESENT, PAST, AND FUTURE TENSES OF TWO VERBS		
	Singular	**Plural**
Present	I live, speak you live, speak he, she, it lives, speaks	we live, speak you live, speak they live, speak
Past	I lived, spoke you lived, spoke he, she, it lived, spoke	we lived, spoke you lived, spoke they lived, spoke
Future	I will live, speak you will live, speak he, she, it will live, speak	we will live, speak you will live, speak they will live, speak

▶ **Exercise 1** **Identifying the Present, Past, and Future Verb Tenses.** In each blank below, write *present*, *past*, or *future* to identify the underlined verb.

EXAMPLE: Nat complained about the heat. _____*past*_____

1. Banks offer many services. _____

2. The truck drove over the speed limit. _____

3. I will report on precipitation. _____

4. The waiter handed us the check. _____

5. The wind causes the temperature to drop. _____

▶ **Exercise 2** **Using the Present, Past, and Future Tenses.** In each blank below, write the tense of the verb indicated in parentheses.

EXAMPLE: The morning bell just _____*rang.*_____ (ring, *past*)

1. I _____ my homework right after school. (do, *present*)

2. The car _____ only the rear wheel of my bike. (hit, *past*)

3. I _____ here until you return. (stay, *future*)

4. Nancy _____ the group on the hike. (lead, *past*)

5. The band _____ in a benefit performance. (sing, *future*)

6. My mother _____ the plants everyday. (water, *present*)

7. Laurie _____ her purse in her backpack. (keep, *present*)

8. Sally _____ the refreshments. (buy, *future*)

9. The back wheels of the car _____ in the mud. (stick, *past*)

10. Jim _____ the evening newspaper. (deliver, *present*)

22.2 The Present, Past, and Future Tenses
• Practice 2

▶ **Exercise 1**   **Using the Present, Past, and Future Tenses.**   In each blank below, write the tense of the verb indicated in parentheses.

EXAMPLE: He ___*came*___ into the living room. (come, *past*)

1. She _____ around the living room. (run, *present*)
2. We _____ our plans for the weekend. (discuss, *past*)
3. The boat _____ as soon as the cargo of machinery is loaded. (sail, *future*)
4. Natasha _____ listening to the music. (enjoy, *past*)
5. He _____ musical comedies. (like, *present*)
6. I _____ you my new leather jacket. (lend, *future*)
7. These arguments _____ you that I am right. (convince, *future*)
8. Although the car is old, it _____ well. (run, *present*)
9. The shopper _____ to see the manager. (ask, *past*)
10. The man in the corner _____ lead guitar in the band. (play, *present*)

▶ **Exercise 2**   **Identifying the Present, Past, and Future Tenses.**   Identify the tense of the underlined verb in each of the following sentences.

EXAMPLE: Almost everyone <u>likes</u> to hear a story. ___*present*___

1. When I <u>hear</u> a story, I use my imagination. _____
2. Storytelling <u>existed</u> before written history. _____
3. A good story <u>will have</u> action and drama. _____
4. Many tales <u>hold</u> my interest. _____
5. I <u>listened</u> to the legend of King Arthur many times. _____
6. My friend <u>prefers</u> the "trickster" tales from Africa. _____
7. The librarian <u>read</u> us fantasies by Tolkien. _____
8. We <u>will practice</u> storytelling this year. _____
9. First, we <u>choose</u> a story we like. _____
10. We <u>will look</u> for folk tales, myths, or legends. _____

▶ **Exercise 3**   **More Work With the Present, Past, and Future Tenses.**   Identify the tense of the underlined verbs below.

EXAMPLE: Blue jays <u>are</u> interesting. ___*present*___

1. Blue jays <u>have</u> many unusual habits. _____
2. A jay <u>will steal</u> nuts from a squirrel. _____
3. First it <u>frightens</u> the squirrel by flying in circles above it. _____
4. The frightened squirrel <u>drops</u> the nut and quickly runs away. _____
5. The jay <u>will dig</u> up a nut buried by a squirrel. _____
6. Jays <u>make</u> both pleasant and unpleasant sounds. _____
7. Its unpleasant shriek <u>will warn</u> other animals of danger. _____
8. We <u>spotted</u> a bird with blue-and-white wings and tail. _____
9. It <u>had</u> a blue crest on its head and wore a black collar. _____
10. The bird we <u>observed</u> was a blue jay. _____

Name _____ , _____ Date _____

 22.2 # The Present Perfect Tense • Practice 1

The present perfect tense describes an action that begins in the past. Sometimes, the action also ends in the past, but it may continue into the present. The present perfect tense is formed by using the helping verbs *have* or *has* with the past participle.

THE PRESENT PERFECT TENSE OF A REGULAR AND IRREGULAR VERB		
	Singular	**Plural**
search	I have searched	we have searched
	you have searched	you have searched
	he, she, it has searched	they have searched
win	I have won	we have won
	you have won	you have won
	he, she, it has won	they have won

▶ **Exercise 1**   **Using the Present Perfect Tense.**   In each blank below, write the present perfect tense for the underlined verb.

EXAMPLE: I <u>walk</u> over twenty miles in two days. _____*have walked*_____

1. He <u>throw</u> some fine curve balls. _____

2. The eagle <u>catch</u> his dinner. _____

3. The wood <u>crack</u> from lack of care. _____

4. Sandra <u>give</u> clear directions to her house. _____

5. Our turkey <u>cook</u> for six hours already. _____

6. The jellyfish in this area <u>sting</u> several swimmers. _____

7. Our team <u>win</u> the league championship. _____

8. We <u>observe</u> the stars through our telescope. _____

9. They <u>go</u> outdoors. _____

10. The package <u>arrive</u>. _____

▶ **Exercise 2**   **More Work With the Present Perfect Tense.**   Put each verb below into the present perfect tense and use it in a short sentence.

EXAMPLE: refuse

_____*They have refused my help.*_____

1. receive

_____

2. behave

_____

3. lose

_____

4. fly

_____

5. read

_____

22.2 The Present Perfect Tense • Practice 2

▶ **Exercise 1** **Using the Present Perfect Tense.** Rewrite the sentences below, changing each underlined verb to the present perfect tense.

EXAMPLE: Many people buy bicycles.
        Many people have bought bicycles.

1. American and foreign companies produce bicycles.

_____

2. The bicycle helps people travel from place to place.

_____

3. Bicycles often last a lifetime.

_____

4. My doctor recommends bicycling to keep fit.

_____

5. I appreciate the ease of bicycle riding.

_____

6. People pause to chat when they see me resting.

_____

7. Al delivers newspapers using his bike.

_____

8. Some enthusiasts enter the yearly bicycle race.

_____

9. Others attempt bicycle polo.

_____

10. I find friends through my local bicycle club.

_____

▶ **Exercise 2** **More Work With the Present Perfect Tense.** Follow the directions for Exercise 1.

1. Our club prints a newsletter.

_____

2. We mail it to our members.

_____

3. Many readers write comments to our editor.

_____

4. The editor prints some of them.

_____

5. Several reporters develop feature articles.

_____

22.2 The Present and Past Progressive
• Practice 1

Two tenses show continuing action. They are the present progressive and the past progressive. The present progressive is formed by combining the present tense of the helping verb *be* with the present participle.

PRESENT PROGRESSIVE TENSE OF A REGULAR AND AN IRREGULAR VERB	
Singular	**Plural**
I am talking, paying you are talking, paying he, she, it is talking, paying	we are talking, paying you are talking, paying they are talking, paying

The past progressive combines the past tense of the helping verb *be* with the present participle.

PAST PROGRESSIVE OF A REGULAR AND AN IRREGULAR VERB	
Singular	**Plural**
I was talking, paying you were talking, paying he, she, it was talking, paying	we were talking, paying you were talking, paying they were talking, paying

▶ **Exercise 1** **Identifying the Present Progressive and Past Progressive Tenses.** Identify the underlined verb in each sentence below. Write *present pro.* if it is the present progressive and *past pro.* if it is the past progressive.

EXAMPLE: We <u>were wearing</u> Halloween costumes. _____*past pro.*_____

1. I <u>am holding</u> a fortune in my hands. _____

2. We <u>were leading</u> the other teams. _____

3. The Great Dane <u>was chasing</u> a cat. _____

4. The artificial heart <u>is pumping</u> the blood well. _____

5. They <u>were making</u> oatmeal cookies. _____

▶ **Exercise 2** **Using the Present Progressive and the Past Progressive.** In each blank below, write the verb in parentheses, putting it into the tense listed.

EXAMPLE: She ____*is learning*____ U.S. history. (learn, *present progressive*)

1. You _____ a strong future. (build, *present progressive*)

2. The crowd _____ at the comedian. (laugh, *past progressive*)

3. The dock _____ with the tide. (rise, *present progressive*)

4. The elephant _____ his long trunk. (swing, *past progressive*)

5. We _____ some soccer. (play, *past progressive*)

6. I _____ the speakers. (introduce, *present progressive*)

7. They _____ the packages. (wrap, *present progressive*)

8. The farmer _____ his fields today. (plow, *past progressive*)

9. We _____ stranded animals. (rescue, *present progressive*)

10. Chris _____ the bill. (pay, *present progressive*)

Name _____   Date _____

 22.2 # The Present and Past Progressive
• Practice 2

▶ **Exercise 1**   **Using the Present and Past Progressive.**   In each blank below, write the verb in parentheses in the verb tense given.

EXAMPLE: Alan _____*is describing*_____ his trip. (describe, *present progressive*)

1. Ann _____ for someone to interview. (look, *present progressive*)

2. Barbara _____ about a sad memory. (write, *present progressive*)

3. I _____ about being on time. (worry, *past progressive*)

4. We _____ how it looked. (imagine, *past progressive*)

5. They _____ the drama club. (join, *present progressive*)

6. Tom _____ to Michigan. (move, *present progressive*)

7. I _____ the papers on my desk. (arrange, *past progressive*)

8. They _____ the movie. (enjoy, *past progressive*)

9. Terry _____ on a computer program. (work, *present progressive*)

10. The librarian _____ about a new book. (tell, *past progressive*)

11. Marie _____ the paintings. (admire, *past progressive*)

12. We _____ to train the puppy. (begin, *present progressive*)

13. He _____ my directions. (follow, *present progressive*)

14. They _____ the cook. (praise, *past progressive*)

15. I _____ a walk in the woods. (take, *present progressive*)

16. We _____ the game when you arrived. (lose, *past progressive*)

17. Dr. Morgan _____ a call. (expect, *present progressive*)

18. I _____ for a reply to my letter. (wait, *present progressive*)

19. We _____ at the comedian's jokes. (laugh, *past progressive*)

20. Your story _____ more interesting. (become, *present progressive*)

▶ **Writing Application**   **Using the Present and Past Progressive.**   Write a paragraph describing a perfect day as if you were experiencing it right now. Use verbs in the present progressive. Start with *I am enjoying a perfect day.*

_____

_____

_____

_____

_____

_____

_____

_____

22.3 Troublesome Verbs: *Did* and *Done*
• Practice 1

One troublesome verb is *do*. Many people are confused about when to use *did* and *done*. It helps to first memorize the principal parts of the verb *do*.

PRINCIPAL PARTS OF *DO*			
Present	**Present Participle**	**Past**	**Past Participle**
do	(am) doing	did	(have) done

Did is never used with a helping verb, but a helping verb must always accompany *done*.

INCORRECT AND CORRECT USAGE OF *DO*	
Incorrect	**Correct**
They *have did* their homework. I *done* my research.	They *did* their homework. I *have done* my research.

▶ **Exercise 1** **Using *Did* and *Done*.** In the sentences below, circle the correct verb from the two given in parentheses.

EXAMPLE: The crickets have ((done) , did) damage to the crops.

1. We (done, did) a good day's work.

2. Mary has (done, did) papier-mâché projects before this.

3. The class has (done, did) nothing to celebrate Valentine's Day.

4. I (done, did) my paper route in half the time today.

5. The helmet has (done, did) a good job protecting the rider's head.

6. Exercise has (done, did) me a world of good.

7. Melanie has already (done, did) the decorations.

8. Mother (done, did) her shopping at the mall.

9. We (done, did) the assignment without any help.

10. You have (done, did) a kind act.

▶ **Exercise 2** **More Work With *Did* and *Done*.** In each blank below, write the correct use of *did* or *done*.

EXAMPLE: I done cake decorating before. ___*have done*___

1. We have did the yard work for our neighbor. _____

2. May always done the lead in our plays. _____

3. I done the dusting earlier today. _____

4. The loose gravel has did damage to the car's paint. _____

5. The horse done the track in record time. _____

22.3 Troublesome Verbs: *Did* and *Done*
• Practice 2

▶ **Exercise 1**   Using *Did* and *Done.*   Write the correct use of *did* or *done* in each sentence below.

EXAMPLE: They have ____*done*____ all the filming in New York.

1. The flooding _____ more damage than the violent winds.
2. We have _____ what was necessary.
3. Our drama club _____ scenes from Shakespeare's play *Hamlet.*
4. Last summer I _____ a number of odd jobs at home.
5. David has _____ me a big favor.
6. On our trip, this car _____ twenty-five miles per gallon.
7. The mayor has _____ many useful things for this city.
8. No one has _____ the dishes.
9. We _____ this scene over seven times.
10. I _____ all I could.

▶ **Exercise 2**   More Work With *Did* and *Done.*   Follow the directions for Exercise 1.

1. The magician _____ his act on the stage.
2. The runner has _____ a mile in less than four minutes.
3. She has _____ the problem on the blackboard.
4. The horse _____ badly in the race.
5. We _____ the work for you.
6. Ted and Yvonne have _____ their best to win.
7. Have you _____ the dishes yet?
8. I _____ what you asked.
9. You _____ a wonderful job!
10. We have always _____ things this way.

▶ **Writing Application**   Using *Did* and *Done* in Sentences.   Write five sentences using *did.*
Write about things that you have accomplished. Then, write five sentences using *done* with a helping verb. Write about things that other people have accomplished.

1. _____
2. _____
3. _____
4. _____
5. _____
6. _____
7. _____
8. _____
9. _____
10. _____

Name _____ Date _____

 22.3 # Troublesome Verbs: *Lay* and *Lie* • Practice 1

Two verbs that are very different but are often confused are *lay* and *lie*. First, they have different meanings. To *lay* means "to put or place something." To *lie* means "to rest in a reclining position" or "to be situated." Second, their principal parts are different.

PRINCIPAL PARTS OF *LAY* AND *LIE*			
Present	**Present Participle**	**Past**	**Past Participle**
lay	(am) laying	laid	(have) laid
lie	(am) lying	lay	(have) lain

Finally, *lay* always takes a direct object while *lie* does not.

EXAMPLES: I *laid* the book on the table.
I *lay* down for a rest.

▶ **Exercise 1** **Using *Lay* and *Lie*.** In each sentence below, circle the correct verb from the two given in parentheses.

EXAMPLE: The contractor is ((laying) , lying) bricks.

1. I have (laid, lain) the rumor to rest.

2. The house (lays, lies) just west of the ridge.

3. We (laid, lay) our picnic basket on the ground.

4. Matt (laid, lay) on the grass, looking up at the clouds.

5. The chickens are (laying, lying) plenty of eggs every day.

6. The kittens (lain, lie) cozily next to their mother.

7. The team's best hope (lays, lies) with the next batter.

8. We have (laid, lain) out the pictures we like best.

9. Tara (laid, lay) on a metal table to have the X-ray taken.

10. The broken tracks are (laying, lying) a mile outside the train station.

▶ **Exercise 2** **More Work With *Lay* and *Lie*.** Correct each of the underlined verbs below by writing in the correct form of *lay* or *lie*.

EXAMPLE: We have <u>lain</u> our bow and arrows down. ___*laid*___

1. The lost doll <u>laid</u> in the dust. _____

2. The fallen trees are <u>laying</u> side by side. _____

3. The dentist <u>lay</u> out the tools he would need. _____

4. Our family <u>lies</u> the presents under the tree. _____

5. The coyote <u>laid</u> in wait for his prey. _____

6. The creek <u>lays</u> between those two mountains. _____

7. She has <u>lain</u> her head on the pillow. _____

8. The pencil is <u>laying</u> next to the phone. _____

9. Yesterday, I <u>lay</u> some carpet. _____

10. Our house is <u>laying</u> southeast of the river. _____

22.3 Troublesome Verbs: *Lay* and *Lie* • Practice 2

▶ **Exercise 1** **Using *Lay* and *Lie*.** In each blank below, write the correct verb form from the two given in parentheses.

EXAMPLE: Grandma is ___*lying*___ down in her room. (lying, laying)

1. Melissa usually _____ her knapsack in the corner of her room. (lays, lies)
2. I _____ under this tree for hours. (lay, lain)
3. The photographer _____ his equipment down very carefully. (laid, lay)
4. Marsha _____ on the beach, listening to music. (lays, lies)
5. I am _____ your mail on your desk. (laying, lying)
6. The shovel _____ untouched in the garden. (lay, laid)
7. Where have you _____ your hat? (laid, lain)
8. Rolling hills _____ everywhere I looked. (laid, lay)
9. Canada _____ to the north of the United States. (lays, lies)
10. Sharon _____ her book aside and went out. (laid, lay)

▶ **Exercise 2** **More Work With *Lay* and *Lie*.** Follow the directions for Exercise 1.

1. Bob is _____ on the floor, reading a mystery novel. (lying, laying)
2. Who has _____ this calculator on my dresser? (lain, laid)
3. The dog _____ near his master. (lay, laid)
4. I have _____ awake for hours. (laid, lain)
5. We are _____ new carpet in this room. (laying, lying)
6. He often _____ on the floor for hours. (lays, lies)
7. The treasure _____ buried in the backyard. (laid, lay)
8. We were _____ our designs out on the easels. (lying, laying)
9. We _____ our gear down. (laid, lay)
10. Henry is _____ his rock collection here. (lying, laying)

▶ **Writing Application** **Using *Lay* and *Lie* in Sentences.** Write five sentences using the verb *lay* and five sentences using the verb *lie*. Use at least three different forms of the verbs *lay* and *lie*.

1. _____
2. _____
3. _____
4. _____
5. _____
6. _____
7. _____
8. _____
9. _____
10. _____

22.3 Troublesome Verbs: *Set* and *Sit* • Practice 1

Set and *sit* are often confused because they look and sound alike. To tell the difference between the two, remember that *set* means "to put something in place," while *sit* means "to be seated" or "to rest."

PRINCIPAL PARTS OF *SET* AND *SIT*			
Present	**Present Participle**	**Past**	**Past Participle**
set	(am) setting	set	(have) set
sit	(am) sitting	sat	(have) sat

Set is always followed by a direct object; *sit* is not.

DO

EXAMPLE: I *set* the table..
I *sat* in the easy chair.

▶ **Exercise 1** **Using *Set* and *Sit* Correctly.** In each sentence below, circle the correct verb from the two given in parentheses.

EXAMPLE: We (set, (sat)) near the phone, waiting for the call.

1. The teacher (set, sat) her briefcase down.

2. The troublemakers are (setting, sitting) near the back.

3. I (set, sat) my purse on the table.

4. The clerk is (setting, sitting) the grocery bags in the cart.

5. I (set, sat) next to an air conditioner.

6. The audience has (set, sat) patiently, waiting for the show to start.

7. The photograph is (setting, sitting) on my dresser.

8. Our teacher clearly (set, sat) the standards for the class.

9. Each week Don is (setting, sitting) new school records in track.

10. I (set, sat) beside the lake with my line dangling in the water.

▶ **Exercise 2** **More Work With *Set* and *Sit*.** Correct each of the underlined verbs below by writing the correct form of *set* or *sat* in the blank.

EXAMPLE: I set next to my grandparents. _____sat_____

1. My dog always sets in my father's favorite chair. _____

2. I sat the lumber down with a thud. _____

3. We have set here all morning. _____

4. Allison sits the dishes in the cupboard. _____

5. I am sitting a good example for my brother. _____

6. The empty garbage cans are setting near the road. _____

7. The waiter sat the bill beside my plate. _____

8. The saddle is setting in the stable. _____

9. Damon has sat our report on the teacher's desk. _____

10. The cast sits the scenery up before the show. _____

22.3 Troublesome Verbs: *Set* and *Sit* • Practice 2

▷ **Exercise 1** **Using *Set* and *Sit*.** In each blank below, write the correct verb form from the two given in parentheses.

EXAMPLE: Felicia usually ___*sits*___ in the first row. (sits, sets)

1. Mr. Randolph _____ the projector on a table in the back of the room. (set, sat)
2. Tommy _____ next to me in English class. (sets, sits)
3. The trophy is _____ on my mantel for everyone to see. (setting, sitting)
4. Bill _____ on the porch for hours. (set, sat)
5. The storekeeper is _____ jars on the shelf. (setting, sitting)
6. When we play badminton, I _____ the net up. (set, sit)
7. Eva is _____ the books in a pile. (sitting, setting)
8. I have _____ your wet umbrella in the hallway. (set, sat)
9. We _____ on the carpet and listened to a fascinating story. (sat, set)
10. The statue _____ on top of a mountain. (sits, sets)

▷ **Exercise 2** **More Work With *Set* and *Sit*.** Follow the directions for Exercise 1.

1. Ted was _____ on the sidelines. (sitting, setting)
2. Karen _____ at our table during lunch. (sat, set)
3. Wanda _____ her packages on the chair. (set, sat)
4. We are _____ all the boxes together. (setting, sitting)
5. My father usually _____ on this chair. (sits, sets)
6. Daniel _____ his suitcase in the baggage rack. (set, sat)
7. We are _____ the chairs on stage. (sitting, setting)
8. Joan has _____ at her desk for hours. (sat, set)
9. Who is _____ over there? (setting, sitting)
10. Janet _____ her plants in the sunshine. (sat, set)

▷ **Writing Application** **Using *Set* and *Sit* in Sentences.** Write a paragraph describing your classroom. Then, tell how it could be rearranged. Use at least three different forms of the verbs *set* and *sit*.

_____
_____
_____
_____
_____
_____
_____
_____
_____
_____
_____

23 Subject Pronouns • Practice 1

Pronouns used as the subject of a sentence are called subject pronouns.

SUBJECT PRONOUNS	
Singular:	I, you, he, she, it
Plural:	we, you, they

To help you decide on the correct subject pronoun to use, take out any other subjects in a sentence. Then, say the sentence with each of the pronouns you are considering; use the one that sounds right.

▶ **Exercise 1** **Identifying the Correct Subject Pronoun.** Circle the correct subject pronoun from the two in parentheses.

EXAMPLE: Natalie and ((I), me) are nominees for class president.

1. Did you or (I, me) volunteer to pick up the food?

2. You and (me, I) can watch television.

3. The Boy Scouts and (us, we) are good campers.

4. Either you or (they, them) will make the decision.

5. Did Lisa and (her, she) stop by your house?

6. Neither (we, us) nor the Red Cross can provide enough medical supplies.

7. My mother and (me, I) are about the same size.

8. Either the fire department or (they, them) should be called.

9. (She, her) and I will miss each other.

10. Has Mark or (he, him) passed the finish line yet?

▶ **Exercise 2** **Using the Correct Subject Pronoun.** An incorrect pronoun has been used in each sentence. Write in the correct subject pronoun in the blank.

EXAMPLE: My brother and me went to the zoo. ____I____

1. We and them will battle for the trophy. _____

2. Neither you nor her has been elected. _____

3. Bill and me collect baseball cards. _____

4. Either they or us will get the new equipment. _____

5. Bill and him have gone on a bike ride. _____

6. Miriam and me joined the swim team. _____

7. Neither we nor them know when the parade starts. _____

8. You and him look very much alike. _____

9. Either it broke by itself or him broke it. _____

10. Neither you nor me like the cake. _____

Name _____ Date _____

 23 # Subject Pronouns • Practice 2

▶ **Exercise 1** **Identifying the Correct Subject Pronoun.** Complete each sentence below with the correct subject pronoun in parentheses.

EXAMPLE: Dr. Turner and ___*he*___ performed the experiment.   (he, him)

1. Ruth and _____ will be on television.   (I, me)

2. Either Erica or _____ will check the calculations.   (her, she)

3. The Hendersons and _____ are amateur golfers.   (we, us)

4. Neither the manager nor _____ like the idea.   (them, they)

5. You and _____ can change the tire.   (me, I)

6. Mr. Miller and _____ agree to try the product.   (he, him)

7. Both Julia and _____ took piano lessons.   (her, she)

8. Our rivals and _____ are well-matched.   (we, us)

9. The Rangers or _____ play here today.   (they, them)

10. Roy and _____ wrote to their state senator.   (he, him)

▶ **Exercise 2** **More Work With Subject Pronouns.** Follow the directions for Exercise 1.

1. The travel agent and _____ planned the trip.   (they, them)

2. The visitors and _____ admired the building.   (us, we)

3. You and _____ will enjoy the new exhibit.   (she, her)

4. Fred and _____ began a small newsletter.   (me, I)

5. The fireman and _____ checked the building.   (he, him)

6. Teresa and _____ spend time in the greenhouse.   (me, I)

7. Douglas and _____ made the rules.   (they, them)

8. You and _____ worked well together.   (she, her)

9. The fifth graders and _____ organized the book fair.   (we, us)

10. Phil and _____ took pictures of old houses.   (he, him)

▶ **Writing Application** **Using Subject Pronouns in Sentences.** Write ten sentences with compound subjects. Use one or more of the following subject pronouns in each sentence: *I, you, he, she, it, we,* and *they.*

1. _____

2. _____

3. _____

4. _____

5. _____

6. _____

7. _____

8. _____

9. _____

10. _____

23 Objective Pronouns • Practice 1

Objective pronouns work in three ways in a sentence: as direct objects, indirect objects, and objects of a preposition.

OBJECTIVE PRONOUNS	
Singular:	me, you, him, her, it
Plural:	us, you, them

USES OF THE OBJECTIVE PRONOUNS		
Direct Object		DO
	Margaret drew it.	
Indirect Object	IO	DO
	Margaret drew her the picture.	
Object of a Preposition		OBJ
	Margaret drew with it.	

It may be difficult to choose the correct pronoun to use when you have a compound object. To help you, take out the other object and try the pronouns you are considering by themselves.

▶ **Exercise 1** **Using Objective Pronouns.** Circle the correct pronoun from the two given in parentheses. In the blank, tell how it is being used.

EXAMPLE: I gave (she, (her)) the correct answer. _____indirect object_____

1. Bob will sit behind (she, her). _____

2. Our employer gave (we, us) a raise. _____

3. The coach spoke to (he, him). _____

4. The pickup truck carried (we, us) to the lake. _____

5. A snake slithered toward John and (I, me). _____

6. Mr. Danners sold Sarah and (I, me) some skates. _____

7. Our tour group was just ahead of (they, them). _____

8. Mrs. Fowler introduced (she, her) to us. _____

9. Nancy lent my friends and (I, me) a paddle boat. _____

10. I suggested you and (he, him) for the committee. _____

▶ **Exercise 2** **More Work With Objective Pronouns.** Complete each sentence below with the type of objective pronoun given in parentheses.

EXAMPLE: Dirk offered John and ____me____ a soft drink.   (indirect object)

1. If you need my book, I will get _____ .   (direct object)

2. When I saw Beth, I waved to _____ .   (object of a preposition)

3. I want Manuel and _____ for my assistants.   (direct object)

4. Aunt Jane sent Mary and _____ plane tickets.   (indirect object)

5. On their wedding day, he gave _____ money.   (indirect object)

6. Do not argue with _____ .   (object of preposition)

7. I will walk behind the senator and _____ .   (object of a preposition)

8. Mother made Dad and _____ some waffles.   (indirect object)

9. We were so quiet that the deer didn't hear _____ .   (direct object)

10. The train left without _____ .   (object of a preposition)

23   Objective Pronouns • Practice 2

▶ **Exercise 1**   **Identifying Objective Pronouns.**   Underline the correct pronoun from the two given in parentheses. Then, tell how it is being used: *object of a preposition, direct object,* or *indirect object.*

EXAMPLE: The carpenter told (we, us) a story. ____*indirect object*____

1. An enthusiastic volunteer spoke to Gerald and (me, I). _____
2. The librarian reserved (she, her) a copy of the book. _____
3. The pianist played a song for Larry and (we, us). _____
4. Marcia went to the museum with (him, he) and his mother. _____
5. The manager showed Martha and (me, I) around the plant. _____
6. Stephen drew Sheila and (she, her) a portrait. _____
7. The guide showed (them, they) around the campus. _____
8. Mrs. Fitzpatrick had a friendly talk with (they, them). _____
9. Mr. Turner reminded Mary Louise and (we, us) of the time. _____
10. Everyone laughed except Linda and (me, I). _____

▶ **Exercise 2**   **More Work With Objective Pronouns.**   Follow the directions for Exercise 1.

1. Sue saw Joan and (she, her) at the stables. _____
2. Andrew offered John and (me, I) a ride on his bicycle. _____
3. You told Mark and (us, we) the wrong answer. _____
4. Joseph showed (he, him) the ranch. _____
5. The scouts didn't notice the birds above (they, them). _____
6. Connie visited (they, them) last week. _____
7. The art teacher showed (we, us) some examples of O'Keeffe's art. _____
8. When we were in Chicago, we called (her, she). _____
9. Does this ring belong to (him, he)? _____
10. Jack sat between Shirley and (she, her). _____

▶ **Writing Application**   **Using Objective Pronouns in Sentences.**   Write ten sentences about unusual things that could happen. Use one of the following pronouns in each sentence: *me, you, him, her, it, us,* and *them.*

1. _____
2. _____
3. _____
4. _____
5. _____
6. _____
7. _____
8. _____
9. _____
10. _____

23 Possessive Pronouns • Practice 1

Possessive forms of personal pronouns show ownership. Sometimes, these pronouns come before a noun, as in the sentence "*Her* paper was excellent." Others are used by themselves, as this example shows: "The judges liked *ours*."

POSSESSIVE PRONOUNS			
Used Before Nouns		Used by Themselves	
my	its	mine	its
your	our	yours	ours
his	their	his	theirs
her		hers	

Do not use an apostrophe with a possessive pronoun.

▶ **Exercise 1**   **Using Possessive Pronouns.**   Complete each sentence below with a possessive pronoun.

EXAMPLE: Your dog dug a hole in ____*our*____ lawn.

1. Your car has four doors, while _____ has two.

2. _____ clock stopped, and I was late for school.

3. We found _____ cat several miles from home.

4. The infant already responds to _____ name.

5. We have our plan, and they have _____.

6. _____ car ran out of gas on the freeway.

7. Did you see _____ towel?

8. The redwood tree releases _____ seeds in a fire.

9. We lent them our camera. _____ was out of film.

10. Jack gave _____ butterfly collection to the school.

▶ **Exercise 2**   **Using Possessive Pronouns Correctly.**   In each sentence below, a possessive pronoun is used incorrectly. Write the correct form in the blank.

EXAMPLE: The tree drops it's leaves each fall. ____*its*____

1. Isn't that coat your's? _____

2. You can tell ours'—it's the one with the blue ribbon. _____

3. His's suitcase was stolen. _____

4. The orchard is their's but they let us pick the fruit. _____

5. The town got it's name from a nearby river. _____

6. This is my fishing pole; her's is against the fence. _____

7. Mother's fudge is good, but your's is better. _____

8. His' skateboard just broke in half. _____

9. Our house was safe, but their's was flooded. _____

10. The cat sharpened its' claws on a nearby tree. _____

23 # Possessive Pronouns • **Practice 2**

▶ **Exercise 1** **Using Possessive Pronouns.** Complete each sentence below with a possessive pronoun.

EXAMPLE: This baseball is ___ours.___

1. This briefcase is mine, but that briefcase is _____.

2. _____ is the house with the green shutters.

3. _____ cousin is a wonderful athlete.

4. We gave the nursery school _____ picture books.

5. Barbara said that this scarf is _____.

6. My soup is very hot. Is _____?

7. Please hand me _____ umbrella.

8. Have all the students in the class finished _____ reports?

9. The Nelsons borrowed our fan. _____ is broken.

10. Tommy said _____ mother was going to Ohio.

11. _____ father told me about the first trip to the moon.

12. Neil Armstrong and "Buzz" Aldrin landed _____ spacecraft.

13. _____ was an adventure of importance.

14. _____ trip was so successful that others have since followed.

15. Scientists in _____ country had never studied moon rocks.

16. The moon is _____ close neighbor.

17. _____ light comes from the sun, just as ours does.

18. _____ weight would be less on the moon than on Earth.

19. The moon's atmosphere is different from _____.

20. Astronauts must carry _____ own supply of air.

▶ **Writing Application** **Using Possessive Pronouns in Sentences.** Write a brief paragraph comparing your family to someone else's. Use at least five different possessive pronouns.

_____

_____

_____

_____

_____

_____

_____

_____

_____

_____

23 Using Different Pronoun Forms • Practice 1

There are three cases of personal pronouns: nominative, objective, and possessive. Each case functions in different ways in a sentence.

	THE THREE CASES OF PERSONAL PRONOUNS AND THEIR FUNCTIONS	
Cases	Pronoun Forms	Uses
Nominative	I, you, he, she, it, we, they	*Subject:* He umpired the game. *Predicate Pronoun:* The one to ask is he.
Objective	me, you, him, her, it, us, them	*Direct Object:* Jan helped her. *Indirect Object:* Bob gave me a job. *Object of a Preposition:* I called to her.
Possessive	my, mine, you, yours, his, hers, its, our, ours, their, theirs	*To Show Ownership:* The blue binder is mine. Our costumes look great.

▷ **Exercise 1**   **Identifying Different Pronoun Cases.**   In the blanks below, label each underlined personal pronoun as *nominative, objective,* or *possessive.*

EXAMPLE: Dana went to her for advice. _____*objective*_____

1. You are holding up traffic. _____
2. Ours is the best school in the district. _____
3. The vacation had its great moments. _____
4. I told her a secret. _____
5. The manager of the store is she. _____
6. Roger asked me. _____
7. My new haircut looks terrible. _____
8. Did they practice this afternoon? _____
9. Mrs. Bunting baked Spencer and me a cake. _____
10. The Hirschels and we will go in one car. _____

▷ **Exercise 2**   **Using Different Pronoun Cases.**   Complete each sentence below with the pronoun case indicated in parentheses. There may be several pronouns that will work equally well.

EXAMPLE: Martin gave _____*her*_____ the keys to the cabin.   (objective)

1. _____ wants some new paperbacks to read.   (nominative)
2. The coach showed _____ a new technique.   (objective)
3. Here are _____ shoes! (possessive)
4. The dancer to watch is _____.   (nominative)
5. Either our group or _____ will win the spelling bee.   (possessive)
6. I report to _____.   (objective)
7. _____ house has a large front yard.   (possessive)
8. The highway patrol will catch _____.   (objective)
9. Did _____ ask her name? (nominative)
10. My answer is correct; _____ isn't.   (possessive)

23 Using Different Pronoun Forms • Practice 2

▶ **Exercise 1** **Identifying Different Pronoun Cases.** Identify the case of each underlined personal pronoun below.

EXAMPLE: He asked me to walk the dog.   _nominative_

1. They took a new route to school. _____
2. Daniel sent me a letter. _____
3. Can you come to my party? _____
4. Marilyn led them across the street. _____
5. The musician who will be playing is he. _____
6. The dancer hurt her leg. _____
7. It was they who presented the awards. _____
8. Our neighbor cuts the grass twice a week. _____
9. My mother read me an article from the evening newspaper. _____
10. Everyone went swimming except Kevin and him. _____

▶ **Exercise 2** **More Work With Pronoun Forms.** Follow the directions for Exercise 1.

1. He often draws cartoons. _____
2. The baby grasped her bottle. _____
3. They rehearsed the skits all morning. _____
4. Michelle sent us a greeting card. _____
5. The students who are going to Washington are they. _____
6. Gordon gave Nancy and her some flowers from his garden. _____
7. The person who will speak to us is she. _____
8. The auditorium is ours for the afternoon. _____
9. I have known Bert and him since we were in kindergarten. _____
10. The photographer showed them some cameras and lenses. _____

▶ **Writing Application** **Telling About Pronoun Cases.** Write a paragraph explaining the uses of the nominative case. Include examples of each use.

_____
_____
_____
_____
_____
_____
_____
_____
_____
_____

24.1 Subjects and Verbs • Practice 1

One important rule in writing is that a singular subject must be used with a singular verb, and plural subjects must be used with plural verbs. In other words, the subject and verb of a sentence must be in agreement.

AGREEMENT OF SUBJECT AND VERB	
Singular	**Plural**
I want a ride.	My friends want a ride.
The church looks lovely.	The churches look lovely.
He plays in a band.	They play in a band.
The man feels healthy.	The men feel healthy.

Most nouns are made plural by adding -s or -es. This is not the case with plural verbs. The only verb form to which an -s is added is the third person singular.

► Exercise 1   **Making Subjects and Verbs Agree.**   Circle the word in parentheses below that makes the subject and verb of the sentence agree.

EXAMPLE: Taxes ((climb) , climbs) higher most of the time.

1. The cake (mix, mixes) looks too thin.

2. Your dog (bark, barks) at night.

3. Milt (like, likes) the high jump.

4. Our (forest, forests) provide a home for many creatures.

5. Usually, his movies (get, gets) good reviews.

6. Dachshunds (stand, stands) low to the ground.

7. (He, They) acts like a clown too often.

8. Our neighbor often (borrow, borrows) tools from us.

9. The fresh (cake, cakes) tastes delicious.

10. They (meet, meets) twice a month.

► Exercise 2   **More Work With Subject and Verb Agreement.**   Correct the underlined word in each sentence below so that the subject and verb are in agreement.

EXAMPLE: Mary dress fashionably.   _dresses_

1. We sees the Golden Gate Bridge. _____

2. Bird fly south for the winter. _____

3. The bed sit below the window. _____

4. They adds the numbers on a calculator. _____

5. The horses' hooves clinks on the road. _____

6. I enters from the left side of the stage. _____

7. We plays in the band. _____

8. My great-grandmother send money on my birthday. _____

9. The kite soar high in the sky. _____

10. The woman weave cloth on a loom. _____

24.1 Subjects and Verbs • Practice 2

▷ **Exercise 1**   **Making Subjects and Verbs Agree.**   For each sentence below, write the verb that agrees with the subject.

EXAMPLE: Many animals _____*live*_____ in tropical forests. (live, lives)

1. Plants _____ thickest along the edges of tropical forests. (grow, grows)
2. The tropical forest _____ warm and humid. (remain, remains)
3. The trees _____ year round. (grow, grows)
4. The branches _____ over one hundred feet. (reaches, reach)
5. This level _____ called the canopy. (is, are)
6. Orchids _____ from the branches of trees. (hang, hangs)
7. Some forest animals _____ through the air from branch to branch. (glides, glide)
8. A gibbon _____ through the treetops. (swing, swings)
9. Many insects _____ on rotting jungle wood. (live, lives)
10. Birds _____ around these forests during the day. (flies, fly)

▷ **Exercise 2**   **More Practice Making Subjects and Verbs Agree.**   Follow the directions for Exercise 1.

1. The elderly man _____ in the easy chair, talking to a friend. (sit, sits)
2. The boys _____ the craftsman make a chair. (watch, watches)
3. Katherine and Thomas _____ at the amusing story. (laugh, laughs)
4. That successful author _____ to write another novel. (plan, plans)
5. The artist _____ about the colors she will use. (think, thinks)
6. The leaves _____ color every fall. (change, changes)
7. The meal _____ soup or salad. (include, includes)
8. The children _____ around the fire. (huddle, huddles)
9. The taxes _____ up every year. (go, goes)
10. The mice _____ all the cheese. (eat, eats)

▷ **Writing Application**   **Writing Sentences With Subjects and Verbs That Agree.**   Write ten sentences about your neighborhood. Make sure the subjects and verbs agree.

1. _____
2. _____
3. _____
4. _____
5. _____
6. _____
7. _____
8. _____
9. _____
10. _____

24.1 Compound Subjects and Verbs • Practice 1

When a compound subject is connected by *and*, the verb is usually plural. But when the parts of the compound subject are thought of as one person or thing, the verb is singular.

COMPOUND SUBJECTS JOINED BY *AND*
Shirts and a new tie *are* on my shopping list.
Chicken and broccoli *is* a popular Chinese dish.

Two singular subjects joined by *or* or *nor* take a singular verb. Two plural subjects joined by *or* or *nor* take a plural verb. When singular and plural subjects are joined by *or* or *nor*, the verb agrees with the subject closer to it.

COMPOUND SUBJECTS JOINED BY *OR* OR *NOR*
Neither Sue nor Pam *has* her ice skates.
Tigers or lions *are* what I went to the zoo to see.
The magazines or the book *has* the information you need.

> **Exercise 1** **Making Compound Subjects and Verbs Agree.** Circle the verb that agrees with the subject of each sentence below.

EXAMPLE: The parents and children ((play) , plays) on opposite teams.

1. Black and white (is, are) my favorite color combination.

2. The trees and shrubs (look, looks) nice today.

3. Place mats or a tablecloth (go, goes) in the picnic basket.

4. Trucks and tractors (slow, slows) traffic down.

5. Neither the men nor the women (want, wants) that rule.

6. Either Sally or Eric (bring, brings) the main course.

7. Shirt and tie (look, looks) best at a formal dinner.

8. Either chicken or steak (taste, tastes) good when barbequed.

9. Neither the couch nor the chairs (look, looks) right in the room.

10. Swimming and running (is, are) good ways to exercise.

> **Exercise 2** **More Work With Compound Subjects and Verbs.** Circle the verb that agrees with the subject of each sentence below.

EXAMPLE: Canada and the United States ((stay) , stays) friendly.

1. Neither my coat nor my dresses (is, are) in the suitcase.

2. Dell and Amy really (like, likes) science.

3. The St. Bernard and the terrier (play, plays) together.

4. Either the cheese or the fish (is, are) bad.

5. The eggs and the milk (go, goes) in next.

6. Neither the sheets nor the bedspread (fit, fits) the bed.

7. *Life* and *Monopoly* (is, are) my favorite games.

8. The cows or sheep (move, moves) to another pasture in the afternoon.

9. A salamander or snake (live, lives) under the rock.

10. The coaches and the managers (run, runs) the teams.

24.1 Compound Subjects and Verbs • Practice 2

▶ **Exercise 1** **Making Compound Subjects and Verbs Agree.** Write the verb that agrees with the subject of each sentence below.

EXAMPLE: Sam and Randy ___are___ examining the globe. (is, are)

1. Land and water _____ drawn to scale on a globe. (is, are)
2. On a globe or a map, an inch or a centimeter _____ for a much larger unit of measurement. (stand, stands)
3. Neither these globes nor this map _____ my street. (show, shows)
4. Valerie and Katy _____ distance on a globe. (measure, measures)
5. Maps and globes _____ different uses. (has, have)
6. Either the globe or the maps _____ here. (belong, belongs)
7. Neither bridges nor airports _____ labeled on the map. (is, are)
8. Bill or John _____ the map that shows products. (has, have)
9. The atlas or a few globes _____ helpful to us. (is, are)
10. The scientists or their assistants _____ this map. (use, uses)

▶ **Exercise 2** **More Practice With Compound Subjects and Verbs.** Write the verb that correctly completes each sentence.

1. Rob or Fred _____ basketball after school. (plays, play)
2. The teacher or the students _____ the display to visitors. (explain, explains)
3. Neither Grace nor Kirk _____ the name. (remember, remembers)
4. A laboratory and an office _____ on the first floor. (is, are)
5. Beef and broccoli _____ a popular Chinese dish. (is, are)
6. The elephants and the giraffes _____ the zoo visitors. (ignore, ignores)
7. The angle or the speed _____ every few minutes. (change, changes)
8. Dodie and Steve _____ clothing made of leather. (dislikes, dislike)
9. Oak trees and large rocks _____ the landscape. (dot, dots)
10. Mom or Dad _____ us as we swim. (watch, watches)

▶ **Writing Application** **Writing Sentences With Compound Subjects.** Write ten sentences about different people, places, or things. Begin each sentence with a compound subject. Make sure the compound subject and the verb agree.

1. _____
2. _____
3. _____
4. _____
5. _____
6. _____
7. _____
8. _____
9. _____
10. _____

24.1 Pronoun Subjects and Verbs • Practice 1

An indefinite pronoun used as the subject of a sentence must agree with the verb. Some indefinite pronouns are always singular and therefore take a singular verb. Some are always plural and require a plural verb. For those pronouns that can be either singular or plural, look back at the noun that they replace. If the noun is singular, the pronoun is also singular.

INDEFINITE PRONOUNS				
Plural	**Singular or Plural**		**Singular**	
anybody	everybody	nothing	both	all
anyone	everything	one	few	any
anything	much	other	many	more
each	neither	somebody	others	most
either	nobody	someone	several	none
everybody	no one	something		

▶ **Exercise 1**   **Making Pronoun Subjects and Verbs Agree.**   In each sentence below, circle the verb that agrees with the pronoun subject.

EXAMPLE: Everybody in the office (know, (knows)) how to type.

1. Few of us (like, likes) Brussels sprouts.

2. All of the work (is, are) ready for you to inspect.

3. Nothing (get, gets) in his way.

4. Each of the stores (contribute, contributes) a gift.

5. Most of my friends (want, wants) to dance.

6. Several of the homes (have, has) fire damage.

7. Nobody (laugh, laughs) at his jokes.

8. None of the equipment (belong, belongs) to me.

9. Many of the teachers (give, gives) homework every night.

10. Each of our pets (try, tries) to please us.

▶ **Exercise 2**   **More Work With Pronoun Subject and Verb Agreement.**   In each sentence below, write the form of the verb that agrees with the pronoun subject.

EXAMPLE: Everybody _____helps_____ with school clean-up.   (help)

1. Most of the newspaper _____ advertisements.   (be)

2. Neither of my younger brothers _____ cartoons.   (watch)

3. Few of the people _____ for the whole day.   (stay)

4. All of the jewelry _____ antique.   (look)

5. Everything in the box _____ to the Goodwill.   (go)

6. Someone _____ that idea every year.   (suggest)

7. Both of my parents _____ the opera.   (enjoy)

8. All of those interested _____ on Tuesday.   (vote)

9. One of my friends _____ a gymnast.   (be)

10. Everyone _____ for a speedy recovery.   (hope)

24.1 Pronoun Subjects and Verbs • Practice 2

Exercise 1 **Making Pronoun Subjects and Verbs Agree.** In the sentences below, write the form of the verb that agrees with the subject.

EXAMPLE: Both of my parents _____*practice*_____ law.   (practice, practices)

1. All of our courts _____ part of our government.   (is, are)
2. Many of the tax cases _____ to a tax court.   (goes, go)
3. Few of the cases _____ to the Supreme Court.   (get, gets)
4. Everything usually _____ in a lower court.   (begins, begin)
5. Everybody on the Supreme Court _____ on the cases to review.   (vote, votes)
6. One of the members _____ as chief justice.   (serves, serve)
7. Each of the justices _____ an office and a staff.   (has, have)
8. No one _____ every case to be reviewed.   (expect, expects)
9. One of the requirements for a review _____ time.   (is, are)
10. Anybody without money _____ as a poor person.   (apply, applies)

Exercise 2 **More Work With Pronoun Subjects and Verbs.** Follow the directions for Exercise 1.

1. Someone from the office _____ every day.   (call, calls)
2. Either of the girls _____ the newspaper.   (deliver, delivers)
3. Each of the men _____ fish in the lake.   (catch, catches)
4. Somebody _____ a daily progress report.   (write, writes)
5. Others _____ his courage.   (admire, admires)
6. Nobody _____ to travel so far in one day.   (want, wants)
7. Most of the viewers _____ the magician.   (admire, admires)
8. Neither of the pieces _____ to this game.   (belong, belongs)
9. Anything about birds _____ me.   (interest, interests)
10. Much of the collection _____ new.   (look, looks)

Writing Application **Writing Sentences With Pronoun Subjects and Verbs.** Use each of the following ten indefinite pronouns as the subject of a sentence: *most, others, nothing, everyone, one, other, several, most, few,* and *much.*

1. _____
2. _____
3. _____
4. _____
5. _____
6. _____
7. _____
8. _____
9. _____
10. _____

24.2 Pronouns and Antecedents • Practice 1

A pronoun and its antecedent, or the word that it stands for, must always agree. A singular antecedent takes a singular pronoun. A plural antecedent takes a plural pronoun. If the antecedents are compound, use the following rule: Use a singular pronoun when the antecedents are joined by *or* or *nor*, and use a plural pronoun when the antecedents are joined by *and*.

PRONOUNS AND THEIR ANTECEDENTS	
Antecedent	**Example**
Singular	The gentleman said *he* would wait.
Plural	The women called *their* lawyer.
Compound joined by *or* or *nor*	Neither Mike nor Dick brought *his* lunch money.
Compound joined by *and*	The parents and children sang *their* favorite songs.

▶ **Exercise 1**   **Making Pronouns and Antecedents Agree.**   Fill in each blank below with a pronoun that agrees with its antecedent.

EXAMPLE: The cab driver said _____*his*_____ car needed a tune-up.

1. The custodian took _____ lunch break at noon.

2. Thomas Edison obtained 1,100 patents for _____ inventions.

3. The fire engine had _____ siren blaring.

4. Mary owns one of the hamsters; _____ is the brown one.

5. Gene and Greg gave _____ mother an apron.

6. Dad bakes bread, and _____ is delicious.

7. Either Jack or Brandon gives _____ speech text.

8. The pilots said _____ could fly the new plane.

9. Both the doctor and his assistant gave _____ opinions.

10. John and I wanted to help out; _____ offer wasn't in time.

▶ **Exercise 2**   **More Work With Pronouns and Antecedents.**   Rewrite the sentences below to correct any pronoun-antecedent errors.

EXAMPLE: The men must wear his coats and ties into the restaurant.

_____*The men must wear their coats and ties into the restaurant.*_____

1. Anne and Bob made her parents a photograph album.

_____

2. My dress does not fit right, so they must be altered.

_____

3. Either Sara or Nicole gives their speech next.

_____

4. My little sister played with its stuffed toy.

_____

5. The members of the team practiced its dribbling.

_____

24.2 Pronouns and Antecedents • Practice 2

▶ **Exercise 1**   **Making Pronouns and Antecedents Agree.**   Fill in each blank below with a pronoun that agrees with its antecedent.

EXAMPLE: Jake trained ____his____ dog to do tricks.

1. The astronomers said that _____ were studying storms on Mars.

2. My coat is clean, but Julie must take _____ coat to the cleaners.

3. Rachel and Donald told about _____ trip to the museum.

4. The woman related _____ story to the police.

5. Neither Fred nor Anthony brought _____ baseball bat.

6. Joan and Linda started _____ science project.

7. Mary always leaves _____ umbrella in the hallway.

8. Either Paul or Claude takes _____ turn next.

9. When Bill and Debbie play tennis, _____ use lightweight rackets.

10. Either Kenneth or Alan brought _____ camera.

▶ **Exercise 2**   **More Work With Pronouns and Antecedents.**   Follow the directions for Exercise 1.

1. Abby asked _____ father if she could keep the hamster.

2. Did Jed and Ethan find _____ pet gerbil?

3. Either Maria or Janet will give _____ recital today.

4. The boy still remembers when he got _____ dog.

5. Neither Sue Jones nor Brenda Smith takes _____ cat outside.

6. Bill and Bob are reading a letter from _____ grandfather.

7. Dr. Anna Quinn had to cancel _____ office hours today.

8. My uncle showed me _____ stamp collection.

9. Neither Paul nor John ate _____ dessert.

10. When Maria sees a sad movie, _____ usually cries.

▶ **Writing Application**   **Using Pronouns and Antecedents in Sentences.**   Write ten sentences about famous people. Use a pronoun and an antecedent in each sentence.

1. _____

2. _____

3. _____

4. _____

5. _____

6. _____

7. _____

8. _____

9. _____

10. _____

25.1 # Using Adjectives to Compare • **Practice 1**

Adjectives can compare items. To do this, adjectives have three degrees of comparison: positive, comparative, and superlative. Most one- and two-syllable adjectives form the comparative by adding *-er* to the end of the word and the superlative by adding *-est* to the end.

DEGREES OF COMPARISON FORMED BY ADDING *-ER* and *-EST*		
Positive	**Comparative**	**Superlative**
rich	richer	richest
sweet	sweeter	sweetest
tidy	tidier	tidiest

In words ending in *-y*, like *tidy*, the *-y* is often changed to *-i* before adding *-er* or *-est*.

▶ **Exercise 1** **Forming Positive, Comparative, and Superlative Adjectives.** Fill in the chart below with the missing positive, comparative, and superlative adjectives.

EXAMPLE:

crisp	*crisper*	*crispest*
Positive	**Comparative**	**Superlative**
1. _____	paler	_____
2. wild	_____	_____
3. _____	_____	quickest
4. small	_____	_____
5. _____	_____	curliest
6. _____	happier	_____
7. clean	_____	_____
8. _____	_____	dirtiest
9. _____	firmer	_____
10. tall	_____	

▶ **Exercise 2** **More Work With Positive, Comparative, and Superlative Adjectives.** Write a second sentence using the underlined adjective as described.

EXAMPLE: Today, the sky is cloudy.

　　　　　Comparative: _____*Today, the sky is cloudier than yesterday.*_____

1. Am I <u>early</u>?

   Superlative: _____

2. My grandfather is <u>old</u>.

   Comparative: _____

3. This bridge is <u>narrow</u>.

   Comparative: _____

4. The bus driver looks <u>sleepy</u>.

   Comparative: _____

5. The weather is the <u>calmest</u> I have seen it.

   Positive: _____

25.1 Using Adjectives to Compare • Practice 2

▶ **Exercise 1** **Forming the Degree of Comparison of One- and Two-Syllable Adjectives.** Fill in the chart below with the missing comparative and superlative forms of each adjective.

EXAMPLE: thick

thick   *thicker*   *thickest*

Positive	**Comparative**	**Superlative**
1. kind	_____	_____
2. mean	_____	_____
3. rich	_____	_____
4. shiny	_____	_____
5. cloudy	_____	_____
6. white	_____	_____
7. tall	_____	_____
8. big	_____	_____
9. young	_____	_____
10. wild	_____	_____
11. strong	_____	_____
12. old	_____	_____
13. soft	_____	_____
14. plain	_____	_____
15. pretty	_____	_____
16. bright	_____	_____
17. sweet	_____	_____
18. cold	_____	_____
19. smooth	_____	_____
20. sad	_____	_____

▶ **Exercise 2** **More Work With Degrees of Comparison of One- and Two-Syllable Adjectives.** Follow the directions for Exercise 1.

Positive	**Comparative**	**Superlative**
1. high	_____	_____
2. angry	_____	_____
3. rich	_____	_____
4. shiny	_____	_____
5. small	_____	_____
6. new	_____	_____
7. hard	_____	_____
8. nice	_____	_____
9. healthy	_____	_____
10. dull	_____	_____

25.1 Using Adjectives With *More* and *Most*

• Practice 1

Another way to form the comparative and superlative forms of adjectives is to add *more* and *most*. All adjectives with more than two syllables will use these words to form comparisons. Even some one- and two-syllable adjectives can use them to form comparisons.

SOME MODIFIERS REQUIRING *MORE* AND *MOST*		
Positive	**Comparative**	**Superlative**
delicious	more delicious	most delicious
attractive	more attractive	most attractive
willing	more willing	most willing
alert	more alert	most alert

▶ **Exercise 1** **Forming Degrees of Comparison With *More* and *Most*.** Fill in the chart below with the degrees of comparison that are missing.

EXAMPLE:

pleasing	more pleasing	most pleasing
Positive	**Comparative**	**Superlative**
1. _____	more convenient	_____
2. _____	_____	most generous
3. _____	more useful	_____
4. apparent	_____	_____
5. protective	_____	_____
6. _____	_____	most unfair
7. _____	_____	most understanding
8. _____	more faithful	_____
9. profitable	_____	_____
10. _____	more surprising	_____

▶ **Exercise 2** **More Work With Forming Comparisons Using *More* and *Most*.** Use *more* and *most* to form the comparative or superlative form of each adjective shown in parentheses below.

EXAMPLE: She was the _____*most disagreeable*_____ girl I ever met. (disagreeable)

1. Your answer is _____ than the one he gave. (reasonable)
2. Smoking is _____ to your lungs. (harmful)
3. Are oaks _____ than maple trees? (impressive)
4. This is the _____ project I have done. (worthwhile)
5. Silk is _____ than cotton. (expensive)
6. That child is _____ than the others. (talkative)
7. You are the _____ friend I have. (considerate)
8. It is _____ that you arrived now. (fortunate)
9. This is a _____ letter than your last one. (interesting)
10. This camp has made me _____ than I was before. (homesick)

25.1 Using Adjectives With *More* and *Most*
• Practice 2

▶ **Exercise 1**   **Using Adjectives With *More* and *Most*.** Use *more* and *most* to form the comparative or superlative form of each adjective shown in parentheses.

EXAMPLE: This trip was _____*more enjoyable*_____ than the last one. (enjoyable)

1. From there we had the _____ view of all. (magnificent)
2. This hotel is _____ than the new one. (luxurious)
3. Sue bought furniture that is _____ than ours. (modern)
4. Angela's solution is the _____ one of all. (sensible)
5. This assignment is the _____ one so far. (difficult)
6. She is the _____ baby sitter I know. (responsible)
7. This is the _____ film I have ever seen. (interesting)
8. A blue sofa would be _____ than a gray one. (attractive)
9. His paintings are _____ than hers. (colorful)
10. This is the _____ report in the class. (thoughtful)

▶ **Exercise 2**   **More Practice Using Adjectives With *More* and *Most*.** Follow the directions for Exercise 1.

1. Our new buses are _____ than our older ones. (comfortable)
2. This is the _____ building in town. (exciting)
3. The book describes the _____ events of our time. (incredible)
4. Who is the _____ scientist—Franklin or Einstein? (famous)
5. That was the _____ story I have ever heard. (outrageous)
6. Peter is _____ about skateboarding than I am. (enthusiastic)
7. Margaret's arguments are _____ than Jack's. (convincing)
8. Last Thanksgiving was the _____ holiday I remember. (eventful)
9. The almond cake is their _____ dessert. (delicious)
10. This magazine is _____ than that one. (interesting)

▶ **Writing Application**   **Using Adjectives With *More* and *Most*.** Write five sentences with adjectives in the comparative degree using *more* and five with adjectives in the superlative degree using *most*.

_____

_____

_____

_____

_____

_____

_____

_____

_____

25.1 Using Adverbs to Compare • Practice 1

Adverbs, like adjectives, have three degrees of comparison: positive, comparative, and superlative. With a one-syllable adverb, the comparative is formed by adding *-er* and the superlative by adding *-est.*

DEGREES OF COMPARISON FORMED BY ADDING *-ER* or *-EST*		
Positive	**Comparative**	**Superlative**
low	lower	lowest
straight	straighter	straightest

Adverbs ending in *-ly* form the comparative and superlative by adding *more* and *most.*

DEGREES OF COMPARISON FORMED BY ADDING *MORE* OR *MOST*		
Positive	**Comparative**	**Superlative**
briefly	more briefly	most briefly
cheerfully	more cheerfully	most cheerfully

▶ **Exercise 1** **Forming the Positive, Comparative, and Superlative Degrees of Adverbs.** Fill in the chart below with the missing positive, comparative, and superlative degrees of the adverbs.

EXAMPLE:

sincerely	more sincerely	most sincerely
Positive	**Comparative**	**Superlative**
1. _____	more slowly	_____
2. long	_____	_____
3. _____	more quietly	_____
4. _____	_____	most carefully
5. willingly	_____	_____
6. _____	_____	most loudly
7. _____	more easily	_____
8. _____	_____	most recently
9. completely	_____	_____
10. often	_____	_____

▶ **Exercise 2** **More Work With Positive, Comparative, and Superlative Adverbs.** Rewrite each sentence below, using the underlined adverb in the form indicated.

EXAMPLE: Matt exercises <u>regularly</u>.

Comparative: *Matt exercises more regularly than I do.*

1. We ride <u>most cautiously</u> on busy streets.

Positive: _____

2. I behaved <u>selfishly</u>.

Comparative: _____

3. You spoke <u>bluntly</u>.

Comparative: _____

4. I hit the nail <u>hard</u>.

Superlative: _____

25.1 Using Adverbs to Compare • Practice 2

▶ **Exercise 1** **Forming the Comparative and Superlative Degrees of Adverbs.** Fill in the chart with the missing comparative and superlative degrees of each adverb listed below. Add *-er* or *-est* to adverbs whenever possible. When necessary, use the words *more* and *most*.

EXAMPLE:

fast   *faster*   *fastest*

Positive	Comparative	Superlative
1. plainly	_____	_____
2. low	_____	_____
3. safely	_____	_____
4. recently	_____	_____
5. quickly	_____	_____
6. deep	_____	_____
7. nearly	_____	_____
8. lively	_____	_____
9. hastily	_____	_____
10. definitely	_____	_____

▶ **Exercise 2** **More Work With the Comparative and Superlative Degrees of Adverbs.** Fill in the chart with the missing comparative and superlative degree of each adverb listed below. Follow the advice given in Exercise 1 regarding the use of *-er* or *-est*.

Positive	Comparative	Superlative
1. softly	_____	_____
2. silently	_____	_____
3. long	_____	_____
4. briefly	_____	_____
5. suddenly	_____	_____
6. hard	_____	_____
7. firmly	_____	_____
8. short	_____	_____
9. carefully	_____	_____
10. distantly	_____	_____

▶ **Writing Application** **Using Adverbs to Compare Actions.** Write a brief paragraph describing how three people perform the same activity. For example, you could describe how people speak, play a game, cook, or work on a project. The people you describe can be real or imaginary. In your paragraph, use at least five adverbs in their comparative or superlative forms. Underline each adverb.

_____

_____

_____

_____

_____

25.1 Avoiding Double Comparisons • Practice 1

If two forms of comparison—for instance, *most* and *-est*—are used in one sentence, the result is a sentence error called a double comparison. To avoid this error, use either *-er* or *more* to form the comparative and *-est* or *most* to form the superlative. Never use both in the same comparison.

CORRECTING DOUBLE COMPARISONS	
Incorrect	**Correct**
I ran *more faster* today than yesterday.	I ran *faster* today than yesterday.
A plum is *more sweeter* than a pear.	A plum is *more sweet* than a pear.
This is the *most cleanest* room.	This is the *cleanest* room.
She worked the *most hardest* of all.	She worked the *hardest* of all.

▶ **Exercise 1** **Avoiding Double Comparisons.** Rewrite the underlined part of each sentence below to eliminate the double comparison.

EXAMPLE: I left more happier after I heard the news. _____*happier*_____

1. These are the most crispest potato chips. _____

2. I have more curlier hair than my sister. _____

3. Fudge tastes the most richest of all candy. _____

4. The crew made the road more wider. _____

5. I promise to call more oftener. _____

6. This cartoon ran the most longest. _____

7. The wood is the most hardest you can buy. _____

8. The music is more louder than I like. _____

9. My dog is the most gentlest on the block. _____

10. I look the most sleepiest in the morning. _____

▶ **Exercise 2** **More Work Correcting Double Comparisons.** Rewrite the underlined portion of each sentence below to eliminate the double comparison.

EXAMPLE: My grandmother is the most oldest member of her family. _____*oldest*_____

1. This test seemed more shorter than the last. _____

2. I am the most handiest at fixing cars. _____

3. That author wrote the most dullest book. _____

4. The kitten grew more bigger each day. _____

5. This grocery store sells meat the most cheapest. _____

6. I can't remember when I've felt more worser. _____

7. The rain fell the most hardest in the valley. _____

8. My brother is the most stubbornest boy around. _____

9. We arrived more later than we thought. _____

10. Our dog obeyed us more better after obedience school. _____

25.1 Avoiding Double Comparisons • Practice 2

▷ **Exercise 1**   Avoiding Double Comparisons.   Most of the sentences below contain double comparisons. Rewrite these sentences correctly. Write *correct* if there are no errors.

EXAMPLE: This pony is more healthier than that one.
          This pony is healthier than that one.

1. The planet Venus is more closer to us than Neptune is.

   _____

2. Here is our most newest model.

   _____

3. Of all these gems, this is the most rarest.

   _____

4. This car uses gasoline the most efficiently.

   _____

5. We heard the most oddest sound before the big storm.

   _____

6. My dog is more smaller than yours.

   _____

7. We began our work earlier than usual.

   _____

8. Robert calculates more faster than Alan.

   _____

9. The more older model still runs well.

   _____

10. Mahogany logs burn longer than pine.

   _____

▷ **Exercise 2**   More Practice Correcting Double Comparisons.   Follow the directions for Exercise 1.

1. Now that the summer tourist crowd is gone it is more quieter.

   _____

2. The vegetables sold at the stand here are the most freshest.

   _____

3. He smiled and acted more friendlier than before.

   _____

4. Betty worked the most hardest during those two weeks.

   _____

5. I awoke more later than my brother.

   _____

25.2 Using *Bad* and *Badly* • Practice 1

Knowing when to use *bad* or *badly* can be a problem. Remember, bad is an adjective and describes a noun. It usually follows linking verbs like *be, look, appear, seem, smell, stay,* and *taste. Badly* is an adverb and follows an action verb.

USING *BAD* AND *BADLY* IN SENTENCES	
bad	The road to the cabin is bad.
	The fish smells bad.
	My cut looks bad.
badly	My sister cleans house badly.
	Today, I swam badly.
	His hands shook badly.

▶ **Exercise 1** **Using *Bad* and *Badly* Correctly.** Circle the correct modifier—*bad* or *badly*—in each sentence below.

EXAMPLE: The rehearsal went (bad, (badly)).

1. Our dog behaves (bad, badly).

2. The smog is (bad, badly) today.

3. The burnt asparagus smells (bad, badly).

4. I draw straight lines (bad, badly).

5. Her science project looks (bad, badly).

6. Mother reacted (bad, badly) to my suggestion.

7. Our lawn mower works (bad, badly).

8. Milk turns (bad, badly) when it isn't refrigerated.

9. My broken arm hurts (bad, badly).

10. The fire seems (bad, badly).

▶ **Exercise 2** **More Work With *Bad* and *Badly*.** Write the correct modifier—*bad* or *badly*—for each sentence below.

EXAMPLE: The color red looks ____bad____ on me.

1. The average score on the test was very _____.

2. The child acts _____ when his parents aren't home.

3. The lawyer wrote the contract _____.

4. Our sailboat handled _____ in the rough water.

5. The results of the hurricane were _____.

6. The speaker's microphone worked _____.

7. The host felt _____ when the guest of honor didn't show up.

8. The foundation under the house was _____.

9. The new plants did _____ in the summer heat.

10. My dog performed _____ in her first dog show.

25.2 Using *Bad* and *Badly* • Practice 2

▶ **Exercise 1** **Using *Bad* and *Badly*.** Write the correct modifier—*bad* or *badly*—for each sentence below.

EXAMPLE: The report on the radio sounded ____*bad*.____

1. This new style of baggy pants looks _____ on me.
2. Paul draws portraits _____.
3. The magician performed _____.
4. The new perfume smells _____ to me.
5. This detergent cleans _____.
6. This fabric wrinkles _____.
7. My brother cooks _____.
8. My new blueberry dessert creation tastes _____.
9. After ten days the cream turned _____.
10. In spite of her lessons, Mary plays _____.

▶ **Exercise 2** **More Practice Using *Bad* and *Badly*.** Follow the directions for Exercise 1.

1. During his illness, Henry looked _____.
2. The plumber repaired the sink _____.
3. In the afternoon the weather turned _____.
4. I felt _____ when I forgot your birthday.
5. Because she worried, she wrote _____.
6. We had problems because we planned the trip _____.
7. The new method of farming works _____.
8. The visibility at the airport remained _____.
9. This painting looks _____ in this spot.
10. These candles flicker and smoke _____.

▶ **Writing Application** **Using *Bad* and *Badly* in Sentences.** Write five sentences using *bad* with various linking verbs. Then, write five sentences using *badly* with action verbs.

1. _____
2. _____
3. _____
4. _____
5. _____
6. _____
7. _____
8. _____
9. _____
10. _____

25.2 Using *Good* and *Well* • Practice 1

Good and *well* often confuse writers. *Good* is an adjective and must always follow a linking verb. *Well* can be either an adverb or adjective. As an adverb, it always follows an action verb. As an adjective, it follows a linking verb and generally refers to a person's health.

EXAMPLES OF *GOOD* and *WELL*		
Word	**Use**	**Example**
Good	Adjective	The warm water feels *good*.
		Your homemade bread tastes *good*.
Well	Adverb	I ride a horse *well*.
		Our candy sold *well*.
Well	Adjective	Your ears look *well* with the infection gone.
		My grandfather feels *well*.

▶ Exercise 1 **Using *Good* and *Well* Correctly.** Circle the correct modifier—*good* or *well*—to complete each sentence below.

EXAMPLE: The first leg of the race went (good, (well)).

1. My brand-new bike rides (good, well).

2. The frozen yogurt tasted (good, well).

3. She handled her disappointment (good, well).

4. The last two movies I've seen have been (good, well).

5. Are you feeling (good, well) now that your fever has dropped?

6. The teacher said my report on the Gold Rush was (good, well).

7. My parents dance (good, well) together.

8. I had the flu, but I am (good, well) now.

9. My teen-age brother drives (good, well).

10. A cool breeze feels (good, well) on a hot day.

▶ Exercise 2 **More Practice using *Good* and *Well*.** Insert the correct modifier—*good* or *well*—to complete each sentence below.

EXAMPLE: The new engine runs _____*well*._____

1. The sand feels _____ between my toes.

2. That dress looks _____ on you.

3. You are looking _____, even after running a marathon.

4. Nancy spoke _____ before the large crowd.

5. Despite the insects, the trees still appear _____.

6. This muffin mix stays _____ for several weeks if refrigerated.

7. These lightweight shoes are _____ for backpacking.

8. I feel _____ enough to be out of bed.

9. The students reacted _____ when the fire alarm went off.

10. The first act of the play was very _____.

25.2 Using *Good* and *Well* • Practice 2

▶ **Exercise 1**   **Using *Good* and *Well*.**   Write the correct modifier—*good* or *well*—for each sentence below.

EXAMPLE: Our first baseman played ____*well*____.

1. During practice Arlene skated _____.
2. Your poster looks _____ here.
3. After a summer at the lake, I will swim _____.
4. Tony is very talented; he sings _____.
5. The sandwiches here taste _____.
6. Although it is old, this table looks _____.
7. Anna had been sick but now seems _____.
8. All winter he stayed _____.
9. The rolls you are baking smell _____.
10. When Peter plays the violin, it sounds _____.

▶ **Exercise 2**   **More Work With Using *Good* and *Well*.**   Follow the directions for Exercise 1.

1. We searched the room _____.
2. During the show, the children listened _____.
3. These flowers smell _____.
4. This cheese tastes _____ to me.
5. When he became _____, he returned to work.
6. This wood burns _____ in our fireplace.
7. As a campsite, this spot looks _____.
8. The breezes feel _____ after our day in the sun.
9. Hats look _____ on you.
10. Those fresh muffins smell _____.

▶ **Writing Application**   **Using *Good* and *Well* in Sentences.**   Write five sentences using *good* and five sentences using *well*.

1. _____
2. _____
3. _____
4. _____
5. _____
6. _____
7. _____
8. _____
9. _____
10. _____

26.1 Periods • Practice 1

A period should be used at the end of declarative and imperative sentences, indirect questions, and most abbreviations and initials.

USES OF A PERIOD	
With a declarative sentence	The rain washed out the road.
With an imperative sentence	Do your homework right now.
With an indirect question	The man asked me where the school was.
With an abbreviation	Prof. Joe Wall presented a slide show.
With initials	My accountant is R. L. Huntley.

▶ **Exercise 1**   **Using Periods.**   Add periods wherever necessary in the sentences below.

EXAMPLE: Gov George Barthold won by a landslide
            Gov. George Barthold won by a landslide.

1. The restaurant is on Almond St just beyond the school

2. Dr D R Farnsworth will pull my wisdom teeth

3. Nancy J Spradling, please set the table now

4. Our newspaper asked when Sen Seth Robbins would arrive

5. I am short—only 5 ft 1 in tall in my stocking feet

6. My relatives have lived in Spokane, Wash, for three years

7. Rep Teresa Willets asked about aid for Allendale Co residents

8. Buy me two lbs of bananas at the store

9. I asked what day of the week Mar 30 fell on

10. Bob asked if 10°C was equal to 50°F

▶ **Exercise 2**   **More Practice Using Periods.**   Write the type of sentence indicated, using periods wherever necessary.

EXAMPLE: Imperative with an abbreviation

        _____*Put in three tsp. of sugar.*_____

1. Declarative with an abbreviation

   _____

2. Imperative

   _____

3. Indirect question

   _____

4. Declarative with initials

   _____

5. Imperative with an abbreviation

   _____

26.1 Periods • Practice 2

▶ **Exercise 1** **Using Periods.** Add periods to the following sentences wherever necessary.

EXAMPLE: Napoleon was about 5 ft 4 in tall
Napoleon was about 5 ft. 4 in. tall.

1. Napoleon Bonaparte was born in Corsica on Aug 15, 1769
2. He was quickly promoted from Pvt to Corp to Sgt
3. "The Little Corporal" was his nickname
4. In battles, he attacked the enemy at its weakest point
5. He expanded his empire by warfare
6. At one time his empire included almost all of Europe
7. On Apr 11, 1814, he gave up his throne
8. His final defeat was at the Battle of Waterloo
9. He died in 1821 on the island of St Helena
10. Some historians have questioned the cause of his death
11. Mr Wyman belongs to a stamp club in Wilmington, Del
12. Mrs Callaghan asked me when I started my stamp collection
13. Look at the color and ink on those stamps
14. This stamped envelope is postmarked Philadelphia, Pa
15. Ed asked whether a magnifying glass was needed
16. I bought this magnifying glass on Willow Ave
17. A dealer on Spruce St sold me these stamps
18. The stamps are from Eng, Fr, and Ger
19. To remove a stamp from an envelope, soak it in water
20. The face of Dr Walter Reed is on a commemorative stamp

▶ **Writing Application** **Using Periods in a Paragraph.** Write a paragraph about an important event in your life. End each declarative sentence, imperative sentence, and indirect question with a period.

_____
_____
_____
_____
_____
_____
_____
_____
_____
_____

26.1 # Question Marks • Practice 1

The question mark is used in two places: at the end of an interrogative sentence and at the end of a word or phrase that asks a question. Do not make the mistake of using a question mark at the end of an indirect question.

USES OF THE QUESTION MARK	
Interrogative sentence	When does the newspaper arrive? Where are you staying?
Word or phrase that asks a question	You'll go to the store. When? He plans to climb that peak. How soon?

▶ **Exercise 1**   **Using Question Marks.**   Place a question mark or period wherever necessary in the sentences below.

EXAMPLE: Do you want salad with dinner   Mashed potatoes
                Do you want salad with dinner?   Mashed potatoes?

1. When does that train come in   On what track

2. What were problems faced by the Pilgrims in the New World

3. I asked when the report was due

4. I left a message for you to call me   Why didn't you

5. Are you going to Martha's to study   When

6. Can you figure out these directions

7. Dan asked if he could borrow the car   What did you say

8. What is your favorite dessert   Favorite movie

9. You said that Bret can help   If so, when

10. Which painting do you like the best

▶ **Exercise 2**   **More Practice Using Question Marks.**   Place a question mark or period wherever necessary in the sentences below.

EXAMPLE: You made this cake   But for whom
                You made this cake.   But for whom?

1. Why me   I'm already too busy

2. How long should I cook it   And at what temperature

3. I asked you what happened to the window   Did you break it

4. Come by around dinner   Is 6:00 P.M. convenient

5. Gerry said to meet after school   Where

6. Your arm is in a cast   For how long

7. The teacher asked what year WWII began   What would you answer

8. Did you lock the front door   Turn off the iron

9. We asked him about that   So what do you think he said

10. Can you organize these cards   By when

26.1 Question Marks • Practice 2

Exercise 1 **Using Question Marks.** Add the missing question marks and periods in the sentences below.

EXAMPLE: She asked me to list the U.S. Presidents   But why
She asked me to list the U.S. Presidents.   But why?

1. Have you read "Charles," by Shirley Jackson
2. When did Edgar Allan Poe and Charles Dickens meet   Why
3. The capital of Brazil was moved from Rio de Janeiro to Brasilia   When
4. How large is the planet Jupiter
5. Were you able to see the comet
6. Can you meet with me tomorrow   Where
7. How did they choose a student representative
8. Who recited the poem by Walt Whitman
9. Marie Curie discovered radium   When
10. If we leave early, we will have time to stop at the zoo
11. Who is expected to win the long jump
12. Arthur will speak to us about computers   At what time
13. Carol said there is a rehearsal this afternoon   Where
14. What new records have been purchased for the library
15. One of the building plans was accepted   Which one
16. Who left this message for me   Why
17. Did you meet a journalist when you visited the newspaper
18. When will we talk about the class trip   With whom
19. Which of these pictures do you like best   Why
20. Can you think of a way to solve this problem   How

Writing Application **Writing Questions.** Write ten questions about a person, place, or thing. Use some complete sentences and some words or phrases following a complete sentence.

1. _____
2. _____
3. _____
4. _____
5. _____
6. _____
7. _____
8. _____
9. _____
10. _____

26.1 Exclamation Marks • Practice 1

An exclamation mark signals strong emotion or feeling. It should be used at the end of exclamatory sentences, strong or forceful imperative sentences, and interjections expressing strong emotion.

USES OF THE EXCLAMATION MARK	
Use an Exclamation Mark With:	Example
an exclamatory sentence	I got accepted to Stanford! We won first place!
an imperative sentence that contains a forceful command	Stay out of the road! Do as I say!
an interjection expressing strong emotion	Ouch! That hurts. Wow! That rainbow is beautiful.

▶ **Exercise 1**　**Using Exclamation Marks.**　Insert an exclamation mark where necessary in the following sentences. Then, indicate the type of sentence it is, using the following code:

　　1—exclamatory sentence　　2—forceful imperative　　3—strong interjection

EXAMPLE: _____ Catch that thief

　　　　　___2___ Catch that thief!

1. _____ It's wonderful to see you looking so healthy

2. _____ Hey Come over here for a minute.

3. _____ Gosh I'm glad to see you

4. _____ Answer your father

5. _____ Stop that man

6. _____ Surprise I'll bet you didn't know we were coming.

7. _____ Your performance was breathtaking

8. _____ Call the fire department

9. _____ I'm completely exhausted

10. _____ Run so you don't miss the bus

▶ **Exercise 2**　**More Work With Exclamation Marks.**　If the use of the period and exclamation mark in a sentence below is correct, write C. If it is incorrect, cross out the incorrect punctuation mark and write the proper one above it.

EXAMPLE: ___C___ Help me! I can't swim.

1. _____ Read the first paragraph for us!

2. _____ Oh my! You startled me.

3. _____ What a wonderful vacation that was.

4. _____ Wow. That was a photo-finish race.

5. _____ I'm absolutely thrilled that you won the election!

6. _____ Well. That guy is a poor sport.

7. _____ Watch out for that car.

8. _____ I washed my hair today!

9. _____ Darn. I forgot my homework at home.

10. _____ That's a splendid suggestion!

26.1 Exclamation Marks • Practice 2

▶ **Exercise 1**   **Using Exclamation Marks.**   Add the necessary exclamation mark(s) to each item below.

EXAMPLE: I knew it
          I knew it!

1. Listen to me

2. On your mark   Get set   Go

3. Deliver this message immediately

4. What a wonderful idea

5. Sit down

6. Oh   This is truly a surprise.

7. Hey   It's not time to begin.

8. Be still

9. Never   I cannot agree.

10. Goodness   You must consider the consequences.

▶ **Exercise 2**   **More Practice Using Exclamation Marks.**   Follow the directions for Exercise 1.

1. Ah   I've found it.

2. Look out

3. Hurray   We finished first.

4. Wow   We saw a really magnificent view.

5. Open the window at once

6. Super   That's an extraordinary idea.

7. Drop the ball

8. Impossible   This report can't be true.

9. Get out

10. What a ridiculous story

▶ **Writing Application**   **Using Exclamation Marks to Show Strong Feelings.**   Write a short, dramatic scene in which two characters show strong feelings. Use exclamation marks after exclamatory sentences, after sentences giving strong commands, and after interjections.

_____

_____

_____

_____

_____

_____

_____

_____

_____

26.2 # Commas in Compound Sentences
• Practice 1

A compound sentence is formed from two simple sentences joined by a comma and a coordinating conjunction. The coordinating conjunctions are *and, but, for, nor, or, so,* and *yet.*

THE COMMA IN COMPOUND SENTENCES
Simple Sentence, Coordinating Conjunction, Simple Sentence
I ran after the ice-cream truck, *but* he didn't see me. Donald went to get hamburgers, *and* Margie set the table. Wendy turned the radio down, *so* I was finally able to study.

Note: If the two sentences forming the compound are very short, the comma can be omitted.

▶ **Exercise 1** **Using Commas in Compound Sentences.** Insert commas where necessary in the sentences below. Some sentences may not need a comma.

EXAMPLE: Nancy will handle the tickets and I will order the food.
Nancy will handle the tickets, and I will order the food.

1. I called home for I was going to be late.

2. Mom washed and Dad dried.

3. We can get dinner now or we can go to the movie.

4. Bill couldn't come today nor is he likely to come tomorrow.

5. The photographer grabbed his camera for the sunset was lovely.

6. I studied history for hours yet I still had trouble on the test.

7. She has never skied before so I suggested that she take lessons.

8. The road was newly paved but the lines had yet to be painted on.

9. The car was just what I wanted and it was the right price.

10. The boy sang and the girl danced.

▶ **Exercise 2** **More Work Using Commas in Compound Sentences.** Combine the two sentences in each numbered item below as a compound sentence, using a comma and a conjunction.

EXAMPLE: I pulled the weeds. My brother mowed the lawn.
I pulled the weeds, and my brother mowed the lawn.

1. We tried to make reservations tonight. The restaurant was booked.

_____

2. I enjoy preparing the salad. My mother likes to do the desserts.

_____

3. We must get this leak fixed. The whole basement might flood.

_____

4. I earned money baby-sitting. I was able to buy the concert tickets.

_____

5. We came out to practice soccer. The field was too wet.

_____

26.2 Commas in Compound Sentences
• Practice 2

▶ **Exercise 1**   **Using Commas in Compound Sentences.**   In each of the following sentences, insert commas where they are needed.

EXAMPLE: A husky is a large dog but a sheepdog is larger.
   A husky is a large dog, but a sheepdog is larger.

1. I turned on the light for it was getting dark.
2. I think we should take a vote but Alan wants to wait.
3. We can stay and explore or we can return tomorrow.
4. I explained the procedure but they didn't understand.
5. Anna wants to join the art club for she loves to paint.
6. Terry calls once a week but Bill telephones every day.
7. Alice was shy so Barbara did all the talking.
8. Summer has arrived yet the days are still chilly.
9. We can walk to the park or we can take our bicycles.
10. They did not seem confused nor did they ask for help.

▶ **Exercise 2**   **More Practice Using Commas in Compound Sentences.**   Follow the directions for Exercise 1.

1. I trained my dog to sit but Bob never trained his dog.
2. Our dog is a mongrel for his parents were different breeds.
3. Our dog seems intelligent yet he can't do many tricks.
4. Mark's dog lives outdoors so Mark keeps the dog house warm.
5. Bring your dog on the picnic or leave him with your dad.
6. I read about many breeds of dogs and I learned the ones that would be best for me.
7. Sally will walk her dog in the park today or she will take him to the beach.
8. Chris has always wanted a dog but he cannot have one in an apartment.
9. Bill's dog did not behave well so he enrolled the dog in obedience school.
10. I cannot visit that dog-lover's home for I am afraid of her dogs.

▶ **Writing Application**   **Using Commas to Punctuate Compound Sentences.**   Write ten compound sentences. Use a comma and one of the following conjunctions to join each part: *and, but, for, nor, or, so,* and *yet.*

_____
_____
_____
_____
_____
_____
_____
_____
_____
_____

26.2 Commas in a Series • Practice 1

A series is considered a list of three or more items. When a sentence contains a series of words or phrases, the items should be separated by commas.

COMMAS USED IN A SERIES OF WORDS AND PHRASES	
Series of Words	I met the principal, the secretary, and the custodian. Apples, oranges, and bananas were all on sale.
Series of Phrases	The mouse ran across the floor, under the table, and out the door. The path takes us by the lake, through a pass, and into the meadow

An exception to this rule: When each item in the series is followed by a conjunction, no comma is used.

EXAMPLE: You may paint or color or draw.

▶ **Exercise 1**　**Using Commas in a Series.**　Insert commas into the sentences below wherever necessary. Some sentences may not require any commas.

EXAMPLE: You can paint scenery sew costumes or build sets.
　　　　　　You can paint scenery, sew costumes, or build sets.

1. The dog sniffed barked and growled at the stranger.

2. You can have eggs or cereal or French toast.

3. So far, we have driven through New Hampshire Vermont and Maine.

4. I grabbed my books rushed out the door and caught the bus.

5. The man sprayed the trees shrubs and the grass.

6. My dad plans to grow peanuts corn and hay this year.

7. Will you buy rent or lease a car?

8. The child had wandered out the door down the drive and into the street.

9. I addressed stamped and mailed the envelopes.

10. We can't decide whether to buy a boat or a raft or a kayak.

▶ **Exercise 2**　**More Work Using Commas in a Series.**　Finish each sentence below by adding a series that requires commas.

EXAMPLE: Every morning before school I . . .
　　　　　　Every morning before school, I___shower, dress, and eat.___

1. At the beach I enjoy looking at . . .

_____

2. . . . are my favorite subjects in school.

_____

3. I plan to visit . . . this year.

_____

4. When I help around the house, I . . .

_____

5. . . . are the best shows on TV right now.

_____

26.2 # Commas in a Series • Practice 2

▶ **Exercise 1** **Using Commas With Items in a Series.** In each of the following sentences, add commas where they are needed.

EXAMPLE: Redwoods pines and firs are all needle-leaf trees.
Redwoods, pines, and firs are all needle-leaf trees.

1. Memphis Nashville and Chattanooga are cities in Tennessee.

2. We met the writer producer and director of the television show.

3. As John made the winning shot, the fans gasped cheered and began shouting his name.

4. We must have volunteers who are willing to supply soda to cook hamburgers and to prepare a salad.

5. They could not decide whether to take their vacation in June July or in August.

6. To decorate her room, Caitlin added a rug a bookcase and a poster.

7. Jasmine has many pets, including a dog a cat a bird and a hamster.

8. You can peel the potatoes make the lemonade and set the table.

9. It was so cold that Kurt wore a shirt a sweater and a jacket.

10. Would you like to go to the beach take a hike or watch a movie?

▶ **Exercise 2** **More Practice Using Commas With Items in a Series.** Follow the directions for Exercise 1.

1. From my window, I can see pigeons sparrows robins and starlings.

2. I wrote folded and sealed the letter without remembering to enclose the pictures.

3. We walked along the waterfront past the marina and beyond the shops.

4. Boston has harbors public parks and historic places to visit.

5. Alex Patty Chris and Ian are all planning to visit Susan after she moves to Detroit.

6. You should just take a deep breath close your eyes and calm down.

7. At the nursery, Wes looked at trees for the front flowers for the back and houseplants for inside.

8. Books magazines and flowers are all good gifts for someone who is sick.

9. On Saturday, Melinda got a haircut had her nails done and bought a new pair of shoes.

10. Barry wants to take guitar lessons write new songs and become a performer.

▶ **Writing Application** **Writing Sentences With Items in a Series.** Write ten sentences about things to do, things to see, or things to listen to. In each sentence, include three or more words or phrases in a series.

1. _____

2. _____

3. _____

4. _____

5. _____

6. _____

7. _____

8. _____

9. _____

10. _____

26.2

Commas With Introductory Words and Phrases • Practice 1

A comma should be used after an introductory word or phrase. Introductory words include mild interjections (*oh, my, true*) or the name of a person you are addressing. Introductory phrases may be a prepositional phrase or a phrase that acts like another part of speech.

USING COMMAS WITH INTRODUCTORY WORDS AND PHRASES	
Introductory Words	My, that was a difficult workout.
	Bill, are you good at multiplication?
Introductory Phrases	In the morning, we'll go fishing.
	Blowing wildly in the wind, the trees weathered the fierce storm.

▶ **Exercise 1** **Recognizing Introductory Words and Phrases.** Write the introductory word or phrase in each sentence below and add the necessary comma.

EXAMPLE: _____ *No,* _____ No we don't have any sunglasses at this store.

1. _____ With this freeze the crop will suffer.

2. _____ To hear the speaker I moved up to the front.

3. _____ Joan have you returned those library books?

4. _____ During the night a storm developed.

5. _____ Well your stroke looks a little sloppy.

6. _____ Yes Marilyn can stay for dinner.

7. _____ Calling my friends I got enough volunteers.

8. _____ True we have a small budget for the project.

9. _____ With your good attitude you'll get the job.

10. _____ Jill turn off the radio.

▶ **Exercise 2** **Using Commas With Introductory Words and Phrases.** Insert a comma wherever necessary in each sentence below.

EXAMPLE: No you can't have another snack before dinner.
 No, you can't have another snack before dinner.

1. Dressed in crazy costumes we went to a Halloween party.

2. With a loud crash the vase hit the marble floor.

3. Shawn do you think we have enough sand here?

4. Well your hem still seems to be a little uneven.

5. To get emergency help in our town you dial 911.

6. After a ten-minute delay the movie finally started.

7. Jason I'm over here next to the refreshment stand.

8. Yes I think you're right about that.

9. With this great invention I can make a fortune.

10. To memorize your speech you must go over it a number of times.

26.2 Commas With Introductory Words and Phrases • Practice 2

Exercise 1 **Using Commas With Introductory Words and Phrases.** Place a comma after the introductory word or phrase in each sentence below.

EXAMPLE: After six weeks of training she began a new job.
After six weeks of training, she began a new job.

1. Yes I am concerned about saving the whales.
2. Because of the bad weather we will need to cancel the game.
3. At every club meeting Mary asks for suggestions.
4. Oh I do have one more thing to say.
5. Leaning on the podium Mr. Price spoke to the students.
6. Henry will you read your story to me?
7. According to the latest report our play was a success.
8. In the new book I found three stories that I had already read.
9. True this is a priceless collection of jewels.
10. On their vacation in Mexico City they took three hundred pictures.

Exercise 2 **More Practice Using Commas With Introductory Words and Phrases.** Follow the directions for Exercise 1.

1. Well we are all very glad that the mystery is solved.
2. With the talent on our team how can we lose?
3. No I have not seen the newly designed airplane.
4. Mr. James please tell me about your trip to Italy.
5. Seeing the play for the first time we were impressed.
6. In spite of her faults Janice is a very likable person.
7. Yes you may go to the movies this afternoon.
8. Dr. Knudsen I've had a sore throat for three days.
9. Tapping her fingers on the table Tabitha sighed.
10. Hoping to meet his cousin Ray waited at the train station.

Writing Application **Writing Sentences With Introductory Words and Phrases.** Write ten sentences describing what you think homes of the future will be like. Use an introductory word or phrase in each sentence.

_____

_____

_____

_____

_____

_____

_____

_____

26.2 Commas With Interrupting Words and Phrases • Practice 1

Sometimes, a word or phrase will interrupt the flow of the main sentence. Commas are placed around these words or phrases to set them off from the rest of the sentence. The commas show the reader that the information provided by the words and phrases, although helpful, is not essential to the main sentence.

USING COMMAS WITH INTERRUPTING WORDS AND PHRASES	
Interrupting Words and Phrases	**Example**
To name a person being addressed	She told you, Joe, to come at noon.
	When do the flags arrive, Mr. Hall?
To rename a noun	My sister, the French major, is graduating.
	The newt, a small salamander, ran into the water.
To set off a common expression	We will, nevertheless, continue to look.
	That book, in my opinion, will be a bestseller.

▶ **Exercise 1** **Recognizing Interrupting Words and Phrases.** Write the interrupting word or phrase in each sentence below, adding the necessary commas.

EXAMPLE: _____, I believe,_____ You are I believe here to see me.

1. _____ Are you sure John that you added correctly?

2. _____ My bike a ten-speed has a flat tire.

3. _____ Mr. Penn our neighbor is selling his house.

4. _____ That performance however is sold out.

5. _____ I went to Disney World a theme park.

6. _____ The design Mrs. Talbot looks good.

7. _____ The road ahead I think is blocked.

8. _____ The kilt a pleated skirt comes from Scotland.

9. _____ Our friendship Melanie is important to me.

10. _____ No operation is necessary in my opinion.

▶ **Exercise 2** **More Work With Interrupting Words and Phrases.** Insert commas around the interrupting words or phrases in the sentences below.

EXAMPLE: You can be sure my friend that I will write.
You can be sure, my friend, that I will write.

1. The elk a large deer is found in North America.

2. Are you sure Helen that you can't come swimming?

3. You need a haircut in my opinion.

4. Is it all right Dad if I use the power saw?

5. My grandmother a native of Ohio went back for a visit.

6. It is a crocodile not an alligator in that pond.

7. Your reservation it seems was canceled.

8. The dress is red my favorite color.

9. Boll weevils long-snouted beetles can damage cotton.

10. Advertising is necessary Mary if we want to sell our product.

26.2 Commas With Interrupting Words and Phrases • Practice 2

Exercise 1 **Using Commas With Interrupting Words and Phrases.** Add commas where necessary in each of the following sentences.

EXAMPLE: Dover the capital of Delaware is a shipping port.
Dover, the capital of Delaware, is a shipping port.

1. This dance Eleanor is one of my favorites.
2. Venice the famous Italian city has over 150 canals.
3. What we should remember of course is our purpose.
4. When Bobby is the next baseball game?
5. Walt Disney an American cartoonist created Mickey Mouse.
6. This new invention will I believe save you time.
7. Your garden Mrs. Tyler looks very well planned.
8. My parents are however more enthusiastic than I am.
9. They are visiting Laura my cousin in Arizona.
10. Please Phil try to get here earlier tomorrow.

Exercise 2 **More Practice Using Commas With Interrupting Words and Phrases.** Follow the directions for Exercise 1.

1. Bill Lee a left-handed pitcher won more than one hundred games.
2. Here is a book Natalie about the Olympics.
3. Jan Morris a travel writer described her trip to Vienna.
4. Many items that you packed John are really not necessary.
5. His fans no doubt will be eager to hear his recording.
6. Listen Matt to that wonderful sound.
7. Edgar Allan Poe the author of many horror tales is also the inventor of the detective story.
8. Your ideas nevertheless have some merit.
9. That beautiful bridge the Golden Gate is the background in many tourists' photographs.
10. You will I am sure be proud of your accomplishments.

Writing Application **Using Interrupting Words and Phrases in Sentences.** Write ten sentences about different hobbies. Use one of the following interrupting words or phrases in each sentence: *true, in fact, for example, I think, it seems, after all, I believe, in my opinion, a popular pastime, a leisure-time activity.*

1. _____
2. _____
3. _____
4. _____
5. _____
6. _____
7. _____
8. _____
9. _____
10. _____

26.2 # Commas in Letters • Practice 1

In a friendly letter, commas are used in three places: the heading, the salutation, and the closing.

COMMAS IN LETTERS	
The heading	35 Andover Ct. Denver, Colorado 80204 (Between city & state) May 6, 2000 (After the number of the date)
The salutation	Dear Mr. Boyd, (After the salutation)
The closing	With warm regards, (After the closing)

▶ **Exercise 1** **Using Commas in Letters.** Insert a comma wherever necessary in the items below.

EXAMPLE: Dear Grandma Mavis
Dear Grandma Mavis,

1. 894 Jenkins Blvd. Knoxville Tennessee 37901 June 12 2001

2. Sincerely yours

3. Your friend

4. 56 Grant Ave. Mobile Alabama 36652 October 19 2000

5. Dear Mr. Alberti

6. My dear Mrs. Martin

7. 469 Rowland Drive Wichita Kansas 67202 January 13 2002

8. Yours truly

9. Dear Mom and Dad

10. 1444 Sutro Lane Pittsburgh Pennsylvania 15219 August 9 2001

▶ **Exercise 2** **More Work Using Commas in Letters.** Write down the information requested, adding commas wherever necessary.

EXAMPLE: A salutation to a brother or sister
_____*Dear Leigh,*_____

1. The heading for the address of a relative of yours _____

_____

_____

2. The salutation for a letter to your next-door neighbor _____

3. The closing for a letter to your grandparents _____

4. The heading for a letter from your school _____

_____

_____

5. The salutation for a letter to your teacher _____

26.2 Commas in Letters • Practice 2

▶ **Exercise 1** **Using Commas in Letters.** Add commas where necessary in each heading, salutation, and closing below.

EXAMPLE: Dear Arlene
Dear Arlene,

1. 211 Old Country Road Pearl River New York 10965 December 7 2000
2. Dear Ellen
3. Your friend
4. Fondly
5. Dear Uncle Ted
6. 753 Water Street Danbury Connecticut 06810 June 10 2001
7. My dear Michelle
8. Bye for now
9. 27 Commerce Street Dallas Texas 75240 January 9 2003
10. Love

▶ **Exercise 2** **More Practice Using Commas in Letters.** Follow the directions for Exercise 1.

1. 22 Park Lane Phoenix Arizona 85029 August 3 2001
2. Yours truly
3. 320 Market Street Plainview New York 11803 March 28 2002
4. Dear Mr. Tyler
5. Sincerely
6. Dear Melanie
7. My dear Aunt Jo
8. With love
9. Your nephew
10. Dear George

▶ **Writing Application** **Using Commas in a Letter.** Write a short friendly letter to a real or imaginary friend. Include a heading, salutation, and a closing.

_____

_____

_____

_____

_____

_____

_____

_____

_____

_____

26.2 Commas in Numbers • Practice 1

Knowing when to use commas with numbers can be confusing. Generally, numbers of more than three numerals use commas to make them easier to read. Also, numbers in series use commas to separate them.

NUMBERS WITH COMMAS	
More than three numerals	a crowd of 23,491; a cost of $497,322.00
Numbers in a series	Study pages 16, 19, and 23.

There are some large numbers that are exceptions to the rule and are not punctuated by commas.

NUMBERS WITHOUT COMMAS	
ZIP Code	36192
Telephone number	(800) 921–5555
Page number	Page 1142
Year	2002
Serial number	566–09–000
House number	3035 Radcliff Avenue

▶ **Exercise 1** **Using Commas in Numbers.** Rewrite the numbers in each sentence below, inserting commas where necessary. Some will not require commas.

EXAMPLE: We can expect at least 16500 tickets to sell. ___*16,500*___

1. Our history book ends on page 1009. _____

2. Look at diagrams 7 8 and 9. _____

3. The carnival attracted 4500 people. _____

4. The library is located at 2788 Talbot Drive. _____

5. The length of the equator is 24901.55 feet. _____

6. Call me at (415) 952–5555. _____

7. He turned twenty-one in the year 2002. _____

8. Check the glossary on pages 64 65 and 68. _____

9. A square mile is 27878400 square feet. _____

10. The longest river runs 4145 miles. _____

▶ **Exercise 2** **More Work Using Commas With Numbers.** Fill in the requested information, inserting commas where necessary.

EXAMPLE: Your house number and address

___*1694 Hanover Lane*___

1. The amount of money you would like to earn in one year _____

2. Your ZIP code _____

3. An estimate of the number of miles on your family's car _____

4. Your telephone number _____

5. The number of pennies in $16.00 _____

26.2 Commas in Numbers • Practice 2

Exercise 1 **Using Commas in Numbers.** In each sentence below, add commas where necessary. If no commas are needed, write *correct*.

EXAMPLE: The area of Belgium is 11779 square miles.
> _The area of Belgium is 11,779 square miles._

1. Thomas Jefferson inherited 2750 acres of land.
2. The ZIP code for Parson, West Virginia, is 26287.
3. Kentucky has 12161 acres of forested land.
4. My telephone number is (111) 691-5555.
5. The serial number on the toaster is 716 025.
6. One acre equals 43560 square feet.
7. There were 3707000 children born in 1983.
8. This quote is on page 1317 of the reference book.
9. Mount McKinley in Alaska is 20320 feet high.
10. It cost $40948900 to build the Empire State Building.

Exercise 2 **More Practice Using Commas in Numbers.** Follow the directions for Exercise 1.

1. To call the hardware store, dial 555-5600.
2. The Statue of Liberty weighs 450000 pounds.
3. The references are listed on pages 22 23 and 24.
4. Each year 42515800 people visit our national parks.
5. The Earth is an average of 92900000 miles from the sun.
6. In 1906 an earthquake shook San Francisco.
7. The highest mountain peak in South America is 22834.
8. The Pacific Ocean is 64186300 square miles.
9. An article about Benjamin West begins on page 1116.
10. The World Trade Center in New York is 1350 feet high.

Writing Application **Using Large Numbers in Sentences.** Write a paragraph about a real or imaginary place. Use five or more large numbers in your paragraph.

_____

_____

_____

_____

_____

_____

_____

_____

_____

_____

26.3 Semicolons • Practice 1

An independent clause is like a complete sentence: It contains a subject and a verb. Two independent clauses closely related in meaning can be connected by a semicolon (;).

INDEPENDENT CLAUSES PUNCTUATED BY SEMICOLONS
Her tutoring certainly helped; I got an A on that test.
I did not mail the letter; I brought it over myself.
The courtroom was quiet; everyone waited with bated breath.

▶ **Exercise 1**   **Using Semicolons.**   Combine the two sentences in each numbered item below as one sentence, joined by a semicolon.

EXAMPLE: _____ *up; she* _____ The deer looked up. She sensed my presence.

1. _____ I vacuumed. My sister dusted.
2. _____ The drums rolled. The trumpets blared.
3. _____ The ground is wet. It must have rained last night.
4. _____ The command was given. The dog snapped to attention.
5. _____ Our train rocked gently. I was soon dozing.
6. _____ The United States exports wheat. It imports oil.
7. _____ It was a forbidding night. No moon was visible.
8. _____ The team deserved to win. They played flawlessly.
9. _____ I like Cajun food. I like it very much.
10. _____ TV is boring. Give me a good book instead.

▶ **Exercise 2**   **More Practice Using Semicolons.**   Add a semicolon and an independent clause to each independent clause already given below.

EXAMPLE: My sister is tall and blonde

_____ *My sister is tall and blonde; I am short and brunette.* _____

1. I love sports

_____

2. My mother wants me to baby-sit

_____

3. I have only six dollars

_____

4. First we bought the paint

_____

5. High school is different from elementary school

_____

26.3 Semicolons • Practice 2

▷ **Exercise 1** **Using Semicolons.** In each of the following sentences, add a semicolon where necessary.

EXAMPLE: Benjamin Franklin was a printer he ran a newspaper in Philadelphia.
Benjamin Franklin was a printer; he ran a newspaper in Philadelphia.

1. We are going to stop at the museum it is presenting an exhibit of African art.

2. These books are about the American Revolution they were written by Easter Forbes.

3. Daniel is a serious photographer he has taken hundreds of photographs.

4. The stories she told me were fascinating they were about her childhood.

5. You are invited to my graduation come to the school auditorium on Friday at 7:30 p.m.

6. Let's go over to Jason's house we can see his new puppies.

7. I read the news today it was quite upsetting.

8. Dominick got a new desk it is made of oak.

9. This bedspread is too small for the bed the bed is a queen, but the spread is a twin.

10. The ticket counter opens at eight o'clock Brett plans to be there at 7:30.

▷ **Exercise 2** **More Practice Using Semicolons.** Follow the directions for Exercise 1.

1. The movie was entertaining the characters and the plot held my interest.

2. Sunday afternoon is my favorite time I listen to music with my friends.

3. This committee wants to know your opinions let us hear from you.

4. These rooms are quite similar they are both used for conferences.

5. There is a concert in the park tonight an orchestra will play the "1812 Overture."

6. I highly recommend this book to you you will definitely like the main character.

7. Ted got back from his vacation in Florida today he had visited his grandparents in Miami.

8. Vinnie got the award for most-improved player he really worked hard this year.

9. There's a big sale on shoes at the mall we should at least go look at them.

10. I have to make an appointment for a haircut I can't stand this style anymore.

▷ **Writing Application** **Using Semicolons in Your Own Writing.** Write ten sentences about things you have done in the past month. In each sentence, use a semicolon to join two independent clauses.

1. _____

2. _____

3. _____

4. _____

5. _____

6. _____

7. _____

8. _____

9. _____

10. _____

26.3 # Colons • **Practice 1**

A colon is used primarily after an independent clause to introduce a list of items. The colon often follows such words as *the following, as follows, these,* or *those*. It is never used with a list that follows a verb or preposition. The colon also has some other uses.

USES OF THE COLON	
To introduce a list after an independent clause	You have your choice of three vegetables: corn, peas, or spinach.
To separate hours and minutes	8:40 A.M. 9:20 P.M.
After the salutation in a business letter	Dear Mr. Porter: Dear Mrs. Wilder:
On warnings and labels	Note: Keep refrigerated after opening.

▶ **Exercise 1**　**Using Colons.**　Insert colons into the sentences below wherever they are needed. Some sentences may not need a colon.

EXAMPLE:　I have packed the following a camera, an ice chest, and suitcases.
　　　　　I have packed the following: a camera, an ice chest, and suitcases.

1. The bottle read "Warning Keep out of reach of children."

2. Dear Miss Kashan

3. *Masterpiece Drama* can be seen at 11 00 a.m. and 9 00 p.m. on Friday.

4. Some of people's fears include these spiders, the dark, and heights.

5. For my birthday I got a CD player, a sweater, and a new book.

6. My mother likes these magazines *Good Gardening, Persons,* and *Daily Living.*

7. Note These curtains may be ordered in other sizes.

8. You must take the following classes English, history, and science.

9. The following roads will be closed by today Arden, Atherton, and Darnell.

10. Caution Roads Slippery When Wet

▶ **Exercise 2**　**More Work Using Colons.**　Add the information requested below, using colons where needed.

EXAMPLE:　I addressed the letter to . . .
　　　　　　_____*I addressed the letter to "Gentlemen:"*_____

1. Our family celebrates the following holidays . . .

　_____

2. Let's meet from . . . A.M. to . . . P.M.

　_____

3. The sign read ". . ."

　_____

4. My best features are these . . .

　_____

5. Some popular boys' (or girls') names include the following . . .

　_____

26.3 Colons • Practice 2

▶ **Exercise 1**   **Using Colons.**   In each item below, add colons where needed.

EXAMPLE: We visited three Canadian cities Calgary, Edmonton, and Winnipeg.
We visited three Canadian cities: Calgary, Edmonton, and Winnipeg.

1. The works of three poets will be featured in the magazine this month Edna St. Vincent Millay, William Carlos Williams, and Robert Frost.

2. We play on the following dates May 15, May 18, or May 21.

3. The three dives I am able to perform are these the cannonball, the backward somersault, and the jack knife.

4. I left the beach at 430 p.m. and arrived at Grandmother's house at 645 P.M.

5. Caution Do not set or store container where temperature exceeds 120 F.

6. The movie can be seen at the following times 145, 330, and 515.

7. When you tour Wyoming, be sure to see these places Yellowstone National Park, Fort Laramie, and Devils Tower National Monument.

8. Choose a book about one of these topics animals, conservation, or oceanography.

9. The first three United States Vice Presidents were the following John Adams, Thomas Jefferson, and Aaron Burr.

10. Dear Ms. Wilson

11. The facts lead to these conclusions we are wasting our resources, we are damaging our health, and we are doing damage to the environment.

12. The play begins at 800, so we should leave the house no later than 700.

13. I met the following people at the party James, Felicia, and Aaron.

14. Dear Sir or Madam

15. Warning Guard dogs protect this property.

▶ **Writing Application**   **Using Colons.**   (1) Write two sentences, each of which includes a list requiring a colon before it. (2) Write a sentence that includes a list which should not have a colon before it. (3) Write a sentence that gives the time of day in hours and minutes. (4) Write a warning or label with a colon.

_____

_____

_____

_____

_____

_____

_____

_____

_____

_____

_____

_____

26.4 Quotation Marks in Direct Quotations
• Practice 1

Always use quotation marks to enclose a direct quotation, or a person's exact words. Using other punctuation—such as commas and end marks—will depend on whether the quotation also has a *he said* or *she said* phrase, and where it is located in the quotation.

PUNCTUATING DIRECT QUOTATIONS	
Introductory words	The coach asked, "Will you be at practice?" The boy replied, "Sure, coach, I'll come."
Interrupting words	"I'm afraid," the officer said, "you were speeding." "Is there any chance," the driver asked, "that you could be mistaken?"
Concluding words	"Which dog is yours?" the woman inquired. "Mine is the Sheltie," the girl answered.

▶ **Exercise 1**   **Using Quotation Marks in Direct Quotations.**   Insert quotation marks and commas where necessary in the sentences below.

EXAMPLE: Watch your step! Mother called.
"Watch your step!" Mother called.

1. Benjamin Franklin wrote One today is worth two tomorrows.

2. Do I have to wear that stupid costume in the play? the boy complained.

3. What if my father worried I can't find the car keys?

4. We are going to visit an observatory the teacher announced.

5. Papyrus I wrote in my report was a kind of paper used by the Egyptians.

6. My sister shouted excitedly Here comes the parade!

7. Is it easier I asked for me to come to your house?

8. Do you want to play baseball during recess? Bob asked.

9. Our neighbor reported I watched a fascinating program on sharks.

10. Colton suggested Imitation is the sincerest form of flattery.

▶ **Exercise 2**   **More Work Using Quotation Marks in Direct Quotations.**   Complete the sentences below, correctly punctuating the direct quotation and the *he said* or *she said* phrase.

EXAMPLE: My father asked . . .
*My father asked,*_____ *"What movie did you see?"* _____

1. . . . my friend said.

_____

2. Our teacher explained . . . _____ .

3. . . . I asked . . . .

_____

4. Our neighbor asked . . .

_____

5. . . . she shouted.

_____

26.4 Quotation Marks in Direct Quotations
• Practice 2

▶ **Exercise 1**　**Using Quotation Marks in Direct Quotations.**　Insert commas and quotation marks where necessary in the sentences below.

EXAMPLE:　This is a picture of my mother said Carol.
　　　　　　　"This is a picture of my mother," said Carol.

1. Sam asked Do you want to go to the baseball game?
2. This movie Robin said is really exciting.
3. Pick up these puzzle pieces immediately! Mom ordered.
4. Miss Harris added We are going to have to work quickly.
5. This building is a city landmark Jeff explained.
6. Do not the museum guide warned touch the displays.
7. When can I see your science project? Steve asked.
8. Please read me another story pleaded the child.
9. Captain Lee said My next voyage will be to the Bahamas.
10. Simone asked Did you just get home?

▶ **Exercise 2**　**More Practice Using Quotation Marks With Direct Quotations.**　Insert commas and quotation marks where necessary in the sentences below.

1. John suggested We could drive to Sturbridge for the day.
2. What activities have been planned? Emily inquired.
3. Bruce thought This Brazilian jazz group is wonderful.
4. The new schedule announced Marilyn will begin tomorrow.
5. I can Stephen volunteered come an hour early to help.
6. Michael announced I think I'll run for class president.
7. How asked Michael's sister can I help you campaign?
8. I'll need to create several large posters answered Michael.
9. Perhaps suggested Michael's dad we can all help.
10. Let's get started this evening said Michael's mom.

▶ **Writing Application**　**Writing Sentences With Direct Quotations.**　Write ten sentences. In each one, tell what a character in a book or movie might say after visiting your school.

1. _____
2. _____
3. _____
4. _____
5. _____
6. _____
7. _____
8. _____
9. _____
10. _____

26.4 Quotation Marks With Other Punctuation
• Practice 1

Commas and periods always go inside final quotation marks.

COMMAS AND PERIODS IN DIRECT QUOTATIONS	
Commas	"I found an oyster shell," Doris announced.
Periods	Jay said, "We should practice our skit."

The location of question marks and exclamation marks can vary. Place them inside the final quotation marks if they are part of the quotation. Place them outside if they are part of the complete sentence but not part of the question.

QUESTION MARKS AND EXCLAMATION MARKS IN DIRECT QUOTATIONS	
Inside the quotation marks	I asked, "When will we get there?"
	He cried, "That monkey bit me!"
Outside the quotation marks	Did you say, "Let's cut class tomorrow"?
	I have told you a hundred times, "Look before crossing the street"!

▶ **Exercise 1** **Using Quotation Marks With Other Punctuation.** In the blank, write the punctuation mark and indicate whether it should go inside or outside the quotation marks.

EXAMPLE: _____!____inside_____ Elsie pointed excitedly, "I see the ship"

1. _____ The guide commented, "This is the throne"
2. _____ "I made the team" Jim yelled happily.
3. _____ "Lindbergh was a famous aviator" the teacher explained.
4. _____ I asked, "How far is Mars from Earth"
5. _____ Please don't say "I ain't got it"
6. _____ "We've got an emergency" the policeman shouted.
7. _____ The child mumbled, "Let me stay at home"
8. _____ Which one of you said, "I'm buying the food"
9. _____ "Blackberries grow nearby" Jill said.
10. _____ Why did you say, "That's a stupid idea"

▶ **Exercise 2** **Using Quotation Marks With Other Punctuation.** Insert commas, periods, question marks, and exclamation marks wherever they are needed in the sentences below.

EXAMPLE: The cook asked, "Can someone hand me a sponge"
The cook asked, "Can someone hand me a sponge?"

1. "Run faster" my team cried.
2. I questioned, "Did you have your purse with you in the car"
3. We were ecstatic when the woman said, "Here is a little reward"
4. "I am nearsighted" George explained.
5. "Do you like my oil painting" the painter asked.
6. "I'll never trust you again" Nora shouted.
7. How did Kate know I said, "I'll surprise her with the present"
8. "We are growing almonds" Ruth told their visitors.
9. I cried sadly, "My project is a complete disaster"
10. The repairman reported, "The dishwasher is now fixed"

26.4 Quotation Marks With Other Punctuation
• Practice 2

▶ **Exercise 1**   **Using Quotation Marks With Other Punctuation Marks.**   Insert commas, periods, question marks, and exclamation marks where needed in the sentences below.

EXAMPLE: I was annoyed when you yelled, "I'm staying here"
  I was annoyed when you yelled, "I'm staying here!"

1. "Aunt Martha called while you were in school" said Lynn
2. Marissa volunteered, "I can help you in math"
3. Ruth asked, "Why did you choose that bicycle"
4. The policeman shouted, "Go back to your houses immediately"
5. I was thrilled when he said, "You can leave now"
6. Why did Marie say, "Kim should be treasurer"
7. How did Ira know I wrote, "Ira took the cookies"
8. Howard muttered, "I can explain why I'm late"
9. Jack wondered, "When did the Johnsons move here"
10. "Take your time" advised the teacher

▶ **Exercise 2**   **More Practice Using Quotation Marks With Other Punctuation Marks.**   Follow the directions for Exercise 1.

1. "Please bring me the evening paper" said Paul
2. Don't you dare say, "I didn't do it"
3. The detective blurted out "This case is extraordinary"
4. Thea inquired "How much longer will I have to wait"
5. The waitress asked "What would you like to order"
6. "I'd like to be a volunteer tutor" said Patrick
7. Maureen asked "What subject would you teach"
8. "Don't you think I'd be a good reading teacher" asked Patrick
9. "Wow" exclaimed Maureen "That would be a perfect job for you"
10. Patrick suggested "You'd be good at it, too, Maureen"

▶ **Writing Application**   **Writing Sentences With Quotation Marks and Other End Marks.**   Write ten sentences, each with a direct quotation. Use commas, periods, exclamation marks, and question marks to end your direct quotations.

1. _____
2. _____
3. _____
4. _____
5. _____
6. _____
7. _____
8. _____
9. _____
10. _____

26.4 # Quotation Marks for Dialogue • Practice 1

When punctuating dialogue, follow the general rules for using quotation marks, capital letters, and other punctuation marks. Start a new paragraph each time the speaker changes. If a speaker says two or more lines without interruption, put quotation marks at the beginning of the first sentence and at the end of the last one.

WRITING DIALOGUE
"I can hardly wait to see the Grand Canyon!" Mary said excitedly. "I hear it is beautiful."
"You won't be disappointed," her father commented. "I think you will find it as breathtaking as you imagine."
Her mother explained, "It looks just like the postcards you see. The colors are so vibrant. I think the Grand Canyon is nature's greatest oil painting!"

▶ **Exercise 1** **Using Quotation Marks for Dialogue.** Put in quotation marks wherever they are needed in the following dialogue.

EXAMPLE: We had better get started now, the bus driver called.
"We had better get started now," the bus driver called.

1. I hate taking swimming lessons every summer! Dorothy complained.

2. But why? Jessica inquired. I think swimming is lots of fun, especially in warm weather.

3. Oh, they always force you to do things you don't want. Last year they made me do a back dive and I did a belly flop!

4. I'll bet it wasn't that bad, Jessica said. You're probably just exaggerating it.

5. You think so? Well, how would you feel if you had two hundred people watching you from a viewing stand? Believe me, it was embarrassing!

▶ **Exercise 2** **Paragraphing Dialogue.** Circle the first word in each sentence that requires indentation for a new paragraph.

"What can we get Dad for his birthday?" Bob asked. "Unfortunately," Nicole said, "I haven't got a clue. He is the most difficult person to buy for!" "Last year we got him slippers. The year before that it was a magazine subscription," recalled Bob. Nicole sighed, "Not very exciting, huh? Wait, I've got it. He loves to fish. How about giving him a certificate for a day on one of those fishing boats?" "Now that's more like it. I think he would love it," Bob exclaimed. "Let's do it!"

26.4 Quotation Marks for Dialogue • Practice 2

▶ **Exercise 1** **Using Quotation Marks in Dialogue.** Turn the numbered sentences below into a dialogue. Add missing punctuation marks and start a new paragraph whenever the speaker changes.

EXAMPLE: (1) Are you all right? he asked.
(2) I'm fine I replied.

_____ *"Are you all right?" he asked.* _____

_____ *"I'm fine," I replied.* _____

(1) Tomorrow announced Mom is Open School Night. (2) How can I find your classroom? (3) It's on the third floor I replied. (4) Walk in the front door, turn left, and go up three flights. (5) The room number is 307. (6) Will any of your work be on display? Mom asked. (7) Yes I said our writing folders will be on our desks. (8) The story I wrote about our cat is my best piece of writing. (9) Mom slowly inquired Is there anything I should know before I go? (10) Honestly I protested you don't need to worry.

_____

_____

_____

_____

_____

_____

_____

_____

_____

_____

▶ **Exercise 2** **More Practice Using Quotation Marks in Dialogue.** Follow the directions for Exercise 1.

(1) Fred, are you busy? Naomi asked. (2) No, why? replied Fred. (3) Well, I'm planning a surprise party for Barbara, and I could use your help. (4) What would you like me to do? asked Fred. (5) Two things, answered Naomi. (6) First, I was hoping you would design theinvitations. (7) And second, it would be a real help if you would keep Barbara out of the house while I decorate. (8) You can count on me said Fred. (9) Terrific! said Naomi enthusiastically. (10) I am totally Fred responded at your service.

_____

_____

_____

_____

_____

_____

_____

_____

_____

26.4 Underlining and Quotation Marks
in Titles • Practice 1

Some titles and names are underlined while others are enclosed in quotation marks. The charts below give examples of each.

TITLES THAT ARE UNDERLINED	
Books	Fahrenheit 451
Plays	You Can't Take It with You
Magazines and Newspapers	Harper's, Daily Herald
Movies	E.T.
Television Series	You Are There
Paintings and Sculptures	Mona Lisa, The Thinker
Air and Space Vehicles	Spitfire, Apollo 8
Ships and Trains	Oriana, Silver Meteor

TITLES THAT ARE ENCLOSED IN QUOTATION MARKS	
Stories	"The Lottery"
Chapters	"Getting Ideas for Speeches"
Articles	"A Mother's Fight for Justice"
Episodes	"Mirror Image" (an episode from The Twilight Zone series)
Songs	"Take Me Out to the Ball Game"

▶ **Exercise 1** **Using Underlining and Quotation Marks.** Underline or enclose in quotation marks each of the titles or names given below.

EXAMPLE: A Trap (short story)
"A Trap"

1. Nite Owl

2. The Secret Garden (book)

3. The Artist's Studio (painting)

4. Blue Moon (song)

5. The Witness (movie)

6. Bull's Eye! (article)

7. I Love Lucy (TV series)

8. Viking I (spacecraft)

9. The Monkey's Paw (short story)

10. Our Town (play)

▶ **Exercise 2** **More Practice Using Underlining and Quotation Marks.** Write in each blank below whether the title or name in the sentence needs *underlining* or *quotation marks*.

EXAMPLE: _____underlining_____ I like to read Sports Illustrated.

1. _____ The artist Donatello did the statue St. George.

2. _____ I watched Forest in the Clouds from the *Nature* series.

3. _____ The Russian spacecraft Salyut 7 was in space for over 211 days.

4. _____ We are to read the chapter called Learning the Keyboard.

5. _____ They wrote a song about the train, called The Santa Fe.

6. _____ Have you read the novel Exodus, by Leon Uris?

7. _____ We read the Raleigh Times.

8. _____ I still enjoy watching reruns of 90210.

9. _____ Manet painted Luncheon on the Grass.

10. _____ My Dad always sings Yesterday.

26.4 Underlining and Quotation Marks in Titles • Practice 2

▶ **Exercise 1**   **Using Underlining and Quotation Marks.**   Each sentence below contains a title or name that needs to be underlined or enclosed in quotation marks. Punctuate the title or name correctly.

EXAMPLE: In class we are reading the novel Johnny Tremain.

1. I shall see the musical comedy My Fair Lady.
2. Mr. Greene flew to France on the Concorde.
3. I am going to subscribe to USA Today.
4. The painting The Dream is shown in this book.
5. Lizard Music is the title of an amusing book.
6. I am reading the chapter titled The Chase.
7. Today we will hear the next episode, The Way Out.
8. Flowers for Algernon is an unusual story.
9. Who starred in the movie Gone With the Wind?
10. Ursula LeGuin wrote the book Wizard of Earthsea.
11. I have read the novel My Side of the Mountain three times.
12. The first chapter of this book is called How Insects Adapt.
13. Jack, I think you should read this article, How to Say You're Sorry and Mean It.
14. For the bride and groom's first dance, the disc jockey played Elvis Presley's song Love Me Tender.
15. The second episode was called Beyond the Limits.

▶ **Writing Application**   **Using Titles in Sentences.**   Write ten sentences. Include a different title in each sentence.

1. _____
2. _____
3. _____
4. _____
5. _____
6. _____
7. _____
8. _____
9. _____
10. _____

26.5 # Hyphens in Numbers and Words • Practice 1

Numbers and words often contain hyphens.

HYPHENS IN NUMBERS	
Use a Hyphen When You Write	**Examples**
the numbers twenty-one through ninety-nine	forty-six eighty-seven
a fraction used as an adjective	The race was one-third over.

HYPHENS IN WORDS		
Use a Hyphen	**Examples**	
after a prefix followed by a proper noun or adjective	mid-July	pro-American
with the prefixes *all-, ex-, self-*, and the suffix *-elect*	ex-Senator	self-appointed
	all-league	President-elect
with compound modifiers	fifty-five	around-the-clock

▶ **Exercise 1**   **Using Hyphens in Numbers and Words.**   Rewrite each phrase or number below to add a hyphen where needed. If no hyphen is necessary, write *C*.

EXAMPLE: _____*C*_____ the antinuclear movement

1. _____ one half of the money
2. _____ the all star game
3. _____ feeling put upon by friends
4. _____ an excited ex felon
5. _____ thirty seven late entries
6. _____ one third water and two thirds vinegar
7. _____ a pro Mexican soccer crowd
8. _____ ate raw sea urchins
9. _____ a second rate job
10. _____ a self winding watch

▶ **Exercise 2**   **More Practice Using Hyphens.**   Insert hyphens where necessary in the sentences below. If no hyphen is necessary, write *C*.

1. He was voted all around best athlete. _____
2. I was elected sergeant at arms. _____
3. The stadium was two thirds full. _____
4. We have to move by mid March. _____
5. That was in the post Kennedy era. _____
6. You must meet with the treasurer elect. _____
7. It was the best selling novel of the year. _____
8. I need twenty five volunteers for the charity auction. _____
9. My grandfather was a self educated man. _____
10. We sat in the dining room for dessert. _____

26.5 Hyphens in Numbers and Words • Practice 2

▶ Exercise 1   **Using Hyphens in Numbers and Words.**   Rewrite each of the sentences below, adding hyphens where necessary. If no hyphens need to be added, write *correct*.

EXAMPLE: A music festival will be held in mid July.

_____ *A music festival will be held in mid-July.* _____

1. There are twenty six amendments to our Constitution.

   _____

2. Sue was given an award as best all around athlete.

   _____

3. Antarctica occupies one tenth of the world's land area.

   _____

4. My uncle operates his own business; he is self employed.

   _____

5. The social studies test was one half written and one half oral.

   _____

6. The senator elect held a victory party.

   _____

7. There is much pro British feeling where we spent our vacation.

   _____

8. Bill is less self conscious than he used to be.

   _____

9. The ex president wrote a book about politics.

   _____

10. Our library has more than five hundred volumes.

   _____

▶ Exercise 2   **More Practice Using Hyphens in Numbers and Words.**   Follow the directions for Exercise 1.

1. The singer recorded some all time favorites.

   _____

2. The movie theater was three fourths empty.

   _____

3. Two thirds of the year has already passed.

   _____

4. The population of Finland is over four million.

   _____

5. The law was passed during the pre Reagan years.

   _____

26.5 Hyphens at the Ends of Lines • Practice 1

If a word must be divided at the end of a line, the general rule is to divide it only between syllables. The dictionary should be used when you are unsure where the syllables fall. Several other rules will also help you hyphenate words correctly at the ends of lines.

FOUR RULES FOR WORD DIVISION
1. Never divide a one-syllable word.
Incorrect: It was a frei-   ght train.   *Correct:* It was a freight train.
2. Never divide a word so that one letter stands alone.
Incorrect: I was all a-   lone.   *Correct:* I was all alone.
3. Never divide proper nouns or proper adjectives.
Incorrect: Rem-   brandt painted this.   *Correct:* Rembrandt painted this.
4. Divide a hyphenated word only after the hyphen.
Incorrect: I bought thir-   ty-five balloons.   *Correct:* I bought thirty-five balloons.

▶ **Exercise 1**   **Using Hyphens to Divide Words.**   Rewrite each word below, inserting a hyphen to show where the word can be divided. If the word cannot be divided, leave it untouched.

EXAMPLE: _____*gas-light*_____ gaslight

1. _____ juicy
2. _____ magic
3. _____ self-control
4. _____ Spanish
5. _____ nugget
6. _____ elect
7. _____ penance
8. _____ Yellowstone
9. _____ project
10. _____ mid-September

▶ **Exercise 2**   **More Practice Hyphenating at the Ends of Lines.**   Draw vertical lines between syllables that can be divided at the end of a line. Circle words that should not be divided at the end of a line.

EXAMPLE: forest for | est   walked (walked)

1. evict
2. custom
3. Bolivia
4. legal
5. noise
6. tasty
7. Grandmother
8. stillness
9. kept
10. boiler

11. doorway
12. column
13. blazed
14. all-time
15. passage
16. scenic
17. pro-German
18. maintain
19. neutral
20. about

26.5 Hyphens at the Ends of Lines • Practice 2

▶ **Exercise 1** **Using Hyphens to Divide Words.** Use a hyphen to show how you would divide each word listed below if it were to occur at the end of a line. If a word cannot be broken, simply rewrite the word. If you are not sure of how to divide a word, look up the word in a dictionary.

EXAMPLE: quarter _____quar-ter_____

1. perform _____
2. agent _____
3. group _____
4. enormous _____
5. handbook _____
6. unicorn _____
7. concern _____
8. bring _____
9. overheard _____
10. overdue _____

11. glance _____
12. dolphin _____
13. ticket _____
14. equality _____
15. open-ended _____
16. lunch _____
17. lion _____
18. step-son _____
19. addition _____
20. view _____

▶ **Writing Application** **Dividing Words at the Ends of Lines.** Write ten sentences about things that are fun to do. Make each sentence at least two lines long. Divide the last word in line one of each sentence so that part of the word is on line one and part of the word is on line two. Use a dictionary to check the syllables in each word you divide.

1. _____
   _____
2. _____
   _____
3. _____
   _____
4. _____
   _____
5. _____
   _____
6. _____
   _____
7. _____
   _____
8. _____
   _____
9. _____
   _____
10. _____
   _____

26.5 # Apostrophes Used to Show Ownership
• Practice 1

To show ownership or possession, an apostrophe and sometimes an *-s* are used.

FORMING POSSESSIVES	
Forming the Possessive	**Example**
Add 's to singular nouns	Mother's book teacher's comment
Add 's to singular nouns ending in *s*	chorus's trophy Kris's paper
	(Exception: If there are too many *s* sounds, drop the last *s* as in *Dickens'* *novel*)
Add an apostrophe to plurals ending in *s*	cats' howling friends' reunion
Add 's to plurals not ending in *s*	geese's food children's toys

▶ **Exercise 1**   **Using Apostrophes to Show Ownership.**   Write the possessive form of each phrase below in the space provided.

EXAMPLE: the presentation of the group _____*the group's presentation*_____

1. the curls of the lass _____
2. the nest of the birds _____
3. the blanket of the child _____
4. the response of the crowd _____
5. the calendar of the doctor _____
6. the ruling of the officials _____
7. the feed of the chickens _____
8. the help of the clerk _____
9. the bracelet of Tess _____
10. the vote of the women _____

▶ **Exercise 2**   **More Practice Using Apostrophes to Show Ownership.**   Write the possessive form of each underlined noun below in the blank provided.

EXAMPLE: _____*deputy's*_____   I followed the deputy suggestion.

1. _____ We have to gather the sheep wool.
2. _____ I read the writer latest biography.
3. _____ Next week is the governors conference.
4. _____ The Jenkins party is next week.
5. _____ We are going camping in our friends trailer.
6. _____ I want to see the class new computer.
7. _____ You should follow the lawyer advice.
8. _____ It's time to harvest the farmers crops.
9. _____ Bill is going to the annual men barbecue.
10. _____ Our neighbors house needs painting.

26.5 Apostrophes Used to Show Ownership
• Practice 2

▶ **Exercise 1**   **Using Apostrophes to Show Ownership.**   Write the possessive form of each underlined noun below.

EXAMPLE: The judge remarks were lengthy.   _judge's_

1. The artist latest painting sold for $10,000. _____
2. The boss office is down the hall. _____
3. As I came closer, I could hear Sharon voice. _____
4. The children singing and playing were delightful. _____
5. All of the rooms ceilings are fifteen feet high. _____
6. The mouse squeak could be heard from afar. _____
7. Mr. Smith calls himself the people candidate. _____
8. A sign hung in the window of my father store. _____
9. I shall read two of Charles Dickens books. _____
10. This baseball has ten players autographs on it. _____

▶ **Exercise 2**   **More Practice Using Apostrophes to Show Ownership.**   Follow the directions for Exercise 1.

1. The scientist argument was very convincing. _____
2. Hercules adventures are extremely varied. _____
3. Have you seen Mr. Wallach coin collection? _____
4. The women decision was to begin a monthly newsletter. _____
5. Bess baked bread is the best I have ever tasted. _____
6. The youngsters ages are six, ten, and twelve. _____
7. Several designers fashions are on display in the department store. _____
8. Doris cousin ran along the shore. _____
9. The audience applauded the musician performance. _____
10. The mice cage is kept in the science laboratory. _____

▶ **Writing Application**   **Using Nouns to Show Ownership.**   List the possessive form of five singular and five plural nouns. Use each possessive noun in a sentence.

_____

_____

_____

_____

_____

_____

_____

_____

_____

_____

26.5 Apostrophes in Contractions • Practice 1

In contractions, the apostrophe shows where one or more letters have been omitted. Generally, contractions are used in informal writing.

COMMONLY USED CONTRACTIONS		
aren't (are not)	haven't (have not)	don't (do not)
isn't (is not)	hadn't (had not)	doesn't (does not)
wasn't (was not)	can't (can not)	shouldn't (should not)
weren't (were not)	couldn't (could not)	won't (will not)
hasn't (has not)	didn't (did not)	wouldn't (would not)
I'll (I will)	he'll (he will)	we'll (we will)
you'll (you will)	she'll (she will)	they'll (they will)
I'm (I am)	it's (it is)	where's (where is)
you're (you are)	we're (we are)	John's (John is)
he's (he is)	they're (they are)	
she's (she is)	who's (who is)	
I'd (I would)	she'd (she would)	who'd (who would)
you'd (you would)	we'd (we would)	Sara'd (Sara would)
he'd (he would)	they'd (they would)	

▷ **Exercise 1** **Using Apostrophes in Contractions.** In the blank, write the contractions that would be used in place of the underlined words.

EXAMPLE: _____doesn't_____ She <u>does not</u> practice the piano enough.

1. _____ <u>Who is</u> that in the red coat?
2. _____ <u>They would</u> have told me.
3. _____ Martha will do it if <u>he will</u> do it too.
4. _____ That gas station <u>would not</u> take checks.
5. _____ <u>Nancy is</u> already in the car.
6. _____ The paint <u>was not</u> dry.
7. _____ I think <u>he would</u> be able to fix the car.
8. _____ If <u>you are</u> in town, stop by.
9. _____ The meat <u>should not</u> be frozen.
10. _____ I <u>have not</u> heard the song.

▷ **Exercise 2** **More Practice With Apostrophes in Contractions.** In the blank, write the words that can be used in place of the underlined contraction.

EXAMPLE: _____she is_____ The teacher said that <u>she's</u> next.

1. _____ <u>I'd</u> go if I could.
2. _____ He <u>won't</u> tell your great news.
3. _____ If <u>you're</u> not ready, you will not pass.
4. _____ I <u>couldn't</u> find the shoes I wanted.
5. _____ The baby sitter <u>can't</u> stay.
6. _____ <u>He'll</u> bring the slide projector.
7. _____ <u>George'd</u> get the groceries.
8. _____ My Dad called, "<u>They're</u> here!"
9. _____ Tonight <u>I'll</u> letter the signs.
10. _____ I <u>wouldn't</u> try that if I were you.

26.5 Apostrophes in Contractions • Practice 2

▶ **Exercise 1**   **Using Apostrophes in Contractions.**   Write the contractions that can be used in place of the underlined words in the sentences below.

EXAMPLE: The music <u>was not</u> loud enough. _____*wasn't*_____

1. <u>He is</u> writing a mystery story. _____
2. Natalie asked if <u>we will</u> take care of her dog. _____
3. They <u>have not</u> heard of a musicologist. _____
4. Maria <u>has not</u> met our friend Simon. _____
5. <u>They will</u> probably ask us to come along. _____
6. <u>Who will</u> volunteer to act as secretary? _____
7. <u>Where is</u> the latest edition of the newspaper? _____
8. <u>I am</u> sure we will stop at the Air and Space Museum. _____
9. Earl speaks Spanish, but he <u>cannot</u> speak French. _____
10. The attorneys <u>are not</u> sure how long the trial will last. _____

▶ **Exercise 2**   **More Practice Using Apostrophes in Contractions.**   Write the contraction that can be used in place of the underlined words.

1. I think <u>you will</u> enjoy reading this novel. _____
2. <u>I would</u> like to make some suggestions. _____
3. The tour <u>does not</u> include a stop at the Alamo. _____
4. <u>It is</u> important for you to consider the alternatives. _____
5. They <u>do not</u> want to attract a large crowd. _____
6. I think <u>you would</u> enjoy seeing San Francisco. _____
7. Please tell Larry that <u>I will</u> be late. _____
8. Diane <u>could not</u> remember the time they arrived. _____
9. <u>She will</u> probably send us a letter with all the details. _____
10. <u>Who is</u> going to begin the discussion? _____

▶ **Writing Application**   **Using Contractions in a Dialogue.**   Write a dialogue in which one person shows another person how to do something. Use at least ten contractions to give your dialogue the feel of real people talking in a natural way.

_____

_____

_____

_____

_____

_____

_____

_____

_____

_____

26.5 Avoiding Problems With Apostrophes

• Practice 1

Sometimes, the apostrophe is used incorrectly. Remember, never use an apostrophe with possessive personal pronouns.

POSSESSIVE PERSONAL PRONOUNS		
my	his	our
mine	her	ours
your	hers	their
yours	its	theirs

Do not confuse *its* and *it's*, *theirs* or *there's*, *whose* and *who's*, or *your* and *you're*. Remember that those containing the apostrophes stand for the contractions *it is*, *there is*, *who is*, and *you are*.

▷ **Exercise 1**   **Using Apostrophes Where Necessary.**   Circle the correct word in parentheses.

EXAMPLE: I ate the rest of ((yours) , your's).

1. (Its, It's) your turn at bat.

2. The child wanted (hers, her's) immediately.

3. (Whose, Who's) notebook is this?

4. Look, (theirs, there's) the lake!

5. Maybe we will get (ours, our's) tomorrow.

6. (Your, You're) friend is at the door.

7. I thought (his, his') science project was excellent.

8. Will (yours, your's) look like that drawing?

9. (Theirs, There's) is the red van with the flat tire.

10. I feel (your, you're) going to win the scholarship.

▷ **Exercise 2**   **More Practice Avoiding Apostrophe Errors.**   Write a sentence correctly using each of the words listed below.

EXAMPLE: it's

       I heard that it's supposed to rain.

1. there's

     _____

2. whose

     _____

3. you're

     _____

4. its

     _____

5. who's

     _____

26.5 # Avoiding Problems With Apostrophes
• Practice 2

▶ **Exercise 1** **Using Apostrophes Where Necessary.** Rewrite each sentence below using the correct word in parentheses.

EXAMPLE: May I borrow (you're, your) pencil?

_____ *May I borrow your pencil?* _____

1. (Who's, Whose) joining the team?

   _____

2. The best science exhibit was (there's, theirs).

   _____

3. Jane felt that (her's, hers) was the better party.

   _____

4. (It's, Its) not too late to try out for the team.

   _____

5. Carlos, give us (you're, your) opinion, please.

   _____

6. I think I know (who's, whose) responsible for this.

   _____

7. (Our's, Ours) was the best dance routine.

   _____

8. Now the sun is at (it's, its) highest point in the sky.

   _____

9. Look, (there's, theirs) the house I was born in.

   _____

10. Maybe (you're, your) right after all.

   _____

▶ **Exercise 2** **More Practice Using Apostrophes Where Necessary.** Follow the directions for Exercise 1.

1. Let's follow this stream to (it's, its) source.

   _____

2. (Who's, Whose) idea was it to camp here?

   _____

3. The highest grades were Phil's and (her's, hers).

   _____

4. (You're, Your) victory clinched the tournament for us.

   _____

5. (There's, Theirs) was the greatest accomplishment.

   _____

Capitals for Sentences and the Word *I*
• Practice 1

Capital letters signal the start of sentences and important words. A capital always begins the first word of a sentence, whether it is a statement, question, or direct quotation. Also the word *I* is always capitalized.

CAPITALS USED WITH SENTENCES AND THE WORD *I*	
Always Capitalized	**Examples**
the first word in a sentence	*Raccoons* got into the trash last night.
	Where will the signal come from?
the first word in a direct quotation	Mike said, "*The* lawn needs water."
	"*If* I do it," Jan said, "will you pay me?"
the word *I*	*I* wondered if *I* had enough time.

▶ **Exercise 1** **Using Capitals to Begin Sentences.** Underline the word or words that should be capitalized in each sentence below.

EXAMPLE: the boys asked, "can we go to the movies?"

1. when i was younger, i took lessons on the clarinet.

2. clipper ships were built with tall masts and sharp lines.

3. "crocodile hide," our teacher said, "is sometimes made into leather."

4. she asked, "does the recipe call for brown sugar?"

5. i will do it only if you have the proper safety equipment.

6. my mother asked, "can you help me vacuum the family room?"

7. the reporter noted, "killer bees have been found in the United States."

8. i have several valuable stamps in a collection i started last year.

9. "when i was a boy," my grandfather recalled, "i loved to play leapfrog."

10. our speaker said, "a nutritious diet is important to your health."

▶ **Exercise 2** **More Work With Capital Letters.** Complete each blank below with an appropriate word or words. Capitalize the word if necessary.

EXAMPLE: Mother said, "_____*Bread*_____ is on sale at the market."

1. _____ wants to go to the beach with us.

2. Mother asked, "_____ should I serve dinner?"

3. You can get Vitamin C from _____.

4. I said, "_____ is my favorite food."

5. Either _____ go or you go, but we can't both go.

6. "_____ topic have you chosen for your report?" the teacher asked.

7. _____ told her, "_____ can't decide on a subject."

8. Our _____ broke down and had to be repaired.

9. "On Halloween," Nan said, "_____ start trick-or-treating about seven."

10. _____ are a fast form of transportation.

27 # Capitals for Sentences and the Word *I*
• Practice 2

▶ **Exercise 1**   **Supplying Capital Letters.**   Underline the word or words that should be capitalized in each sentence below.

EXAMPLE: <u>the</u> two teams were playing hockey.

1. all twelve hockey players were skating briskly early in the morning.
2. there was one player i began to watch closely.
3. i said to my dad, "watch number 27."
4. he was swinging at the puck.
5. my dad asked, "do you think he will score?"
6. "yes," i replied, "i do."
7. instead, the player passed the puck to a teammate.
8. i yelled, "that was a great pass!"
9. i saw the forward shoot the puck into the net.
10. he scored a goal.

▶ **Exercise 2**   **More Work With Capital Letters.**   Follow the directions for Exercise 1.

1. a few people were waiting at the bus stop.
2. the teacher asked, "did your experiment work?"
3. i decided i should revise my story.
4. answer the question.
5. i remember the first day i went to school.
6. they asked her to show how to use the machine.
7. i think i can finish the book by tomorrow.
8. Tim said, "this new chair is very comfortable."
9. the cabin attendant announced, "fasten your seatbelts."
10. our science laboratory is an interesting place.

▶ **Writing Application**   **Using Capital Letters Correctly.**   Write ten sentences about a place you know well. Make sure each sentence begins with a capital letter and that the word *I* is always capitalized.

1. _____
2. _____
3. _____
4. _____
5. _____
6. _____
7. _____
8. _____
9. _____
10. _____

Name _____ Date _____

Capitals for Names of People and Places

• Practice 1

When naming a specific person or place, capital letters should be used.

CAPITALS FOR SPECIFIC NAMES AND PLACES	
Persons	Louisa May Alcott, J. Edgar Hoover, Mickey Mouse
Streets and Roads	Mill Road, Washington Avenue, Fifth Avenue
Cities and States	Santa Fe, Chicago, Paris, Wisconsin, Oregon
Nations and Continents	Egypt, Finland, Australia, South America
Land Forms	Mount Shasta, the Central Valley, Virgin Islands, the Mojave Desert
Bodies of Water	Gold Lake, Hudson Bay, Arabian Sea, Yukon River, the Pacific Ocean

▷ **Exercise 1**   **Using Capital Letters With Specific People and Places.**   Underline each letter that should be capitalized in the sentences below.

EXAMPLE: <u>h</u>ank <u>a</u>aron hit 755 home runs in his career.

1. britain fought a war over the falkland islands.

2. The lowest point below sea level is found in death valley, california.

3. robert e. peary was the first person to reach the north pole.

4. Many animal studies are done on the galápagos islands in ecuador.

5. john f. kennedy defeated richard m. nixon in a close election in 1960.

6. The arabian desert is 70,000 square miles in size.

7. The President of the united states lives on pennsylvania avenue.

8. The sacramento river empties into the san francisco bay.

9. The most recent eruption of mount st. helens in washington was 1984.

10. The mysterious Bermuda Triangle is found in the atlantic ocean.

▷ **Exercise 2**   **More Work With Capitalizing Specific Names and Places.**   Fill in each blank below with an appropriate word or words. Capitalize when necessary.

EXAMPLE: I once took a boat to _____*Catalina Island*_____.

1. The ocean nearest my home is _____.

2. My address is _____.

3. My grandfather's full name is _____.

4. I have visited these states: _____.

5. I would like to travel to the country of _____.

6. The closest mountains to my home are _____.

7. It would be fun to go fishing in the _____ River.

8. Canada is located on the _____ continent.

9. Italy is near the _____ Sea.

10. The most famous city near my home is _____.

27 Capitals for Names of People and Places
• Practice 2

▶ **Exercise 1** **Using Capitals for Names of People and Places.**   Underline each letter that should be capitalized.

EXAMPLE: gerald r. ford was born in omaha, nebraska.

1. madeline spencer spent a month in greece last summer.

2. great bear lake is located in canada.

3. the snake river is over 1,000 miles long.

4. dr. john s. knickerbocker's office is at the end of main street.

5. In 1519 hernando cortes discovered mexico.

6. mount kilimanjaro is in africa.

7. victoria c. woodhull ran for President in 1872.

8. The book Antoinette has been reading is by j. r. r. tolkien.

9. lake george is a popular vacation spot.

10. stan laurel and oliver hardy made comic films.

11. The rocky mountains stretch across much of north america.

12. lake erie is more than 9,000 miles long.

13. west virginia and kentucky have large deposits of coal.

14. The second largest river in europe is the danube.

15. atlanta and denver are capital cities.

16. The largest lake in africa is lake victoria.

17. levi hutchins invented the alarm clock.

18. james l. plimpton designed the first roller skates.

19. harriet tubman helped slaves escape to freedom.

20. charles lindbergh was the first person to fly solo across the atlantic.

▶ **Writing Application** **Using the Names of People and Places in Sentences.**   Write ten sentences, using the name of a specific person or place in each sentence.

1. _____

2. _____

3. _____

4. _____

5. _____

6. _____

7. _____

8. _____

9. _____

10. _____

Capitals for Names of Specific Things
• Practice 1

The name of *specific* things—such as special days, events, or objects—should always be capitalized.

CAPITALS FOR SPECIFIC THINGS	
Historical Periods, Events, and Documents	Industrial Revolution, Civil War, Declaration of Independence
Days, Months, and Holidays	Saturday, October, Thanksgiving
Organizations and Schools	Girl Scouts, Miller Elementary School
Government Bodies and Political Parties	the Congress, the Republican Party
Races, Nationalities, and Languages	Eskimo, Chinese, French
Monuments, Memorials, and Buildings	Statue of Liberty, the Vietnam Memorial, the Eiffel Tower
Religious Faiths	Judaism, Christianity, Hinduism
Awards	Oscars, Caldecott Medal
Air, Sea, Space, and Land Craft	*Double Eagle II, Lusitania, Skylab 2, Rambler*

▶ **Exercise 1**　**Using Capitals for the Names of Specific Things.**　Underline the letters of words requiring capitals in the sentences below.

EXAMPLE: The liberty bell was cracked in September of 1752.

1. Four presidents are sculptured in the monument of mount rushmore.
2. One form of mass transit is the system called amtrak.
3. memorial day is usually celebrated on the last Monday in may.
4. Most people in turkey are muslims.
5. In somalia, the official languages are somali and arabic.
6. The concorde flew from New York to paris 3 hours 30 minutes.
7. The tallest building in the world is the sears tower in Chicago.
8. The symbol of the democratic party is the donkey.
9. Satellites have been launched from the space shuttle *Discovery*.
10. Two women are now members of the supreme court.

▶ **Exercise 2**　**More Work Capitalizing Specific Things.**　In each pair, one item is general and one is specific. Underline the letters in the specific item that need capitalizing.

EXAMPLE:

	a lawyer's contract	the equal rights amendment
1.	a single-engine plane	the spirit of st. louis
2.	the medal of honor	an achievement award
3.	a conservative group	the republican party
4.	our elected group	the congress
5.	father's day	a day for fathers
6.	bill of rights	a list of guaranteed rights
7.	a church group	christians
8.	the sewing group	national sewing association
9.	the model t	an old car
10.	June	the month for weddings

27 Capitals for Names of Specific Things
• Practice 2

▶ **Exercise 1**   **Using Capitals for the Names of Specific Things.**   Write each specific thing requiring capitals in the sentences below. Add the necessary capital letters.

EXAMPLE: On July 4, 1776, congress accepted the declaration of independence.

       July, Congress, Declaration of Independence

1. Our class is learning about the constitution.

2. The lions club will sponsor a picnic next Saturday.

3. the mayas and the aztecs lived in mexico.

4. Fernando speaks english, spanish, and italian.

5. The sears tower in chicago, illinois, is 1,450 feet high.

6. Pearl Buck won the nobel prize.

7. washington's birthday is celebrated in February.

8. Rae sailed along the coast of maine on the <u>mattie</u>.

9. we visited carpenter's hall and independence hall.

10. The maplewood school is open Monday through Saturday.

11. The candidates from the republican party will speak here on Tuesday.

12. The golden kite award was presented to M. E. Kerr.

13. skylab 2 gave american astronauts a chance to spend more time in space than ever before.

14. The first Sunday after labor day is grandparent's day.

15. The treaty of versailles was rejected by the senate.

Name _____ Date _____

 27 # Capitals for Titles of People • Practice 1

There are three kinds of titles: social, professional, and family titles. Generally, you capitalize these titles only when they come before a person's name or in direct address. You also capitalize a family title when it refers to a specific person, but does not follow a possessive noun or possessive pronoun.

CAPITALS WITH SOCIAL, PROFESSIONAL, AND FAMILY TITLES		
Title	**Examples**	**Use in a Sentence**
Social	Miss, Madam, Mister, Sir, Mesdames	Could you help me, *Sir*? Our guest is *Mr.* David Gatley. I seated the *m*esdames at the table.
Professional	Senator, Mayor, Judge, Doctor, Sergeant, Rabbi, Sister, Professor	The service was led by *Father John*. Did the men finish the drill, *Corporal*? The *d* octor cured the man.
Family	Mother, Father, Aunt, Uncle, Grandmother, Grandfather	I love *Uncle John's* farm. Is this the picture you meant, *Mother*? Your *Father* will be able to fix it.

▶ **Exercise 1**   **Capitalizing Titles of People.**   Underline each title below that requires capitalization. Some sentences may have no titles requiring capitalization.

EXAMPLE: Ask <u>sister</u> Joan to come to the chapel.

1. Can you tell us, congresswoman Filante, how you will vote on the issue?

2. The doctor is at lunch right now.

3. I understand judge Canyon will hear the case.

4. Was that lieutenant Randolph who just walked up?

5. Who is your favorite French author, professor?

▶ **Exercise 2**   **More Work Capitalizing Titles of People.**   Use each title below in two ways—first, where it requires a capital and, second, where it does not.

EXAMPLE: private

I am Private Thomas Jackson reporting for duty.

That private wears his uniform with pride.

1. uncle

_____

_____

2. governor

_____

_____

3. attorney

_____

_____

4. doctor

_____

_____

5. mother

_____

_____

27 Capitals for Titles of People • Practice 2

Exercise 1 **Using Capitals for Titles of People.** Underline each title that requires capitalization.

EXAMPLE: The new course is taught by <u>professor</u> Cooper.

1. The commander of the ship is captain Jones.
2. Last spring, doctor Martin traveled abroad.
3. At night aunt Bonnie reads mysteries.
4. Today ambassador Burton made the announcement.
5. This soup, cousin Jane, is really delicious.
6. I asked grandmother Smith to show me her album.
7. What is your position on education, governor?
8. The speaker, rabbi Stern, talked about Israel.
9. The officer, captain Lee, was in charge.
10. Is uncle George visiting for the weekend, mother?

Exercise 2 **More Practice Capitalizing Titles of People.** Follow the directions for Exercise 1.

1. Every year uncle Jack has a backyard barbecue.
2. He asks dr. Henderson, his neighbor, to help.
3. Then aunt Irene sends out invitations.
4. Her cousin, judge smith, usually comes.
5. One of the regular guests is coach Ryan.
6. He and aunt Irene organize a volleyball game.
7. My dad's lawyer, attorney Stevens, always plays.
8. His team played a team led by grandpa Max.
9. I wasn't sure grandfather would play.
10. Grandpa, however, scored more points than cousin Ralph.

Writing Application **Using Titles of People in Sentences.** Write ten sentences. In five of these sentences, include different social or professional titles. In the other five sentences, include titles that show different family relationships.

1. _____
2. _____
3. _____
4. _____
5. _____
6. _____
7. _____
8. _____
9. _____
10. _____

Capitals for Titles of Things • Practice 1

Capitals are used with the titles of written works and works of art. You should capitalize the first word and all other key words in these titles. The title of a school course is capitalized only when it is followed by a number or refers to a language.

TITLES OF WRITTEN WORKS, WORKS OF ART, AND SCHOOL COURSES	
Books	*Swiss Family Robinson, Kon-tiki*
Newspapers and Magazines	*The Daily Journal, Outdoor Life*
Short Stories and Poems	"The Loser," "Richard Cory"
Full-length Plays	*My Fair Lady, The Music Man*
Movies	*Strangers on a Train, Star Wars*
Songs	"Hello Dolly," "Puttin' on the Ritz"
Paintings and Sculptures	*Young Woman With a Water Jug, Boxing Match*
School Courses	English 2A, German, Science I

 Exercise 1   **Using Capitals for Titles of Things.**   Circle the letters in the titles below that require capital letters.

EXAMPLE: ⟨t⟩he ⟨e⟩nchanted ⟨c⟩astle —painting

1. *splash* —movie
2. *reader's source* —magazine
3. *the sign of the beaver* —book
4. spanish—school course
5. orlando *eagle* —newspaper
6. "you've got a friend"—song
7. *fiddler on the roof* —play
8. *the thinker* —sculpture
9. *jane eyre* —book
10. "the bridge"—poem
11. *the peasant dance* —painting
12. composition 2—school course
13. "ol' man river"—song
14. *chariots of fire* —movie
15. tucson *daily star*—newspaper
16. *collector's guide*—magazine
17. *the cat in the hat* —book
18. *haystacks* —painting
19. *our town* —play
20. "trees"—poem

Exercise 2   **More Work With Capitalizing Titles of Things.**   Circle any letters in the titles that need capitalizing in the sentences below.

EXAMPLE: The poem "⟨a⟩nnabel ⟨l⟩ee" was written about Poe's wife.

1. *through the looking glass*, by Lewis Carroll, has become a classic book.
2. I try to read the denver *sentinel* on the bus on the way to work.
3. The longest running play in the United States is *cats*.
4. My counselor signed me up for english I next year.
5. I enjoyed reading *that was then, this is now*.
6. Puppets were used in the movie *the muppets take manhattan*.
7. My brother has taken both french and latin in high school.
8. *Hiking* is a magazine for people who enjoy the outdoors.
9. One of Michael Jackson's gold records is "the girl is mine."
10. Thomas Gainsborough painted *the blue boy*.

27 Capitals for Titles of Things • Practice 2

▶ **Exercise 1**   **Using Capitals for Titles of Things.**   Rewrite the following titles, adding capital letters as necessary. Keep the underlining and quotation marks as shown.

EXAMPLE: the sound of music _____*The Sound of Music*_____

1. the good earth _____
2. "spring fever" _____
3. "sounds of silence" _____
4. mathematics 103 _____
5. mona lisa _____
6. national geographic _____
7. the poseidon adventure _____
8. french _____
9. "the split cherry tree" _____
10. "the lady or the tiger?" _____
11. the los angeles times _____
12. science digest _____
13. "the rain in spain" _____
14. life with father _____
15. my fair lady _____
16. animal farm _____
17. the pearl _____
18. history 570 _____
19. the crucible _____
20. "the circuit" _____

▶ **Exercise 2**   **More Practice Using Capital Letters for Titles of Things.**   Follow the directions for Exercise 1.

1. algebra II _____
2. the way we were _____
3. the new york daily news _____
4. the devil and daniel webster _____
5. when the legends die _____
6. "the most dangerous game" _____
7. island of the blue dolphins _____
8. "the fun they had" _____
9. treasure island _____
10. "the road not taken" _____
11. latin _____
12. the sunflowers _____
13. the outsiders _____
14. a raisin in the sun _____
15. "the base stealer" _____
16. the red pony _____
17. a star is born _____
18. fiddler on the roof _____
19. "mother to son" _____
20. popular computers _____

▶ **Writing Application**   **Using Titles of Things in a Paragraph.**   Write a paragraph about the kind of books or movies you enjoy. Include at least three titles.

_____
_____
_____
_____
_____
_____
_____
_____
_____

27 **Capitals in Letters** • **Practice 1**

Friendly letters require capital letters in several places—the heading, the salutation, and the closing.

CAPITALS IN FRIENDLY LETTERS		
Heading	14 Carolyn Drive Newark, New Jersey 07102 August 2, 2001	
Salutations	Dear Ellen, Dear Mr. Rodgers,	My dear Family, Dear Aunt Harriet,
Closings	Always, Your friend,	Fondly, With love,

▶ **Exercise 1** **Using Capitals in Letters.** Underline the words that need capitals in the parts of letters below.

EXAMPLE: with fond regards,

1. my dear sister,
2. 410 camilia lane
   new orleans, lousiana 70130
   April 17, 1999
3. your good friend,
4. dear mrs. dunkin,
5. 1620 vineyard avenue
   baltimore, maryland 21202
   February 14, 2000

6. affectionately,
7. dear grandma ethel,
8. my dear mr. larusso,
9. 1213 dunning way
   akron, ohio 44308
   January 1, 1998
10. 16 sunset lane
    fort wayne, indiana 46802
    November 23, 2001

▶ **Exercise 2** **More Practice in Using Capitals in Letters.** Provide the information requested below, using capitals where necessary.

EXAMPLE: Write a closing for a letter to a friend.

_____ *Thinking of you,* _____

1. Write your address and today's date as it would look in a letter heading.

   _____

   _____

   _____

2. Write the closing you would use in a letter to your parents.

   _____

3. Write the salutation you would use in a letter to an adult neighbor.

   _____

4. Write the salutation you would use in a letter to an aunt or uncle.

   _____

5. Write the closing you would use in a letter to a friend in class.

   _____

27   Capitals in Letters • Practice 2

▷ **Exercise 1**   **Using Capitals in Letters.**   Underline the words that need capitals in the parts of letters below.

EXAMPLE: dear arnold

1. 128 hollings drive
   freeport, maine 04033
   April 20, 2001
2. 418 tremont avenue
   atlanta, georgia 30339
   September 15, 2001
3. dear uncle bill,
4. my dear sister,
5. sincerely,
6. affectionately,

7. 43 tenth street
   berkeley, california 94710
   August 10, 2001
8. 225 highland street
   September 15, 1987
   canton, massachusetts 02021
   may 14, 2001
9. greetings, marcia
10. fondly,

▷ **Exercise 2**   **More Practice Using Capitals in Letters.**   Follow the directions for Exercise 1.

1. 46 lincoln avenue
   hancock,
   new hampshire 03449
   February 16, 2000
2. 791 central avenue
   bloomington, indiana 47401
   August 23, 2001
3. hello, george,
4. howdy, mindy,
5. love,

6. yours truly,
7. 347 willow road
   san antonio, texas 78216
   December 7, 2001
8. 86 kirkland street
   portland, oregon 97233
   June 15, 2000
9. dear aunt karen,
10. your friend,

▷ **Writing Application**   **Using Capitals in Letters.**   Write a letter with a heading, salutation, and closing to a friend. Tell about something you have been doing at home or in school.

_____

_____

_____

_____

_____

_____

_____

_____

_____

_____

_____

Diagraming Sentences • Practice 1

A diagram shows how the parts of a sentence are related.

DECLARATIVE	INTERROGATIVE
Snow is falling.	Do you ski?
Snow | was falling	you | Do ski

IMPERATIVE
Listen!
(you) | Listen

▶ **Exercise 1** **Diagraming Declarative and Imperative Sentences.** Diagram each sentence below. Use the models above if necessary.

1. Snakes crawl.

2. Stop!

3. Birds were singing.

▶ **Exercise 2** **Diagraming Interrogative Sentences.** Diagram each sentence below. Refer to the model if necessary.

1. Are you listening?

2. Has he finished?

Diagraming Sentences • Practice 2

▶**Exercise 1**   **Making Sentence Diagrams.**   Diagram each sentence below.

EXAMPLE: Cyclones move.

Cyclones	move

1. Flowers grow.

2. Kenneth is absent.

3. Is it raining?

▶**Exercise 2**   **More Practice Diagraming Sentences.**   Diagram each of the following sentences.

1. Kathie has been swimming.

2. Did he forget?

3. Tornadoes destroy.

Diagraming Phrases • Practice 1

A prepositional phrase is diagramed to show how it relates the object of the preposition to another word in the sentence. The preposition is written on a slanted line joined to the word the phrase modifies. The object is written on a horizontal line. One-word modifiers are placed on a slanted line below the word they modify.

ADJECTIVE PHRASE	ADVERB PHRASE
The flowers *in the window box* are dying.	The boat arrives early *in the morning.*

APPOSITIVE PHRASE
John, the team captain, is batting now.

To diagram an appositive phrase, put the most important noun in the phrase in parentheses and place it next to the noun it renames, identifies, or explains. Place modifiers beneath the noun.

▶ **Exercise 1**   **Diagraming Adjective and Adverb Phrases.**   Correctly diagram each sentence below.

1. The team with the red shirts is winning.

2. The door closed with a bang.

3. The girl behind me was speaking in a whisper.

▶ **Exercise 2**   **Diagraming Appositive Phrases.**   Correctly diagram each sentence below.

1. Ulysses, the Greek leader, was plotting.

2. Ellen, the runner-up, smiled happily.

Diagraming Phrases • Practice 2

▶**Exercise 1** **Diagraming Phrases.** Diagram the sentences below. Each contains at least one prepositional or appositive phrase.

EXAMPLE: Her vacation, a week in Europe, begins Wednesday.

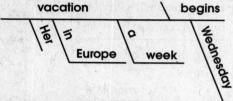

1. The store awning waved in the breeze.

2. Mr. Dobbs, the new grocer, works daily.

3. Our new mall, on the highway, opened recently.

▶**Exercise 2** **More Practice Diagraming Phrases.** Diagram the following sentences. Each contains a prepositional or appositive phrase.

1. The clowns somersaulted over the lions.

2. The coach stood beside the winner.

3. Our teacher, a computer whiz, likes to invent.

Diagraming Compound Sentences • Practice 1

The clauses of a compound sentence are diagramed separately, one under the other. They are connected by a dotted line that looks like a step. The coordinating conjunction or semicolon is written on the step. Notice that a direct object is placed after the verb with a short line separating them.

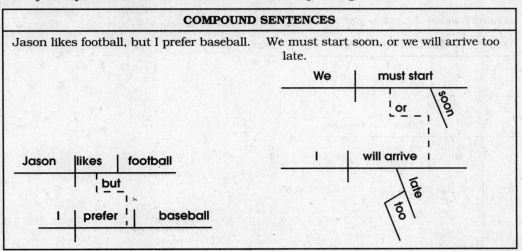

COMPOUND SENTENCES

Jason likes football, but I prefer baseball.   We must start soon, or we will arrive too late.

▶ **Exercise 1**   **Diagraming Compound Sentences.**   Diagram each of the following compound sentences.

1. Adults must have a child with them, or they cannot enter the zoo.

2. The plane developed engine trouble, and the pilot made a forced landing.

3. The police freed the suspect, for they believed his story.

▶ **Exercise 2**   **Interpreting Diagrams.**   Write the compound sentence represented by the diagram below.

1.

Diagraming Compound Sentences • Practice 2

▶ **Exercise 1**   **Diagraming Compound Sentences.**   Diagram each of the following compound sentences.

EXAMPLE: The rains flooded the town, and the wind blew houses away.

1. We like to walk on the beach, and they like to sail.

2. Alaska has mountains and it has beautiful glaciers.

3. That artist draws well and he likes to paint.

4. John left early for the game, but his car broke down.

5. We can go to the beach, or we can sit by the pool.

Answers

14.1 The Noun (Page 1)
Practice 1
Exercise 1 Recognizing Nouns
1. reporters, scene, survivors
2. children, dark
3. neighbors, vacation, mountains.
4. Jason, sneaker, couch
5. Amanda, movie
6. Nancy, team
7. tree, leaf
8. architect, fountain, lobby.
9. Phil, parents, fear
10. Marc, glasses

Exercise 2 Adding Nouns to Sentences
(Sample answers are given.)
1. wallet, money
2. officer, car
3. waiter, water
4. Mom, treat
5. pitch, strike
6. bush, driveway
7. Mr. Walker, bank
8. people, ballet
9. Dad, stew
10. class, New York

14.1 The Noun (Page 2)
Practice 2
Exercise 1 Identifying Nouns
1. James Ullman, books, stories
2. Ullman, America, mountains, Tibet
3. adventurer, mountains
4. Ullman, expedition, Mount Everest
5. climb, novel
6. story, Ullman, Amazon
7. people, adventures, books
8. Readers, knowledge, daring
9. Ullman, world, reporter
10. man, traveler, writer, person
11. works, Jack London
12. stories, settings, characters
13. author, Alaska, gold
14. years, London, school, work
15. jobs, adventures, London, career, writer

Exercise 2 More Work With Nouns
1. ingredients, bread, flour, water, milk, butter, yeast
2. yeast, water
3. sugar, flour, mixture, bowl
4. milk, flour, dough, board
5. dough, loaf, minutes
6. loaves, oven, pans, while
7. bread, pans, loaf, cooling rack
8. cats, kitchen, bread
9. cats, food
10. dinner, chunks, bread, olive oil

Writing Application
Using Nouns to Describe a Room
(Sample answers are given.)
1. armchair
2. bookcase
3. lamp
4. pillows
5. plants
6. rug
7. sofa
8. table
9. TV
10. VCR

I like to watch TV in the den. The TV stand is new and has a shelf for the VCR. The sofa is large and comfortable with lots of pillows. I usually put a bowl of popcorn on the table in front of the sofa, but I'm careful not to spill the popcorn on the rug. Mom has plants under the window in the den. She watches TV from her armchair. Sometimes she turns on the lamp beside her chair to read a book. The bookcase is full of the many books Mom has read while I watch TV!

14.1 Compound Nouns (Page 3)
Practice 1
Exercise 1 Recognizing Compound Nouns
1. Morning glories, lamppost
2. paperback, bestseller
3. playwright, musical comedy
4. Kevin Parker, political science
5. passerby, sidewalk
6. city desk, deadline
7. bathing suit, backpack
8. caretaker, skeleton key
9. seat belt, airplane
10. chopsticks, chow mein

Exercise 2 More Work With Compound Nouns
1. grandfather, nursery rhymes
2. seventy-seven, Roman numerals
3. roommate, runner-up
4. footnote, cross reference
5. contact lens, bedroom
6. folk singer, tall tale
7. stage manager, run-through
8. follow-up, blood pressure
9. Kneepads, skateboards
10. bookkeeper, handwriting

14.1 Compound Nouns (Page 4)
Practice 2
Exercise 1 Finding Compound Nouns
1. salesclerk, goldfish
2. sister-in-law, wheelbarrow
3. clockwork, soap opera
4. left-hander, fastball
5. backpack, snowshoes
6. sleepwalker
7. short story, cowboy, farmhand
8. basketball, football, weekend
9. girlfriend, sheep dog, Siamese cat
10. folktale, countryside
11. handball, milkshake
12. tape recording, courtroom
13. bookmark, bookcase
14. armchair, fireplace
15. eyewitness, policeman
16. mail carrier, greeting cards, mailbox
17. attorney-at-law, chairperson
18. eyeglasses, handwriting, blackboard
19. housekeeper, doorbell
20. applesauce, rice pudding

21. control tower, aircraft
22. footsteps, teddy bear
23. city-state, city hall
24. fool's gold, riverbed
25. spaceship, light-year

Writing Application
Writing Sentences With Compound Nouns
(Sample answers are provided.)
1. My classmates and I went on a class trip.
2. We took a vote and chose an amusement park.
3. First, we rode the roller coaster.
4. Before lunch, we played a game of tag football on the grass.
5. Our teacher won a wristwatch playing ringtoss.

14.1 Common and Proper Nouns (Page 5)
Practice 1
Exercise 1   Recognizing Proper Nouns
1. Fourth of July
2. Mrs. Jacobson
3. Santa Claus
4. Lancers
5. Beach Boys
6. August
7. Henry Wadsworth Longfellow
8. Uncle Albert
9. Japanese
10. Washington Monument

Exercise 2   Distinguishing Between Common and Proper Nouns
(Sample answers are provided.)

	Common Nouns	Proper Nouns
1.	book	*The Time Machine*
2.	street	Broadway
3.	building	Empire State Building
4.	capital	Santa Fe
5.	comic strip	Mutt and Jeff
6.	ballpark	Yankee Stadium
7.	Indian chief	Sitting Bull
8.	first lady	Eleanor Roosevelt
9.	school	Julliard School of Music
10.	continent	South America

14.1 Common and Proper Nouns (Page 6)
Practice 2
Exercise 1   Identifying Common and Proper Nouns
(Sample answers are given.)

	Common Nouns	Proper Nouns
1.	singer	Garth Brooks
2.	lake	Lake Superior
3.	computer	Apple
4.	neighbor	Mr. Beale
5.	country	Poland
6.	football team	Giants
7.	university	Harvard
8.	girl	Helen
9.	scientist	Einstein
10.	president	Franklin D. Roosevelt
11.	war	World War II
12.	heroine	Joan of Arc
13.	comic strip character	Snoopy
14.	department store	Macy's
15.	comedian	Bill Cosby
16.	state	Iowa
17.	club	4-H
18.	doctor	Dr. Wilson
19.	airline	Island Airlines
20.	London	city

Exercise 2   More Work With Common and Proper Nouns
(Sample answers are given.)

	Common Nouns	Proper Nouns
1.	country	China
2.	ballpark	Wrigley Field
3.	school	Beaver Elementary
4.	war	Civil War
5.	language	Spanish
6.	president	George Washington
7.	gulf	Gulf of Mexico
8.	friend	Evelyn
9.	city	San Diego
10.	canal	Panama Canal
11.	hero	Gandhi
12.	baseball team	Red Sox
13.	river	Amazon River
14.	town	Millville
15.	mountain chain	Andes Mountains
16.	monument	Lincoln Memorial
17.	ocean	Pacific
18.	building	Chrysler Building
19.	patriot	Betsy Ross
20.	planet	Saturn

14.2 The Pronoun (Page 7)
Practice 1
Exercise 1   Recognizing Pronouns and Antecedents
(Antecedents are given in parentheses.)
1. her (Allison)
2. their (parakeets)
3. its (Iowa)
4. their (students)
5. He (Mr. Wilson)
6. she (Angie)
7. their (members)
8. her (Mom)
9. its (Mississippi River)
10. their (twins)

Exercise 2   Using Pronouns in Sentences
1. his
2. their
3. their
4. his
5. its
6. it
7. she
8. they
9. their
10. it

14.2 The Pronoun (Page 8)
Practice 2
Exercise 1   Recognizing Pronouns and Antecedents

1. colonists... they
2. Farmers... their
3. woman... she
4. Sybilla Masters... her
5. people... their

194 • Answers

6. tall tales... them

7. bird... its

8. doll...it

9. settler... he

10. boy... he

Exercise 2   More Work With Pronouns and Antecedents

1. seashell... its

2. varieties... they

3. shells... they

4. skeletons...them

5. animals... their

14.2   Personal Pronouns (Page 9)
Practice 1
Exercise 1   Recognizing Personal Pronouns
1. your, 2nd, P
2. I, 1st, S
3. ours, 1st, P
4. she, 3rd, S
5. you, 2nd, S
6. their, 3rd, P
7. its, 3rd, S
8. his, 3rd, S
9. us, 1st, P
10. mine, 1st, S

Exercise 2   Adding Personal Pronouns to Sentences
1. our
2. their
3. me
4. her
5. your
6. his
7. its
8. he
9. her
10. it

14.2   Personal Pronouns (Page 10)
Practice 2
Exercise 1   Recognizing Personal Pronouns
1. you   second person
2. It   third person
3. he   third person
4. His   third person
5. We   first person
6. they   third person
7. My   first person
8. I   first person
9. him   third person
10. she   third person
11. her   third person
12. them   third person
13. your   second person
14. mine   first person
15. we   first person

Exercise 2   More Work With Personal Pronouns
1. your   second person
2. I   first person
3. me   first person
4. us   first person
5. his   third person
6. her   third person
7. our   first person
8. her   third person
9. they   third person
10. we   first person
11. mine   first person
12. yours   second person
13. hers   third person
14. them   third person
15. their   third person

14.2   Demonstrative Pronouns (Page 11)
Practice 1
Exercise 1   Recognizing Demonstrative Pronouns
(Referents are given in parentheses.)
1. That (firecracker)
2. these (pastries)
3. these (tomatoes)
4. this (sweater)
5. Those (meatballs)
6. That (woman)
7. These (curtains)
8. this (stew)
9. That (movie)
10. those (pictures)

Exercise 2   Using Demonstrative Pronouns in Sentences
1. This (or That)
2. That
3. those
4. that (or this)
5. this
6. those
7. this
8. those
9. this
10. these (or those)

14.2   Demonstrative Pronouns (Page 12)
Practice 2
Exercise 1   Recognizing Demonstrative Pronouns
1. These, (paintings)
2. This, (portrait)
3. those, (paintings)
4. This, (gallery)
5. That, (bathtub)
6. These, (birds)
7. This, (household)

8. That, (studio)

9. these, (pictures)

10. those, (letters)

Exercise 2   More Work with Demonstrative Pronouns

1. This, (street)

2. That, (house)

3. Those, (bushes)

4. that, (coins)

5. This, (coin)

6. These, (pennies)

7. Those, (francs)

8. This, (nickel)

9. this, (money)

10. These, (coins)

Writing Application
Using Demonstrative Pronouns
[Sample paragraph is given.]
This school has the largest enrollment in the city. During the summer, these classrooms were renovated. The awards in those showcases belong to the graduating class. Let's go into the auditorium. That student just joined the school band.

15.1   The Verb (Page 13)
Practice 1
Exercise 1   Recognizing Verbs

1. offered, action
2. tastes, condition
3. wears, action
4. gave, action
5. remained, condition
6. felt, condition
7. played, action
8. is, condition
9. seems, condition
10. planned, action

Exercise 2   Adding Verbs to Sentences
(Sample answers are given.)

1. plays
2. checked
3. were
4. looks
5. repeated
6. annoyed
7. attended
8. become
9. sounds
10. learned

15.1   The Verb (Page 14)
Practice 2
Exercise 1   Recognizing Verbs

1. dreamed
2. explored
3. was
4. felt
5. paid
6. taught
7. grew
8. studied
9. worked
10. became

Exercise 2   More Work With Verbs

1. enjoys
2. spent
3. tried
4. felt
5. attended
6. seemed
7. attempted
8. was
9. raced
10. is

Writing Application
Using Verbs in Sentences
(A sample paragraph is given.)
This is how to make a tuna salad sandwich. First, empty a can of tuna into a bowl. Chop celery and add it to the tuna. Mix in a little mayonnaise. Add pepper to taste. Spread it on sandwich bread and add pickles.

15.2   Action Verbs (Page 15)
Practice 1
Exercise 1   Identifying Action Verbs

1. explained
2. planted
3. teased
4. borrowed
5. won
6. promised
7. estimated
8. left
9. started
10. failed

Exercise 2   Adding Action Verbs to Sentences
(Sample answers are given.)

1. remembered
2. likes
3. paced
4. stumped
5. shook
6. searched
7. expects
8. dribbled
9. drew
10. handed

15.2   Action Verbs (Page 16)
Practice 2
Exercise 1   Identifying Action Verbs

1. built
2. produces
3. remember
4. rubs
5. twirls
6. appreciate

7. wonder
8. wrote
9. feared
10. banned

Exercise 2   More Work With Action Verbs
1. selected
2. gathered
3. signaled
4. understand
5. awarded
6. realized
7. recognized
8. heard
9. adjusted
10. chose

Writing Application
Using Verbs in Sentences
(Two sample sentences are given.)
1. Peter chopped wood in the yard.
2. He stacked the wood in a pile.

15.2   Linking Verbs (Page 17)
Practice 1
Exercise 1   Recognizing Linking Verbs
(Linked words are given in parentheses.)
1. sound (violinists/terrible)
2. has been (rail service/irregular)
3. am (I/board)
4. became (crowd/restless)
5. were (Many/jealous)
6. feels (Jerry/listless)
7. should have been (Louisa/careful)
8. smell (cookies/delicious)
9. feels (Linus/secure)
10. remained (Alicia/calm)

Exercise 2   Adding Linking Verbs to Sentences
(Sample answers are given.)
1. Nancy was lucky
2. Some were hard
3. order was large
4. Dorothy felt surprised
5. store stayed open
6. Phil seems confused
7. weather turned cold
8. Luke became actor
9. Jennie sounded excited
10. something smells good

15.2   Linking Verbs (Page 18)
Practice 2
Exercise 1   Recognizing Linking Verbs

1. Rita is artist
2. candidates seem confident
3. trees grow tall
4. bread smelled delicious
5. neighbor sounded frightened

6. magazine looks interesting
7. Mr. Davis was farmer
8. store stayed open
9. We remained partners
10. traveler felt tired

Exercise 2   More Work With Linking Verbs
1. speaker appeared relaxed
2. report sounds accurate
3. I am relative
4. sister remained calm
5. John became impatient
6. Michelle turned red
7. horses were Shetlands
8. item looked new
9. Ted seemed fit
10. dinner smells delicious

Writing Application
Using Linking Verbs in Sentences
(Two sample sentences are given.)
The little girl looked nervous. She appeared to be lost.

15.3   Helping Verbs (Page 19)
Practice 1
Exercise 1   Identifying Helping Verbs
1. will be (serving)
2. should (arrive)
3. has (examined)
4. can (be)
5. has (ordered)
6. did (forget)
7. may know

8. has (taken)

9. am (waiting)

10. should have (tried)

Exercise 2 Adding Helping Verbs to Sentences
(Sample answers are given.)
1. will
2. must have
3. has been
4. may be
5. have
6. has been
7. may
8. should
9. should have
10. has been

15.3 Helping Verbs (Page 20)
Practice 2
Exercise 1 Identifying Helping Verbs

1. can (explain)

2. might (begin)

3. will (look)

4. could be (caused)

5. will (grow)

6. has been (working)

7. might be (solving)

8. is being (used)

9. has (written)

10. have been (fed)

Exercise 2 More Work With Helping Verbs

1. have (written)

2. was (serving)

3. would (become)

4. was (captured) ; was (sentenced)

5. should (remember)

6. had (lived)

7. should have (volunteered)

8. could have (done)

9. might have (been)

10. must have (inspired)

Writing Application
Writing Sentences With Helping Verbs
(Two sample sentences are given.)
I have been making pies at home. Without mother's advice, I never would have learned the secrets of baking.

16.1 The Adjective (Page 21)
Practice 1
Exercise 1 Identifying Adjectives
(Modified words are given in parentheses.)
1. popular (star), enthusiastic (fans), loyal (fans)
2. smallest (building), vast (estate)
3. two (maple trees), old (maple trees), beautiful (maple trees)
4. that (house), large (house), white (house), expensive (house)
5. nervous (I), excited (I), blue (ribbon)
6. expert (fisherman), enormous (fish), that (one)
7. withered (woman), old (woman), silent (audience)
8. Fat (shoelaces), neon (colors), brief (fad), colorful (fad)
9. Diligent (Len), determined (Len), expert (Len)
10. That (fern), feathery (fern), green (fern), beautiful (fern), front (window)

Exercise 2 Adding Adjectives to Sentences
(Sample answers are given.)
1. enormous
2. harmless
3. breathtaking
4. eager
5. shy
6. jubilant, victorious
7. heavy
8. bountiful
9. daring
10. tropical, tiny

16.1 The Adjective (Page 22)
Practice 2
Exercise 1 Recognizing Adjectives
1. clear, cold, deep
2. Old, comfortable
3. frisky, playful
4. new, less, old
5. Red, white
6. Hot, favorite
7. old, silent
8. magnificent
9. Blue, green, brown, orange
10. Chocolate, vanilla, strawberry, gleaming
11. two, good, cheap
12. long, exhausted
13. Frightened, confused, small, their
14. ideal, large
15. older, artistic, athletic
16. Used, good
17. Three, small, my
18. Don's, fancy, new
19. large, wet, bitter
20. funny, interesting

Writing Application
Using Adjectives to Describe a Movie
(A sample paragraph is given.)
    My favorite movie is *Tiny Tim*. In this movie, a very small boy gets into lots of funny mischief. Tim lives in a home for orphans and has many friends his

age, which is about seven years old. He is called Tiny Tim because he is small for his age. In the move, Tiny Tim gets into all kinds of silly trouble doing his chores and everyday routines. Other kids try to help him out, but they make more mistakes and things get very confused and very silly. Everybody laughs at Tim's mistakes and the other children look after him. In the end, a wonderful family adopts Tim.

16.1   Articles (Page 23)
Practice 1
Exercise 1   Identifying Articles
1. a, I
2. a, I; the, D
3. the, D; an, I
4. The, D; an, I; the, D
5. a, I; the, D
6. The, D; the, D; a, I; the, D
7. The, D; a, I; a, I
8. An, I; the, D
9. The, D; an, I
10. an, I; the D

Exercise 2   Using Indefinite Articles
1. a
2. an
3. an
4. a
5. a
6. an
7. a
8. a
9. a
10. an

16.1   Articles (Page 24)
Practice 2
Exercise 1   Using Indefinite Articles
1. a
2. a
3. a
4. an
5. an
6. a
7. a
8. an
9. an
10. an
11. a
12. an
13. an
14. a
15. an
16. a
17. a
18. an
19. a
20. a
21. a
22. an
23. an
24. a
25. an
26. a
27. an
28. a
29. a
30. a
31. an

32. an
33. a
34. a
35. an
36. a
37. an
38. an
39. a
40. a

Writing Application
Using Articles in Sentences
I have received many animals as gifts. I received a pet rabbit once. It was a very soft and an unusually big rabbit. For an especially good report card, I got an exotic bird. Another time, I got a puppy. I am glad to say an elephant was not on the list.

16.1   Proper Adjectives (Page 25)
Practice 1
Exercise 1   Identifying Proper Adjectives
(Modified words are given in parentheses.)
1. Scandinavian (winters)
2. Eskimo (kayak)
3. June (day)
4. Brazilian (restaurants)
5. Caribbean (ports)
6. Mel Gibson (films)
7. Colombian (beans)
8. Italian (ice)
9. Greek (myths)
10. Monet (painting)

Exercise 2   Using Proper Adjectives to Modify Nouns
1. a new Michael Jackson video
2. the Australian soccer team
3. an Italian opera
4. a Middle Eastern diplomat
5. a Mediterranean island
6. the Tchaikovsky overture
7. a White House spokesman
8. Alaskan snowstorms
9. the Idaho potato
10. a California representative

16.1   Proper Adjectives (Page 26)
Practice 2
Exercise 1   Identifying Proper Adjectives

	Proper Adjective	Noun
1.	Georgia	peaches
2.	French	dressing
3.	Beethoven	symphony
4.	Swiss	watch
5.	Panama	hat
6.	Parisian	designer
7.	Spanish	literature
8.	Canadian	team
9.	March	winds
10.	Venezuelan	embassy

Exercise 2   More Work With Proper Adjectives

	Proper Adjective	Noun
1.	Hawaiian	island
2.	Chaplin	movie
3.	Portuguese	coins
4.	Carter	memoirs
5.	Mediterranean	furniture
6.	Christmas	vacation
7.	Irish	leprechaun
8.	Swedish	film
9.	Mexican	restaurant
10.	Chopin	waltz

Writing Application
Writing Sentences With Proper Adjectives
(Samples sentences are given.)
1. The museum exhibited a French painting.
2. I took a course in Spanish history.
3. We love to go to Mexican restaurants.
4. The Peruvian vase was ancient.
5. Greek children performed a play.

16.1 Possessive Adjectives (Page 27)
Practice 1
Exercise 1 Recognizing Possessive Adjectives
1. orchestra, its, finale
2. Mandy, her, family
3. record, its, week
4. stars, their, services
5. you, your, work
6. I, my, umbrella
7. Rick, his, guitar
8. Betsy and I, our, secrets
9. people, their, chairs
10. Denise and Len, their, grandparents

Exercise 2 Using Possessive Adjectives in Sentences
1. their, computer
2. his, collection
3. her, pie
4. its, circulation
5. his, home
6. my, camera
7. its, schedule
8. her, family
9. his, puppy
10. your, report

16.1 Possessive Adjectives (Page 28)
Practice 2
Exercise 1 Recognizing Possessive Adjectives

1.
Andrea said that computers make her life easier.
2.
Computers don't lose their patience.
3.
Eric added, "My homework was done on a computer."
4.
Juan spends his time designing programs.
5.
A student who uses a computer will learn its uses.

6.
Michael, has your school developed any software for science classes?
7.
Mary will show her program to you.
8.
"Donna, your program is saved on a diskette."
9.
The boys have made revisions in their compositions.
10.
Chris says his skills in word processing have improved.

Exercise 2 More Work with Recognizing Possessive Adjectives

1.
Dr. Alice Hamilton is known for her work in medicine.
2.
She helped people in Chicago care for their children.
3.
Dr. Hamilton received her degree in 1893.
4.
The governor appointed the
doctor to head one of his committees.
5.
She studied workers' diseases and their causes.

16.2 The Adverb (Page 29)
Practice 1
Exercise 1 Identifying Adverbs
1. away, Where?
2. thoroughly, To what extent?
3. always, When?
4. well, In what way?
5. unusually, To what extent?
6. sometimes, When?
7. here, Where?
8. hard, In what way?
9. truly, To what extent?
10. home, Where?

Exercise 2 More Work With Adverbs
(Modified words are given in parentheses.)
1. seldom (cries)
2. Yesterday (discovered)
3. usually (arrives)
4. extremely (well), well (did)
5. sometimes (is)
6. gradually (solved)
7. annually (has)
8. quite (annoyed)
9. rapidly (melted)
10. diligently (practices)

16.2 The Adverb (Page 30)
Practice 2
Exercise 1 Finding Adverbs
1. often
2. Yesterday

3. once
4. jokingly
5. Carefully
6. most
7. Eventually
8. very
9. amazingly
10. carefully

Exercise 2 More Work With Adverbs

1. yearly
2. Joyously
3. outside
4. early
5. uptown
6. carefully
7. utterly
8. unusually
9. fully
10. quite

Writing Application
Using Adverbs in Sentences

(Two sample sentences are given.)
1. Rain fell softly as we began the drive.
2. Jean writes often to her friends.

16.2 Adverb or Adjective? (Page 31)
Practice 1
Exercise 1 Distinguishing Between Adjectives and Adverbs

1. adjective
2. adverb
3. adjective
4. adjective
5. adjective
6. adjective
7. adverb
8. adjective
9. adverb
10. adverb

Exercise 2 Writing Adjectives and Adverbs in Sentences

(Sample answers are given.)
1. Jason painted a picture of an upside-down clown. We turned the cooler upside-down to let the water run out.
2. Some considered the job change a backward move. The youngster put his shirt on backward.
3. We planned an early dinner. The plane got in early.
4. All the poisonous chemicals were kept on a high shelf. The sea gulls glided high above us.
5. Pat was the only student who got 100 on the test. Dad was angry only for a few minutes.

16.2 Adverb or Adjective? (Page 32)
Practice 2
Exercise 1 Recognizing Adverbs and Adjectives

1. adjective
2. adverb
3. adverb
4. adjective
5. adjective
6. adverb
7. adverb
8. adjective
9. adverb
10. adjective

Exercise 2 More Work With Adverbs and Adjectives

1. adjective
2. adverb
3. adjective
4. adjective
5. adverb
6. adverb
7. adverb
8. adjective
9. adjective
10. adverb

Writing Application
Using Adverbs and Adjectives in Sentences

(Two sample sentences are given.)
1. Peter is energetically chopping wood.
2. The axe has a long handle.

17 The Preposition (Page 33)
Practice 1
Exercise 1 Identifying Prepositions

1. into, next to
2. without
3. Among, of, for
4. Because of, to
5. from, across
6. through
7. against, since
8. for, on, in
9. from, until
10. except

Exercise 2 Using Prepositions in Sentences

(Sample answers are given.)
1. to
2. for
3. until
4. around
5. under
6. because of
7. about
8. besides
9. through
10. next to

17 The Preposition (Page 34)
Practice 2
Exercise 1 Supplying Prepositions

(Sample answers are given.)
1. on
2. around
3. since
4. before
5. near
6. across
7. in
8. over
9. through
10. except

Exercise 2 More Work With Prepositions

(Sample answers are given.)
1. under
2. like
3. toward
4. oppostite
5. into
6. against
7. on
8. until

9. in
10. by

Writing Application

Using Prepositions in Sentences

(Two sample sentences are given.)
1. The daisies are near the window.
2. The car is in the driveway.

17 Preposition or Adverb? (Page 35)

Practice 1

Exercise 1 Distinguishing Between Prepositions and Adverbs

1. adverb
2. preposition
3. adverb
4. preposition
5. preposition
6. preposition
7. preposition
8. adverb
9. preposition
10. adverb

Exercise 2 Writing Prepositions in Sentences

(Sample sentences are given.)
1. The clouds above us were white and fluffy. The balloon floated high above.
2. There is a surprise inside the box. We stayed inside because of the weather.
3. Someone left the phone off the hook. Please turn the television off.
4. Do not leave the lighter fluid near the grill. The child runs to his mother whenever someone else comes near.
5. Put this box underneath the cellar stairs. Those yellow petals are peach underneath.

17 Preposition or Adverb? (Page 36)

Practice 2

Exercise 1 Recognizing Prepositions and Adverbs

1. adverb
2. preposition
3. preposition
4. adverb
5. adverb
6. preposition
7. adverb
8. preposition
9. preposition
10. adverb

Exercise 2 More Work With Recognizing Prepositions and Adverbs

1. adverb
2. preposition
3. preposition
4. adverb
5. preposition
6. adverb
7. preposition
8. adverb
9. adverb
10. preposition

Writing Application

Using Prepositions and Adverbs in Sentences

(Sample sentences are given.)
1. We went to the movies after lunch.
   Helen arrived first, and we arrived after.

2. Before a live audience, the singer got sick.
   Dad fed the dog before.
3. Sam climbed over the fence.
   The puppy ran over and licked my ice cream cone.
4. Then the puppy pulled the cloth off the table.
   The cap came off as I grabbed the jar.
5. Around the bend came the speeding car.
   The boy ran around to find his lost toy.

18.1 The Conjunction (Page 37)

Practice 1

Exercise 1 Recognizing Coordinating Conjunctions

1. green (or) blue

2. with great accuracy (but) without much feeling.

3. Carol (and) Luke

4. We arrived early, (so) we could … seats.

5. Jason (or) Madeline

6. noisy (yet) well-behaved.

7. would sit (nor) stay

8. We … ballpark, (for) we … heavy.

9. busily (but) quietly

10. luck (and) skill

Exercise 2 Writing Sentences With Coordinating Conjunctions

(Sample sentences are given.)
1. Jeff jumped off the board and into the pool.
2. The reviews were favorable but restrained.
3. The bus never came, so we started walking.
4. The traffic flowed slowly yet smoothly.
5. He or I will do the dishes.

18.1 The Conjunction (Page 38)

Practice 2

Exercise 1 Recognizing Coordinating Conjunctions

1. Today I have tests in mathematics (and) social studies.

2. I went to the game, (but) I left early.

3. Cars were parked in the street (and) in the driveways.

4. Bob reads slowly (and) carefully.

5. Mary wanted to buy those jeans, (so) she saved her allowance money.

6. The book was long (but) enjoyable.

7. The runner stumbled (and) fell.

8. I did not like the movie, (nor) did she.

9. Are you going with us (or) with them?

10. Bill phoned all day, (yet) nobody answered.

Exercise 2   More Work With Coordinating Conjunctions

1. Jill could not get tickets, (nor) could Ed.

2. Do you want lemonade (or) soda?

3. The weather was sunny (but) cool.

4. I'm excited, (for) today is my birthday.

5. Put your bicycle in the garage (or) in the basement.

6. Did they fly (or) drive to Kansas City?

7. The song was simple (but) beautiful.

8. The boat glided silently (yet) rapidly.

9. Please put lettuce (and) mayonnaise in my sandwich.

10. Either you (or) she will be asked to speak.

Writing Application
Using Coordinating Conjunctions in Sentences
(Two sample sentences are given.)
1. Kerri and Marci want to be scientists.
2. Joe wanted to build a telescope, so Ed helped him.

18.1   Correlative Conjunctions (Page 39)
Practice 1
Exercise 1   Finding Correlative Conjunctions

1. (either) walks (or) rides

2. (not only) tender (but also) flaky

3. (Both) Paul (and) family

4. (neither) in its jacket (nor) on the turntable

5. (whether) Shana (or) sister

6. (either) salad (or) vegetable.

7. (not only) set the table (but also) washed the dishes.

8. (Either) Fran ... arrangements, (or) Mom ... angry.

9. (neither) in the closet (nor) under my bed.

10. (both) sausage (and) peppers

Exercise 2   Writing Sentences With Correlative Conjunctions
(Sample answers are given.)
1. The violinist played neither smoothly nor well.
2. I wonder whether you or I should have locked the door.
3. Either the contestant will withdraw that entry, or the judges will disqualify it.
4. I looked for my tennis racket not only in the hall closet but also in the garage.
5. The art teacher both designed and built the sets for the play.

18.1   Correlative Conjunctions (Page 40)
Practice 2
Exercise 1   Finding Correlative Conjunctions

1. (Neither) the bat (nor) the ball belongs to me.

2. My sister reads (both) novels (and) plays.

3. Ralph could not decide (whether) to go (or) to stay at the party.

4. She (neither) agreed (nor) disagreed.

5. Your brother is (both) funny (and) intelligent.

6. The ball landed (either) in the lake (or) in that bush.

7. The food here is (both) inexpensive (and) tasty.

8. (Not only) did we go to the fair (but) we (also) won a prize.

9. The coach would not say (whether) Phil (or) Don would pitch.

10. On ice you must drive (both) slowly (and) carefully.

11. (Both) Eric (and) Aaron play tennis.

12. They (not only) compete (but also) practice.

13. They feel (neither) nervous (nor) upset in a game.

14. Eric studies his opponent (both) before a game (and) during a game.

15. They both play (either) singles (or) doubles.

16. It is hard to say (whether) Eric (or) Aaron is the better player.

17. They select (not only) their equipment (but also) the courts where they will play.

18. Aaron plays (either) during the day (or) during the evening.

19. To play well, they should be (neither) tired (nor) angry.

20. Instead, they should feel (both) focused (and) calm.

Writing Application

Using Correlative Conjunctions to Write About a Sport

(Two sample sentences are given.)
1. Swimming offers not only good exercise but also pleasant relaxation.
2. It can be practiced either in indoor pools or in outdoor waters.

18.2   The Interjection (Page 41)
Practice 1
Exercise 1   Recognizing Interjections
1. Nonsense!
2. Gosh
3. Terrific!
4. Ugh!
5. Sh
6. Oh, no!
7. Whew
8. Alas
9. My
10. Psst

Exercise 2   Writing Interjections in Sentences
(Sample answers are given.)
1. Wow
2. Golly
3. Ouch
4. Oops
5. Nonsense
6. Gosh
7. Terrific
8. Hey
9. Hurray
10. Huh

18.2   The Interjection (Page 42)
Practice 2
Exercise 1   Supplying Interjections
(Sample answers are given.)
1. Hey
2. Ouch
3. Hurray
4. Oh
5. Darn
6. Ugh
7. Nonsense
8. Wow
9. Gosh
10. Hey

Exercise 2   More Work With Supplying Interjections
(Sample answers are given.)
1. Well
2. Terrific

3. Golly
4. Oh
5. Boy
6. My
7. Gosh
8. Oops
9. Hey
10. Psst

Writing Application
Using Interjections in Sentences
(Two sample answers are given.)
1. Hurray! The astronauts are off again.
2. Gosh! I wonder what they will discover.

19.1   The Two Parts of a Sentence (Page 43)
Practice 1
Exercise 1   Finding Simple Subjects and Simple Predicates
1. beach ball rolled
2. Dachshunds were bred
3. book was
4. people reported
5. Len speaks
6. sink was
7. inspector Low held
8. Mr. Bixby assigns
9. No one noticed
10. map was

Exercise 2   Writing Subjects and Predicates
(Sample answers are given.)
1. hatch
2. officer
3. paid
4. party
5. crawled

19.1   The Two Parts of a Sentence (Page 44)
Practice 2
Exercise 1   Finding Simple Subjects and Simple Predicates
1. settlers   arrived
2. governor   called
3. people   came
4. ship   was called
5. settlers   wanted
6. men   worked
7. Women   helped
8. children   were expected
9. houses   were
10. homes   pleased

Exercise 2   More Work With Simple Subjects and Simple Predicates
1. we   moved
2. Uncle Jonathan   will sell
3. I   remember
4. chair   wobbles
5. letters   were written
6. Robert   studied
7. We   felt
8. furniture   looks

9. table   holds

10. seat   swivels

Exercise 3 Writing Subjects and Predicates
(Sample answers are given.)

1. felt
2. Tom
3. enjoyed
4. visited
5. gym
6. sprang
7. teacher
8. finished
9. tried
10. passenger

19.2 Complete Subjects and Predicates (Page 45)

Practice 1

Exercise 1 Recognizing Complete Subjects and Predicates

1. … bicycle/stood …
2. … problem/is …
3. … September/is …
4. … brother/earns …
5. … States/was …
6. … waiter/accepted …
7. … lilies/ floated …
8. … description/joined …
9. … neighborhood/was …
10. This toy/requires …

Exercise 2 Identifying Complete and Simple Subjects and Predicates

1. The tanker/was slowly breaking …
2. The youngest … brothers/has …
3. The manager … Otters/ argued …
4. … crocodile/snoozed …
5. The hedge … house/concealed …
6. The drawer … desk/contained …
7. That girl … trench coat/is …
8. … majority/is …
9. Few of the spectators/stayed …
10. … apology/satisfied …

19.2 Complete Subjects and Predicates (Page 46)

Practice 2

Exercise 1 Complete Subjects and Predicates

1. The elegant lady |glanced nervously at the clock.
2. Old Dr. Wentworth | walked up and down the room.
3. A man in a blue suit |looked out the window.
4. The famous artist | mumbled some words to herself.
5. The pianist, pleasant and handsome,| spoke constantly.
6. The alert hostess |tried to relieve the tension.
7. A young woman | offered the guests cold drinks.
8. This thoughtful offer | helped a bit.
9. All the guests |welcomed the distraction.
10. The conversation | returned to normal.

Exercise 2 More Work With Complete Subjects and Predicates

1. My older cousin | works on his car every weekend.
2. He |checks the pressure in the tires.
3. Paul |opens the hood to check the oil.
4. The oil |must be at the proper level.
5. The old radiator |needs more water.
6. Several quarts of water |must be added.
7. A friend from school | sometimes helps Paul with these chores.
8. The two boys |clean the inside of the car.
9. Other boys from town| wash the outside.
10. Waxing |is the last chore.

Writing Application
Using Complete Subjects and Predicates
(Two sample sentences are given.)

1. Five friends in heavy clothing | sat on a hill late one night.
2. The meteor show | was expected very soon.

19.3 Compound Subjects and Predicates (Page 47)

Practice 1

Exercise 1 Recognizing Compound Subjects

1. Trucks, buses
2. teacher, parent
3. encyclopedia, dictionary
4. director, assistant
5. Rachel, sister
6. threats, pleas
7. bottles, jars
8. judge, justice of the peace, captain
9. Salad, dessert
10. doctor, nurse

Exercise 2 Recognizing Compound Predicates

1. swayed, bent
2. stood, cheered
3. jog, do
4. wrote, illustrated
5. can deposit, withdraw
6. repairs, replaces
7. sanded, wiped
8. rest, write
9. stuff, address, stamp
10. booed, hissed

19.3 Compound Subjects and Predicates (Page 48)

Practice 2

Exercise 1 Recognizing Compound Subjects and Predicates

1. read (and) discuss
2. Mark Twain (and) Edgar Allan Poe
3. Marilyn (or) Evan
4. re-read (and) corrected
5. eats, sleeps, (and) plays
6. Decimals (and) percents

7. Ellen (or) Hal

8. Jim (and) Jane

9. check (and) correct

10. added (and) divided

11. boys (and) girls

12. worked (or) labored

13. boy (or) girl

14. hired (and) started

15. Books (and) supplies

16. visited (and) taught

17. He (and) Mary Mann

18. wrote (and) spoke

19. Schools (and) books

20. taught, practiced law, (and) ran

Writing Application
Writing Sentences With Compound Subjects and Predicates
(Two sample answers are given.)

1. <u>Paints</u> (and) <u>brushes</u> were needed for our art project.

2. We <u>drew</u> (and) <u>colored</u> scenes from our vacations.

19.4 Hard-to-Find Subjects (Page 49)
Practice 1
Exercise 1 Recognizing Hard-to-Find Subjects
1. binoculars
2. place
3. pairs
4. cat
5. season
6. cameras
7. chance
8. nails
9. stamp
10. letter

Exercise 2 Identifying the Subject of a Command or Request
(The subject of all sentences is (you); places for insertion are given.)
1. Jill, ∧ hand
2. ∧open
3. ∧ Do
4. Wendy, ∧ watch
5. Aaron, ∧ stop

19.4 Hard-to-Find Subjects (Page 50)
Practice 2
Exercise 1 Recognizing Commands or Requests
1. (you)
2. Australia
3. British
4. (you)
5. (you)
6. people
7. (you)
8. words
9. Sydney
10. (you)

Exercise 2 Finding the Subject of Sentences That Ask Questions
1. capital
2. Richie
3. you
4. June
5. show
6. museum
7. lessons
8. Arctic Ocean
9. scientists
10. advertisements

Exercise 3 Recognizing Hard-to-Find Subjects
1. whale
2. whales
3. class
4. you
5. you

19.5 Direct Objects (Page 51)
Practice 1
Exercise 1 Finding Direct Objects
1. encores
2. animals
3. ball
4. guest
5. wand
6. orchids
7. lives
8. blueprints, directions
9. articles, stories
10. foot

Exercise 2 Writing Sentences With Direct Objects
(Sample answers are given.)
1. weather
2. the picnic
3. everyone
4. granola bars
5. Frank for his report
6. an empty box
7. a book by Robert Louis Stevenson
8. the drowning child
9. a package to the wrong house
10. the national anthem

19.5 Direct Objects (Page 52)
Practice 2
Exercise 1 Finding Direct Objects
1. bracelet
2. song
3. lottery
4. truth
5. daisies, lilies
6. acrobatics

7. piano
8. door
9. faucet, drain
10. teeth

Exercise 2   More Work With Direct Objects
1. film
2. flowers, vegetables
3. house
4. ingredients
5. them
6. England, France
7. Mrs. Percy
8. dishes
9. charts, pictures, graphs
10. news

Writing Application
Using Direct Objects in Sentences
(Two sample sentences are given.)
1. In June, Alice won the speech <u>contest</u>.
2. Her speech gave <u>reasons</u> for exercise.

19.5   Indirect Objects (Page 53)
Practice 1
Exercise 1   Recognizing Indirect Objects
1. rabbit
2. tourists
3. Clare, me
4. us
5. aunt
6. Alicia
7. Tom, Alex
8. mother
9. Dagwood
10. us

Exercise 2   Writing Sentences With Indirect Objects
1. The mayor gave Nicole a medal.
2. The class sent the charitable organization canned goods.
3. My uncle found me a summer job.
4. I wrote the author of the book a letter.
5. The letter carrier brought me a letter.

19.5   Indirect Objects (Page 54)
Practice 2
Exercise 1   Recognizing Indirect Objects
1. teacher
2. him
3. museum
4. people
5. me
6. her
7. writers, lawyers
8. committee
9. Kenny, me
10. me

Exercise 2   More Work With Indirect Objects
1. mother, father, brother
2. cousin, me
3. magazine
4. him
5. me
6. children
7. me
8. class
9. us
10. Chris

Writing Application

Using Indirect Objects in Sentences
(Two sample answers are given.)
1. My father brought <u>me</u> an interesting book.
2. I read my little <u>sister</u> one of the stories.

19.6   Predicate Nouns (Page 55)
Practice 1
Exercise 1   Recognizing Predicate Nouns
1. mammals
2. corn, spinach
3. beast
4. doctor
5. goat
6. friends
7. captain
8. Lisa, Mark
9. ice cream
10. friend

Exercise 2   More Work With Predicate Nouns
1. columnist/speaker
2. explorers/Lewis, Clark
3. author, illustrator/Maurice Sendak
4. continent, country/Australia
5. Valentina V. Tereshkova/astronaut
6. googol/number
7. career/ programming
8. mayor/Mr. Ramos
9. president/ John F. Kennedy
10. sport/Soccer

19.6   Predicate Nouns (Page 56)
Practice 2
Exercise 1   Recognizing Predicate Nouns
1. novels
2. illustrator
3. beginner
4. astronomer
5. friends
6. machine
7. player
8. dogs, cats, birds
9. dentist
10. nurse
11. mammal
12. maple
13. treasurer
14. uncle
15. emerald
16. golfer
17. orchid
18. volunteer
19. vegetables
20. explorers

Writing Application

Using Predicate Nouns in Sentences
(Two sample sentences are given.)
1. Tom Sawyer was an adventurous boy.
2. Nancy Drew must be a clever <u>detective</u>.

19.6   Predicate Adjectives (Page 57)
Practice 1
Exercise 1   Recognizing Predicate Adjectives
(Modified words are given in parentheses.)
1. impractical (plan)
2. dark (It)
3. hard (puzzle)
4. fishy (story)
5. weary (runners)

6. sour (milk)
7. yellow (maples)
8. cold (water)
9. suspicious (teller)
10. hot, muggy (day)

Exercise 2   Using Predicate Adjectives in Sentences
(Sample answers are given.)
1. shorter
2. terrific
3. exciting
4. refreshing
5. shiny
6. salty
7. scary
8. jubilant
9. delicious
10. smooth

19.6   Predicate Adjectives (Page 58)
Practice 2
Exercise 1   Recognizing Predicate Adjectives

1.
This winter has been cold and damp.
2.
The plans sound perfect to me.
3.
We were ready before noon.
4.
That marching music is lively.
5.
My pet cat is intelligent but mischievous.
6.
Your home cooking always tastes wonderful.
7.
The room looks strange without furniture.
8.
The house will be empty all summer.
9.
I became impatient with the slow service.
10.
The listeners remained quiet and attentive.

Exercise 2   More Work With Predicate Adjectives
1. Mike is interested in computers.
2. You must be mistaken about the time and place.
3. I remained awake and restless all night.
4. The path became narrow and steep.
5. My parents will be happy with this news.
6. This large sculpture is attractive but unsteady.
7. You seem healthy and rested after your vacation.
8. This new fabric feels smooth.
9. My aunt appeared tired after her trip.
10. We were nervous about the noise.

Writing Application
Using Predicate Adjectives in Sentences
(Two sample sentences are given.)
1. The violets look lovely in that new vase.
2. This new toothpaste is perfect for children.

20.1   Adjective Phrases (Page 59)
Practice 1
Exercise 1   Finding Adjective Phrases
1. character   in the story
2. visitor   from another planet
3. Part   of the treasure map
4. road   along the coastline
5. Several   of the eggs
6. sign   on the bench
7. book   about the Pony Express
8. bike   with ten speeds
9. gate   to the playground
10. notebook   with the plaid cover

Exercise 2   Using Adjective Phrases
(Sample answers are given.)
1. Those   cows   in the meadow are Holsteins.
2. The   path   through the woods is twisting.
3. A   student   from another country is attending our school.
4. This   book   about computers is interesting.
5. Please buy a   roll   of stamps.

20.1   Adjective Phrases (Page 60)
Practice 2
Exercise 1   Finding Adjective Phrases
1.
The water near the bottom of this lake is cold.
2.
The water in the ocean is not drinking water.
3.
Many people from the city enjoy water sports.
4.
Faucets in houses bring us a good supply of water.
5.
Water from the ocean evaporates.
6.
Later, the moisture in the atmosphere returns as rain.
7.
Industries along rivers often use the available water.
8.
A house beside a lake is well located.

9.

The tap water <u>in this village</u> tastes wonderful.

10.

The water <u>behind the dam</u> is being saved.

Exercise 2   More Work With Adjective Phrases

1.

The sound <u>of the machinery</u> made us shout.

2.

I will share my ideas <u>on the subject.</u>

3.

The field <u>across the road</u> is where we play softball.

4.

The sign <u>near the road</u> was an advertisement.

5.

Today is a good day <u>for a picnic.</u>

6.

The seat <u>with the cushion</u> is comfortable.

7.

The car <u>behind us</u> was a convertible.

8.

Irene heard the noise <u>of the carpenter</u> repairing the house next door.

9.

The ground <u>outside the building</u> is muddy.

10.

You should follow the advice <u>of this expert.</u>

Writing Application
Using Adjective Phrases in Sentences
(Two sample sentences are given.)
1. I want to visit Washington, D.C., a city <u>with many monuments.</u>
2. In the spring, it is a very pretty city <u>with lots of cherry blossoms.</u>

20.1   Adverb Phrases (Page 61)
Practice 1
Exercise 1   Recognizing Adverb Phrases

1. (crossed)   <u>in small boats</u>

2. (closes)   <u>on Saturdays</u>

3. (delivers)   <u>after school</u>

4. (boils)   <u>at 100° Celsius</u>

5. (big)   <u>for the little boy</u>

6. (plays)   <u>in the school band</u>

7. (curious)   <u>about the large package</u>

8. (led)   <u>along the rim</u>

9. (practices)   <u>for an hour</u>

10. (early)   <u>in the morning</u>

Exercise 2   Recognizing Adverb Phrases
(Sample sentences are given.)
1. Tom peeped through the window.
2. The water was muddy after the storm.
3. The cat reached into the fishbowl.
4. The emcee handed the microphone to the speaker.
5. Our team won by six points.

20.1   Adverb Phrases (Page 62)
Practice 2
Exercise 1   Recognizing Adverb Phrases

1.

She placed my umbrella <u>beside my coat.</u>

2.

Jim plays softball <u>after school.</u>

3.

The books fell <u>with a loud bang.</u>

4.

<u>On Sunday afternoon,</u> I read the sports section.

5.

<u>During the meeting,</u> Jean explained her ideas.

6.

The housekeeper led the visitor <u>to the study.</u>

7.

The entire class agrees <u>with our plan.</u>

8.

He seems afraid <u>of the dark.</u>

9.

We studied that question <u>in the fall.</u>

10. The old newspapers and magazines were piled evenly <u>in stacks.</u>

Exercise 2   More Work With Adverb Phrases

1. E. B. White first (lived)   <u>in Mount Vernon, New York.</u>

2. He (studied)   <u>at Cornell University.</u>

3. He later (wrote)   <u>for *The New Yorker* magazine.</u>

4. His writing is (famous)   <u>for its clarity and simplicity.</u>

5. His essays are (graceful)   <u>in style.</u>

6. His children's books (appeal)   <u>to many adults.</u>

7. In *Charlotte's Web*, he (wrote)   <u>about a spider.</u>

8. In his books, readers (find)   <u>fascinating details.</u>

9. His stories are often (full) of his own experiences.

10. His book *Stuart Little* (describes) in detail a mouse's adventures.

Writing Application
Writing Sentences With Adverb Phrases
(Two sample sentences are given.)
1. Dad drove Mother to the hospital.
2. My baby sister was born in the afternoon.

20.1   Appositive Phrases (Page 63)
Practice 1
Exercise 1   Finding Appositive Phrases

1. (eohippus) , a small hoofed mammal

2. (Dave) , a strong swimmer

3. (plane) , a Boeing 727

4. (lighthouse) , a landmark for sailors

5. (Enrico Caruso) , a famous opera tenor

6. (Ms. Geering) , the next mayor

7. (whale) , the largest mammal on Earth

8. (Mr. Amati) , our neighbor

9. (Serbo-Croatian) , the language of Yugoslavia

10. (me) , the rightful owner

Exercise 2   Using Appositive Phrases
(Sample answers are given.)

1. (Mrs. Parila) , our next-door neighbor, is trying to grow grass.

2. (Tangerines) , my favorite snack, are sweeter than oranges.

3. (Michael Jackson) , a famous rock singer, always wears one glove.

4. (Mr. Walsh) , the school principal, announced the early closing.

5. (Hartford) , our state capital, is home to many insurance companies.

20.1   Appositive Phrases (Page 64)
Practice 2
Exercise 1   Finding Appositive Phrases

1.
Jim Kelly, the star of our show, was on TV.

2.
Gym, my favorite class, is scheduled for today.

3.
This car, an inexpensive model, uses gas efficiently.

4.
We considered two choices, a Mexican restaurant and a French restaurant.

5.
This letter, a message from my mother, arrived today.

6.
Aunt Clara, my mother's sister, lives in Tennessee.

7.
This cabinet was made by Bill Webster, my great-uncle.

8.
The music, jazz of the 1930's, was great.

9.
My friend, a computer whiz, leads a busy life.

10.
The home, an elegant mansion, is owned by a millionaire.

Exercise 2   More Work With Appositive Phrases
1.
Atlanta, the capital of Georgia, is a busy city.

2.
Main Street, a busy thoroughfare, was closed to traffic.

3.
Lisa, my cousin from Maine, will visit us.

4.
The movie, an unusally long show, was a documentary.

5.
We joined the club, a group of serious chess players.

6.
That oil painting, a portrait of an ancestor, has been in the family since 1875.

7.
Paul Revere, a Revolutionary War patriot, was an expert silversmith.

8.
It would be hard to pet a porcupine, an animal with sharp quills.

9.
We will see our cousins, Randy Cruz and Roberta Montoya, on Friday.

10.

I had to choose between two classes,
computer studies and drama.

Writing Application

Using Appositive Phrases

(Two sample sentences are given.)

1. Martin Johnson, a good student, won the prize.
2. Washington, our capital, is a beautiful city.

20.2 Recognizing Independent Clauses (Page 65)

Practice 1

Exercise 1   Recognizing Independent Clauses

1. independent
2. subordinate
3. subordinate
4. independent
5. independent
6. subordinate
7. subordinate
8. subordinate
9. independent
10. independent

Exercise 2   Writing Independent Clauses

1. The ancient Egyptians worshiped cats.
2. Some trains travel at 120 miles per hour.
3. The map of Thailand is shaped like an elephant's head.
4. Ms. Maloney teaches science.
5. We were waiting for the bus.

20.2 Recognizing Independent Clauses (Page 66)

Practice 2

Exercise 1   Recognizing Independent Clauses

1. independent
2. subordinate
3. independent
4. subordinate
5. subordinate
6. independent
7. independent
8. subordinate
9. independent
10. independent

Exercise 2   More Practice Recognizing Independent Clauses

1. independent
2. subordinate
3. subordinate
4. independent
5. subordinate
6. independent
7. subordinate
8. subordinate
9. independent
10. subordinate

Writing Application

Writing Independent Clauses

(Two sample answers are given.)

1. Diana knows the answers.
2. Bill works at the library.

20.2 Forming Compound Sentences (Page 67)

Practice 1

Exercise 1   Identifying the Parts of Compound Sentences

1. water looked, (but) it was
2. Leaves were turning, (and) geese were flying
3. recipe calls, (but) I do use
4. We expected, (for) all had predicted
5. Sharon could make (;) much depended.
6. We must score, (or) Renegades will win
7. No one walked, (for) Mrs. Lewis was
8. work was, (but) it paid
9. Scott did expect, (yet) he entered
10. We have, (so) we might drink

Exercise 2   Writing Compound Sentences

1. Cinderella married the prince, and they lived happily ever after.
2. The inventor had many disappointments, but he didn't give up.
3. Voters must register, or they cannot vote.
4. My sister wants to graduate early, so she is going to summer school.
5. We expected a storm, for the barometer was falling rapidly.

20.2 Forming Compound Sentences (Page 68)

Practice 2

Exercise 1   Writing Compound Sentences

1. Ted brought the rolls, and Robin brought the orange juice.
2. The fans cheered the players on, but the team couldn't even the score.
3. I want to sell my old bicycle, for I have outgrown it.
4. We can take a bus to the theater, or we can leave early and walk there.
5. Susan helped me with my math, and I helped her with her English.
6. I have long, straight hair, but my sister has short, curly hair.
7. Bowling is a very old game, for balls and pins have been found in Egyptian tombs.
8. Dinosaurs were very large, yet their brains were very small.
9. In 1910, there were no electric washing machines, and there were no electric toasters.
10. Frisbees today are made of plastic, but earlier models were made of metal.

Writing Application

Creating Compound Sentences

(Two sample sentences are given.)

1. The morning was gloomy, and the afternoon was sunny.
2. Mary made the salad; Jim set the table.

21.1 Four Kinds of Sentences (Page 69)
Practice 1
Exercise 1 Identifying the Four Kinds of Sentences
1. interrogative
2. imperative
3. imperative
4. exclamatory
5. exclamatory
6. declarative
7. interrogative
8. imperative
9. declarative
10. exclamatory

Exercise 2 Choosing the Correct End Mark for Sentences
1. .
2. .
3. ?
4. ?
5. !
6. .
7. ?
8. .
9. .
10. !

21.1 Four Kinds of Sentences (Page 70)
Practice 2
Exercise 1 Recognizing the Four Kinds of Sentences
1. declarative .
2. interrogative ?
3. imperative .
4. interrogative ?
5. exclamatory !
6. exclamatory !
7. declarative .
8. imperative .
9. interrogative ?
10. declarative .

Exercise 2 More Work With the Four Kinds of Sentences
1. declarative .
2. imperative . or !
3. declarative .
4. imperative .
5. interrogative ?
6. exclamatory !
7. interrogative ?
8. exclamatory !
9. declarative .
10. declarative .

Writing Application
Writing Four Kinds of Sentences
(Two sample sentences are given.)
1. What a beautiful morning! (exclamatory)
2. The sunlight is sparkling on the lake. (declarative)

21.2 Sentence Combining (Page 71)
Practice 1
Exercise 1 Combining Sentences
(Sample sentences are given.)
1. If the weather clears, we may go sailing …
2. Last night Marcie called and invited me …
3. My father and grandfather are building …
4. Jennie, Sue, and I went to the movies.
5. The cookies baking in the oven smelled delicious.

Exercise 2 More Work With Combining Sentences
(Sample sentences are given.)
1. We were able … ourselves because we followed …
2. The horse got out of the barn, ran across the field, and went into …
3. The concert tickets and album raised lots of money.
4. Mr. Gordon, the girls' basketball coach, demands the best …
5. Jogging, swimming, and biking are good exercise.

21.2 Sentence Combining (Page 72)
Practice 2
Exercise 1 Combining Sentences
(Sample sentences are given.)
1. Joe parked the car and carried the groceries into the house.
2. Janice and Terry ran indoors because they were drenched from the sudden rain shower.
3. The exhibit and the bake sale were both successes.
4. I usually arrive early at school since I enjoy walking in the morning.
5. A pet snake lived in a glass tank in Marty's bedroom.
6. Mr. Wilson paints landscapes that he sells at the Community Art Center.
7. The Rangers tasted victory for the first time this season.
8. Two famous ball players were the surprise guests at our awards banquet on Friday.
9. The bank robber, disguised as a policeman, escaped unnoticed into the crowd on the sidewalk.
10. The walrus looks clumsy and sluggish, but it is quite agile in the water.

Exercise 2 More Work With Combining Sentences
(Sample sentences are given.)
1. The flowers that Mother ordered for the party were delivered next door by mistake.
2. The tool shed stays warm during the winter because it has good insulation.
3. Thomas Jefferson, the third president of the United States, helped to write the Declaration of Independence.
4. Stephanie wants to buy a new stereo and a personal computer, but she needs a new bicycle first.
5. Slapping the water with its tail, the beaver swam away, down the river.

21.3 Adding Details to Sentences (Page 73)
Practice 1
Exercise 1 Adding Details to Short Sentences
1. The high-school students are making elaborate plans for the prom.
2. Colorful tropical fish swam in the large salt-water tank.
3. The new Mexican restaurant was full of happy, chattering customers.
4. In spite of her trainer's advice, Judy decided to enter the annual long-distance race.
5. The old colonial house is on a beautiful wooded lot with many pine trees.

Exercise 2 More Work With Short Sentences
(Sample answers are given.)
1. The horror movie badly scared the young child.
2. We thoroughly enjoyed our simple meal of omelets and salad.

3. Brightly colored, sweet-smelling flowers cover the picket fence.
4. Lonely and homesick, Tim hated the wilderness camp where he spent the month of July.
5. Kelly's story about the abandoned mine had good details about the location and the inside.

21.3 Adding Details to Sentences (Page 74)
Practice 2

Exercise 1   Adding Details to Short Sentences
(Sample answers are given.)
1. Under the trees, we ate a picnic lunch of sandwiches and sodas.
2. Its leaves rustling, the tree swayed in the wind outside my window.
3. Afraid of failing their math test, they studied hard every night.
4. Enormous multicolored birds perched in a large gilded cage.
5. Hearing a loud crash and afraid that the roof would cave in, we jumped and ran.
6. After dinner, we gathered around the campfire and roasted marshmallows.
7. Before the guests arrived, Ellen set the table with our best china and silverware.
8. Hurrying to finish the project in time, Les made a serious mistake.
9. We had spaghetti with clam sauce after an exciting day at the beach.
10. On a beautiful spring day, Phil took a hike along the rugged trail leading to the waterfall.

Exercise 2   More Work With Short Sentences
(Sample answers are given.)
1. Our bright, red kite soared high in the sky.
2. In a burst of energy, we painted my room blue in a single day.
3. After the town meeting, Pam spoke persuasively to my father.
4. Last Saturday, Eileen and I rode our new bicycles all afternoon.
5. Terrified, George saw a hazy shape on the staircase of the deserted house.

21.3 Shortening Rambling Sentences (Page 75)
Practice 1

Exercise 1   Shortening Rambling Sentences
(Sample answers are given.)
   Audrey is always very careful about getting assignments down carefully, so she was the best person to call with my question. However, she wasn't home, nor was Angie. By the time I could reach anyone, the library was closed, so I couldn't do the assignment anyway.

Exercise 2   More Work With Shortening Rambling Sentences
(Sample answers are given.)
   We walked for miles through the woods until we finally found a campsite that we liked. There, we pitched our tent beside the stream. Dad went off to fill the water buckets while we gathered sticks for kindling. When we came back to camp, the tent was on the ground, and a raccoon was eating our bread and graham crackers.

21.3 Shortening Rambling Sentences (Page 76)
Practice 2

Exercise 1   (Sample answers are given.)
1. My sister wanted to ride the roller coaster, but because it was raining, we saw a movie instead. On the way home, we stopped for ice cream.
2. Uncle Henry bought a new car. It looked sturdy, but it soon developed problems. Eventually, he had to sell it.
3. Mix three eggs in a bowl. Add half a cup of milk. Beat the ingredients. Dip slices of bread into the mixture. Then, fry the bread on a griddle.
4. Connie's aunt sent her some money, so Connie decided to buy some clothes. She took the bus downtown and bought a new ski jacket and boots.
5. Bill closed his eyes and swung the bat. When it connected with a crack, he started running. He just made it to second base, a second before the throw.

Writing Application
Rewriting Rambling Sentences
(Sample paragraph is given.)
   I thought drive-in movies were a thing of the past until we found one near our summer cottage. Naturally, we asked Dad to take us, and he did. None of us remembers what movie was playing, though. First, Monica made friends with the girls in the next car. Then, Skip and I explored the grounds, especially between the car and the refreshment stand, where we also made some new friends. Dad spent his time cleaning out the trunk of the car. We all accomplished a lot that night.

21.4 Recognizing Fragments (Page 77)
Practice 1

Exercise 1   Recognizing Fragments
1. fragment
2. fragment
3. sentence
4. fragment
5. sentence
6. sentence
7. fragment
8. fragment
9. sentence
10. sentence

Exercise 2   Identifying What is Missing From Fragments
1. an independent clause
2. complete verb
4. a subject and a verb
7. a subject
8. a verb

21.4 Recognizing Fragments (Page 78)
Practice 2

Exercise 1   Recognizing Fragments
1. sentence
2. fragment
3. fragment
4. fragment
5. sentence
6. fragment
7. sentence
8. fragment

9. sentence
10. fragment

Exercise 2   More Work With Fragments
1. sentence
2. sentence
3. fragment
4. fragment
5. fragment
6. sentence
7. fragment
8. fragment
9. fragment
10. sentence

Writing Application
Writing About Fragments and Sentences
(Sample sentences are given.)
1. Mom drove the car.   sentence
2. Mom driving the car   fragment

A sentence is a complete thought. A fragment is missing the part that would make it a complete thought.

21.4   Correcting Fragments (Page 79)
Practice 1
Exercise 1   Connecting Fragments to Nearby Sentences
1. A ship sailed into the harbor flying a strange flag.
2. You may use my binoculars if you are careful with them.
3. We got off the boat with a few seconds to spare.
4. The magician found the card right in my pocket!
5. Then, we took a swim while you finished your set.

Exercise 2   Adding Necessary Words to Change Fragments to Sentences
(Sample answers are given.)
1. All we could find was a parking space too small for our car.
2. The noises began a few minutes before midnight.
3. That plane is carrying one important passenger.
4. People hoping to get a letter wait eagerly for the mail to come.
5. The chairman was elected unanimously.

21.4   Correcting Fragments (Page 80)
Practice 2
Exercise 1   Changing Fragments Into Sentences
(Sample answers are given.)
1. Hal practiced new steps before the dance.
2. We were careful while we worked on the experiment.
3. Once the baseball season begins, I am very busy.
4. Ahead of me loomed the mountain.
5. After the summer vacation, we came home.
6. I wondered how to write without a pen or pencil.
7. Opposite the park stood a hot dog stand.
8. When she began to speak, we all listened.
9. Even though the temperature was warm, I felt cold.
10. From my seat, I could see very well.

Exercise 2   More Work With Fragments and Sentences
(Sample answers are given.)
1. Our school is next to the library.
2. I wonder how the rumor spread.
3. I keep my comb and brush on top of my dresser.
4. You will find the classroom past the principal's office.

5. I will be glad when they are found.

21.4   Recognizing Run-Ons (Page 81)
Practice 1
Exercise 1   Recognizing Run-Ons
1. run-on
2. sentence
3. run-on
4. run-on
5. sentence
6. sentence
7. run-on
8. sentence
9. sentence
10. run-on

Exercise 2   Analyzing Run-On Sentences
1. speaker (,) she
3. tired (,) they
4. doors (,) then
7. stubs (,) they
10. unnecessary (,) no one

21.4   Recognizing Run-ons (Page 82)
Practice 2
Exercise 1   Recognizing Run-ons
1. run-on
2. sentence
3. run-on
4. run-on
5. sentence
6. run-on
7. run-on
8. run-on
9. sentence
10. sentence
11. run-on
12. sentence
13. run-on
14. run-on
15. run-on

Writing Application
Avoiding Run-ons
(A sample paragraph is given.)

Television has both advantages and disadvantages. One advantage is that television provides information and entertainment. One disadvantage of television is the amount of time people spend watching it instead of doing important things.

21.4   Correcting Run-ons (Page 83)
Practice 1
Exercise 1   Preparing to Correct Run-ons
1. C
2. mud∧the
3. easy∧a
4. C
5. China∧they
6. C
7. Park∧it
8. C
9. C
10. drive∧so

Exercise 2   Correcting Run-ons
(Choices of correction methods may vary; samples are given.)
1. … mud. The sun …
2. … easy; a cookbook …
3. … China, where …
4. … Park; it …
5. … drive, so …

21.4   Correcting Run-ons (Page 84)
Practice 2
Exercise 1   Correcting Run-ons
(Sample answers are given.)
1. The smallest dog is the Chihuahua; the tallest dog is the Irish wolfhound.
2. A husky can pull a sled through snow, while a collie can herd sheep.
3. A St. Bernard is the heaviest dog; some St. Bernards weigh over 200 pounds.
4. A person can see better than a dog, but a dog can hear better than a person.
5. Do wild dogs still exist? I heard that there were some living in India.
6. Dogs are not only used as pets. Some dogs are used as guide dogs for the blind.
7. The dog was probably the first mammal to be tamed. People had dogs as pets 12,000 years ago.
8. In some ways, dogs exhibit a great deal of variety; they vary in size, shape, and color.
9. In many ways, dogs are alike; they have sharp teeth and cold, wet noses.
10. The jackal is a type of wild dog, and it is found mainly in Africa and Asia.

Exercise 2   More Work With Run-ons
(Sample answers are given.)
1. What sites did you see in Boston? We saw Faneuil Hall.
2. Last night we had a snowstorm; the accumulation was over a foot.
3. George visited the historic city of Williamsburg. A blacksmith there explained his work.
4. The farm produces several kinds of fresh vegetables; most of them are sold locally.
5. Timothy's desk is made of oak, but Martha's desk is made of mahogany.

21.4   Avoiding Double Negatives (Page 85)
Practice 1
Exercise 1   Correcting Double Negatives
1. anything
2. can
3. any
4. are
5. anywhere

Exercise 2   More Work Correcting Sentences With Double Negatives
1. Max shouldn't ever have tried to fix it himself. Max should never have tried to fix it himself.
2. We haven't heard anything about your trip to Canada. We have heard nothing about your trip to Canada.
3. Your keys weren't anywhere that I could see. Your keys were nowhere that I could see.
4. My father says I never hear anything that he says. My father says I hear nothing that he says.
5. I didn't want help from anybody. I want help from nobody.

21.4   Avoiding Double Negatives (Page 86)
Practice 2
Exercise 1   Correcting Sentences With Double Negatives
(Alternate answer in parentheses.)
1. We had never (hadn't ever) realized that Theodore wrote so well.
2. I can't ever (can never) remember that incident.
3. Ann hasn't said anything (has … nothing) about her new job.
4. This ice cream isn't sold anywhere (is … nowhere) else.
5. There isn't room anywhere (is … nowhere) for this table.
6. They aren't taking any (are … none) of these rumors seriously.
7. I wouldn't ever (would never) make that journey alone.
8. The court hasn't heard any (has … no) testimony yet.
9. The storyteller didn't tell any (told none) of the old legends.
10. I haven't told anybody (have … nobody) about your discovery.

Exercise 2   More Practice Correcting Double Negatives
1. The visitors don't want any (want no) publicity.
2. The end isn't anywhere (is nowhere) in sight.
3. Our newspaper hasn't printed anything (has … nothing) about the event.
4. We can't agree on a location (can … no) for the meeting.
5. The committee didn't select anybody (selected nobody) as chairperson.

22.1   Regular Verbs (Page 87)
Practice 1
Exercise 1   Using Regular Verbs
1. painted
2. C
3. is lacking
4. presented
5. C
6. practiced
7. will jump
8. C
9. divided
10. C

Exercise 2   More Work With Regular Verbs
1. brushing
2. imitated
3. filled
4. hated
5. attending
6. closed
7. show
8. played
9. sprayed
10. saluting

22.1   Regular Verbs (Page 88)
Practice 2
Exercise 1   Using Regular Verbs
1. recommended
2. started
3. living
4. witness

5. stayed
6. remained
7. complaining
8. created
9. learned
10. suggest

Exercise 2　More Work With Regular Verbs
1. explored
2. photographed
3. developed
4. learning
5. learned
6. inhabited
7. been discovered
8. reading
9. deposited
10. formed

Writing Application
Using Regular Verbs in Sentences
(Five sample sentences are given.)
1. My best friend and I walked to town to see a play.
2. She has acted in plays at school.
3. She has played the leading role.
4. While we waited to buy the tickets, we shared a sandwich and joked about our dreams to be actresses!
5. Finally, we were called to go inside.

22.1　Irregular Verbs (Page 89)
Practice 1
Exercise 1　Using Irregular Verbs
(If more than one answer is correct, all are given.)
1. are buying, bought
2. C
3. C
4. will shoot
5. C
6. got
7. had, have had
8. C
9. caught
10. learned

Exercise 2　More Work With Irregular Verbs
1. bought
2. losing
3. brought
4. getting
5. finding
6. paid
7. caught
8. held
9. swung
10. stuck

22.1　Irregular Verbs (Page 90)
Practice 2
Exercise 1　Using Irregular Verbs
1. caught
2. gotten
3. led
4. paid
5. spun
6. lost
7. swung
8. bought
9. had
10. brought
11. paid

12. lost
13. brought
14. caught
15. built
16. stung
17. bought
18. sat
19. laid
20. swung

Writing Application
Using Irregular Verbs
(Sample answer is given.)
When you hear what we have to say about this new cereal, you will want to buy it right away. Just sit down and listen. One person who has tried this great crunchy breakfast food has said she has built her diet around this great food!

22.1　More Irregular Verbs (Page 91)
Practice 1
Exercise 1　Using Irregular Verbs
1. cast
2. cutting
3. burst
4. reading
5. hurt
6. set
7. letting
8. rid
9. costing
10. hit

Exercise 2　More Work With Irregular Verbs
1. rid
2. hurt
3. setting
4. cutting
5. letting

22.1　More Irregular Verbs (Page 92)
Practice 2
Exercise 1　Using Irregular Verbs Correctly
1. have cut
2. let
3. put
4. hurting
5. rid
6. read
7. casting
8. burst
9. cost
10. bid

Writing Application
Using Irregular Verbs in a Summary
(A sample paragraph is given.)
Yesterday, I read the paper and cut coupons to use at the grocery store. I put the coupons in an envelope. Food costs less when I use the coupons.

22.1　Other Irregular Verbs (Page 93)
Practice 1
Exercise 1　Completing the Principal Parts of Irregular Verbs
1. eating, ate
2. throw, thrown
3. spoke, spoken
4. beginning, begun
5. do, doing
6. knowing, knew

7. be, was
8. drank, drunk
9. tear, tearing
10. lie, lain

Exercise 2 Selecting the Correct Forms of Irregular Verbs
1. tore
2. sang
3. throwing
4. lay
5. driven
6. swam
7. begun
8. doing
9. risen
10. flying

22.1 Other Irregular Verbs (Page 94)
Practice 2
Exercise 1 Selecting the Correct Forms of Irregular Verbs
1. drove
2. flown
3. rung
4. swam
5. choose
6. torn
7. threw
8. known
9. rose
10. began
11. did
12. written
13. sang
14. was
15. given
16. spoken
17. ate
18. taken
19. lay
20. drunk

Writing Application
Using Irregular Verbs in Sentences
(Sample answers are given.)

Since last year, I changed by learning a new language. I chose a language for which I knew a few words. I can write sentences, give directions, and speak to a waiter about what I want to eat. I began learning with a tape and book. I also took a course.

22.2 The Present, Past, and Future Tenses (Page 95)
Practice 1
Exercise 1 Identifying the Present, Past, and Future Verb Tenses
1. present
2. past
3. future
4. past
5. present

Exercise 2 Using the Present, Past, and Future Tenses
1. do
2. hit
3. will stay
4. led
5. will sing
6. waters

7. keeps
8. will buy
9. stuck
10. delivers

22.2 The Present, Past, and Future Tenses (Page 96)
Practice 2
Exercise 1
1. runs
2. discussed
3. will sail
4. enjoyed
5. likes
6. will lend
7. will convince
8. runs
9. asked
10. plays

Exercise 2 Identifying the Present, Past, and Future Tenses
1. present
2. past
3. future
4. present
5. past
6. present
7. past
8. future
9. present
10. future

Exercise 3 More Work With the Present, Past, and Future Tenses
1. present
2. future
3. present
4. present
5. future
6. present
7. future
8. past
9. past
10. past

22.2 The Present Perfect Tense (Page 97)
Practice 1
Exercise 1 Using the Present Perfect Tense
1. has thrown
2. has caught
3. has cracked
4. has given
5. has cooked
6. have stung
7. has won
8. have observed
9. have gone
10. has arrived

Exercise 2 More Work With the Present Perfect Tense
(Sample answers are given.)
1. We have received your gift.
2. I have behaved rudely.
3. You have lost my favorite belt.
4. They have flown over 2,000 miles.
5. He has read sixty books this year.

22.2 The Present Perfect Tense (Page 98)
Practice 2
Exercise 1   Using the Present Perfect Tense
1. have produced
2. has helped
3. have lasted
4. has recommended
5. have appreciated
6. have paused
7. has delivered
8. have entered
9. have attempted
10. have found

Exercise 2   More Work With the Present Perfect Tense
1. has printed
2. have mailed
3. have written
4. has printed
5. have developed

22.2 The Present and Past Progressive (Page 99)
Practice 1
Exercise 1   Identifying the Present Progressive and Past Progressive Tenses
1. present pro.
2. past pro.
3. past pro.
4. present pro.
5. past pro.

Exercise 2   Using the Present Progressive and the Past Progressive
1. are building
2. was laughing
3. is rising
4. was swinging
5. were playing
6. am introducing
7. are wrapping
8. was plowing
9. are rescuing
10. is paying

22.2 The Present and Past Progressive (Page 100)
Practice 2
Exercise 1   Using the Present and Past Progressive
1. is looking
2. is writing
3. was worrying
4. were imagining
5. are joining
6. is moving
7. was arranging
8. were enjoying
9. is working
10. was telling
11. was admiring
12. are beginning
13. is following
14. were praising
15. am taking
16. were losing
17. is expecting
18. am waiting
19. were laughing
20. is becoming

Writing Application
Using the Present and Past Progressive
(A sample paragraph is given.)
   I am enjoying a perfect day. I am walking to work and looking at the beautiful flowers in gardens along the way. The sun is shining and the air is refreshing. Birds are singing and the squirrels are hopping on lawns. People are laughing and smiling as they meet.

22.3 Troublesome Verbs: *Did* and *Done* (Page 101)
Practice 1
Exercise 1   Using *Did* and *Done*
1. did
2. done
3. done
4. did
5. done
6. done
7. done
8. did
9. did
10. done

Exercise 2   More Work With *Did* and *Done*
1. done
2. did
3. did
4. done
5. did

22.3 Troublesome Verbs: *Did* and *Done* (Page 102)
Practice 2
Exercise 1   Using *Did* and *Done*
1. did
2. done
3. did
4. did
5. done
6. did
7. done
8. done
9. did
10. did

Exercise 2   More Work With *Did* and *Done*
1. did
2. done
3. done
4. did
5. did
6. done
7. done
8. did
9. did
10. done

Writing Application
Using *Did* and *Done* in Sentences
(Two sample sentences are given.)
1. Last month, I did my exercises every day.
2. Jane has done the most difficult dive.

22.3 Troublesome Verbs: *Lay* and *Lie* (Page 103)
Practice 1
Exercise 1   Using *Lay* and *Lie*
1. laid
2. lies
3. laid
4. lay

5. laying
6. lie
7. lies
8. laid
9. lay
10. lying

Exercise 2   More Work With *Lay* and *Lie*

1. lay
2. lying
3. laid
4. lays
5. lay
6. lies
7. laid
8. lying
9. laid
10. lying

22.3   Troublesome Verbs: *Lay* and *Lie* (Page 104)
Practice 2

Exercise 1   Using *Lay* and *Lie*

1. lays
2. lay
3. laid
4. lies
5. laying
6. lay
7. laid
8. lay
9. lies
10. laid

Exercise 2   More Work With *Lay* and *Lie*

1. lying
2. laid
3. lay
4. lain
5. laying
6. lies
7. lay
8. laying
9. laid
10. laying

Writing Application

Using *Lay* and *Lie* in Sentences

(Two sample sentences are given.)
1. Dad always lays his keys on the hall table.
2. My cat often lies on the sofa.

22.3   Troublesome Verbs: *Set* and *Sit* (Page 105)
Practice 1

Exercise 1   Using *Set* and *Sit* Correctly

1. set
2. sitting
3. set
4. setting
5. sat
6. sat
7. sitting
8. set
9. setting
10. sat

Exercise 2   More Work With *Set* and *Sit*

1. sits
2. set
3. sat
4. sets
5. setting

6. sitting
7. set
8. sitting
9. set
10. sets

22.3   Troublesome Verbs: *Set* and *Sit* (Page 106)
Practice 2

Exercise 1   Using *Set* and *Sit*

1. set
2. sits
3. sitting
4. sat
5. setting
6. set
7. setting
8. set
9. sat
10. sits

Exercise 2   More Work With *Set* and *Sit*

1. sitting
2. sat
3. set
4. setting
5. sits
6. set
7. setting
8. sat
9. sitting
10. set

Writing Application

Using *Set* and *Sit* in Sentences

(Sample paragraphs are given.)
1. Some students sit near the window. The teacher is sitting at her desk. She set the large globe on the shelf. Students are setting their projects up on a table. I sit at my desk to work.
2. We could all sit near the window. The teacher could sit at one of our desks. We could set the globe on another shelf and set the projects on desks. A student could sit at the teacher's desk!

23   Subject Pronouns (Page 107)
Practice 1

Exercise 1   Identifying the Correct Subject Pronoun

1. I
2. I
3. we
4. they
5. she
6. we
7. I
8. they
9. She, I
10. he

Exercise 2   Using the Correct Subject Pronoun

1. they
2. she
3. I
4. we
5. he
6. I
7. they
8. he
9. he
10. I

23 Subject Pronouns (Page 108)
Practice 2
Exercise 1 Identifying the Correct Subject Pronoun
1. I
2. she
3. we
4. they
5. I
6. he
7. she
8. we
9. they
10. he

Exercise 2 More Work With Subject Pronouns
1. they
2. we
3. she
4. I
5. he
6. I
7. they
8. she
9. we
10. he

Writing Application
Using Subject Pronouns in Sentences
(Sample sentences are given.)
1. You and I will enjoy this movie.
2. She and Jack will join us at the theater.

23 Objective Pronouns (Page 109)
Practice 1
Exercise 1 Using Objective Pronouns
(The pronoun is given first, followed by its use.)
1. her, object of a preposition
2. us, indirect object
3. him, direct object
4. us, direct object
5. me, object of a preposition
6. me, indirect object
7. them, object of a preposition
8. her, direct object
9. me, indirect object
10. him, direct object

Exercise 2 More Work With Objective Pronouns
(If more than one answer is correct, all are given.)
1. it
2. her
3. you
4. me, us
5. her
6. it
7. you, him, her, them
8. me, us
9. us
10. me

23 Objective Pronouns (Page 110)
Practice 2
Exercise 1 Identifying Objective Pronouns
1. me—obj of prep
2. her—ind obj
3. us—obj of prep
4. him—obj of prep
5. me—dir obj
6. her—ind obj
7. them—dir obj
8. them—dir obj
9. us—dir obj
10. me—obj of prep

Exercise 2 More Work With Objective Pronouns
1. her—dir obj
2. me—indir obj
3. us—indir obj
4. him—indir obj
5. them—obj of prep
6. them—dir obj
7. us—indir obj
8. her—dir obj
9. him—obj of prep
10. her—obj of prep

Writing Application
Using Objective Pronouns in Sentences
(Two sample sentences are given.)
1. The snowstorm in May amazed me.
2. I'll tell you about its effects.

23 Possessive Pronouns (Page 111)
Practice 1
Exercise 1 Using Possessive Pronouns
(Sample answers are given.)
1. ours
2. My
3. our
4. its
5. mine
6. their
7. his
8. its
9. Theirs
10. his

Exercise 2 Using Possessive Pronouns
(Sample answers are given.)
1. yours
2. ours
3. his
4. theirs
5. its
6. hers
7. yours
8. his
9. theirs
10. its

23 Possessive Pronouns (Page 112)
Practice 2
Exercise 1 Using Possessive Pronouns
(Sample answers are given.)
1. yours
2. Hers
3. His
4. our
5. hers
6. yours
7. my
8. their
9. Theirs
10. his
11. My
12. their
13. Theirs
14. Their
15. our
16. our
17. Its

18. My
19. ours
20. their

Writing Application

Using Possessive Pronouns in Sentences

1. My cousin has a large family. His brothers and sisters are younger than mine. Their house is in the same town as ours.

23 Using Different Pronoun Forms (Page 113)
Practice 1
Exercise 1 Identifying Different Pronoun Cases

1. nominative
2. possessive
3. possessive
4. objective
5. nominative
6. objective
7. possessive
8. nominative
9. objective
10. nominative

Exercise 2 Using Different Pronoun Cases
(Sample answers are given.)

1. She
2. me
3. his
4. she
5. yours
6. him
7. Our
8. them
9. you
10. yours

23 Using Different Pronoun Forms (Page 114)
Practice 2
Exercise 1 Identifying Different Pronoun Cases

1. nominative
2. objective
3. possessive
4. objective
5. nominative
6. possessive
7. nominative
8. possessive
9. objective
10. objective

Exercise 2 More Work With Pronoun Forms

1. nominative
2. possessive
3. nominative
4. objective
5. nominative
6. objective
7. nominative
8. possessive
9. objective
10. objective

Writing Application

Telling About Pronoun Cases
(A sample paragraph is given.)
Nominative pronouns are used as the subject or predicate pronoun.
She likes to swim. (subject)
The swimmer was she. (predicate pronoun)

Objective pronouns are used as direct object, indirect object, object of a preposition.
Jake walked him to school. (direct object)
She gave me the package. (indirect object)
He handed the package to her. (object of a preposition)
Possessive pronouns are used to show ownership.
The lost locket is mine.

24.1 Subjects and Verbs (Page 115)
Practice 1
Exercise 1 Making Subjects and Verbs Agree

1. mix
2. barks
3. likes
4. forests
5. get
6. stand
7. He
8. borrows
9. bagel
10. meet

Exercise 2 More Work With Subject and Verb Agreement
(If more than one answer is correct, all are given.).

1. see
2. Birds
3. sits
4. He, She
5. clink
6. enter
7. he, she
8. sends
9. kites
10. weaves

24.1 Subjects and Verbs (Page 116)
Practice 2
Exercise 1 Making Subjects and Verbs Agree

1. grow
2. remains
3. grow
4. reach
5. is
6. hang
7. glide
8. swings
9. live
10. fly

Exercise 2 More Practice Making Subjects and Verbs Agree

1. sits
2. watch
3. laugh
4. plans
5. thinks
6. change
7. includes
8. huddle
9. go
10. eats

Writing Application

Writing Sentences With Subjects and Verbs That Agree
(Two sample sentences are given.)

1. Many people live in my neighborhood.
2. Each building has many apartments.

24.1 Compound Subjects and Verbs (Page 117)
Practice 1
Exercise 1   Making Compound Subjects and Verbs Agree
1. is
2. go
3. goes
4. slow
5. want
6. brings
7. looks
8. tastes
9. look
10. are

Exercise 2   More Work With Compound Subjects and Verbs
1. are
2. like
3. play
4. is
5. go
6. fits
7. are
8. move
9. lives
10. run

24.1 Compound Subjects and Verbs (Page 118)
Practice 2
Exercise 1   Making Compound Subjects and Verbs Agree
1. are
2. stands
3. shows
4. measure
5. have
6. belong
7. are
8. has
9. are
10. use

Exercise 2   More Practice With Compound Subjects and Verbs
1. plays
2. explain
3. remembers
4. are
5. is
6. ignore
7. changes
8. dislike
9. dot
10. watches

Writing Application
Writing Sentences With Compound Subjects
(Two sample sentences are given.)
1. Gina and Lulu like to shop on Saturday.
2. Mom or Grandma shops with the girls.

24.1 Pronoun Subjects and Verbs (Page 119)
Practice 1
Exercise 1   Making Pronoun Subjects and Verbs Agree
1. like
2. is
3. gets
4. contributes
5. want
6. have
7. laughs
8. belongs
9. give
10. tries

Exercise 2   More Work With Pronoun Subject and Verb Agreement
1. is
2. watches
3. stay
4. look
5. goes
6. suggests
7. enjoy
8. vote
9. is
10. hopes

24.1 Pronoun Subjects and Verbs (Page 120)
Practice 2
Exercise 1   Making Pronoun Subjects and Verbs Agree
1. are
2. go
3. get
4. begins
5. votes
6. serves
7. has
8. expects
9. is
10. applies

Exercise 2   More Work With Pronoun Subjects and Verbs
1. calls
2. delivers
3. catches
4. writes
5. admire
6. wants
7. admire
8. belongs
9. interests
10. looks

Writing Application
Writing Sentences With Pronoun Subjects and Verbs
(Sample sentences are given.)
1. Most of the workers had the day off.
2. Others had to take their place on the job.
3. Nothing was open on the holiday.
4. Everyone enjoyed a day to relax.
5. One of the people works that shift.

24.2 Pronouns and Antecedents (Page 121)
Practice 1
Exercise 1   Making Pronouns and Antecedents Agree
1. his or her
2. his
3. its
4. he or she
5. their
6. his
7. his
8. they
9. their
10. our

Exercise 2 More Work With Pronouns and Antecedents

1. Anne and Bob made their parents a photograph album.
2. My dress fits perfectly, but hers must be altered.
3. Either Sara or Nicole plays her solo next.
4. My little sister played with her stuffed toy.
5. The members of the team practice their dribbling.

24.2 Pronouns and Antecedents (Page 122)
Practice 2
Exercise 1 Making Pronouns and Antecedents Agree

1. they
2. her
3. their
4. her
5. his
6. their
7. her
8. his
9. they
10. his

Exercise 2 More Work With Pronouns and Antecedents

1. her
2. their
3. her
4. his
5. her
6. their
7. her
8. his
9. his
10. she

Writing Application
Using Pronouns and Antecedents in Sentences
(Two sample sentences are given.)
1. President Lincoln gave his speech at Gettysburg.
2. Garth Brooks sang his fans' favorite songs.

25.1 Using Adjectives to Compare (Page 123)
Practice 1
Exercise 1 Forming Positive, Comparative, and Superlative Adjectives

1. pale, palest
2. wilder, wildest
3. quick, quicker
4. smaller, smallest
5. curly, curlier
6. happy, happiest
7. cleaner, cleanest
8. dirty, dirtier
9. firm, firmest
10. taller, tallest

Exercise 2 More Work With Positive, Comparative, and Superlative Adjectives
(Sample answers are given.)
1. Am I the earliest to arrive?
2. My grandfather is older than yours.
3. The bridge is narrower than the road.
4. The bus driver looks sleepier than the passengers.
5. The weather is calm.

25.1 Using Adjectives to Compare (Page 124)
Practice 2
Exercise 1 Forming the Degree of Comparison of One- and Two-Syllable Adjectives

1. kinder/kindest
2. meaner/meanest
3. richer/richest
4. shinier/shiniest
5. cloudier/cloudiest
6. whiter/whitest
7. taller/tallest
8. bigger/biggest
9. younger/youngest
10. wilder/wildest
11. stronger/strongest
12. older/oldest
13. softer/softest
14. plainer/plainest
15. prettier/prettiest
16. brighter/brightest
17. sweeter/sweetest
18. colder/coldest
19. smoother/smoothest
20. sadder/saddest

Exercise 2 More Work With Degrees of Comparison of One- and Two-Syllable Adjectives

1. higher/highest
2. angrier/angriest
3. slower/slowest
4. sharper/sharpest
5. smaller/smallest
6. newer/newest
7. harder/hardest
8. nicer/nicest
9. healthier/healthiest
10. duller/dullest

25.1 Using Adjectives With *More* and *Most* (Page 125)
Practice 1
Exercise 1 Forming Degrees of Comparison With *More* and *Most*

1. convenient, most convenient
2. generous, more generous
3. useful, most useful
4. more apparent, most apparent
5. more protective, most protective
6. unfair, more unfair
7. outstanding, more outstanding
8. faithful, most faithful
9. more profitable, most profitable
10. surprising, most surprising

Exercise 2 More Work With Forming Comparisons Using *More* and *Most*

1. more reasonable
2. most harmful
3. more impressive
4. most worthwhile
5. more expensive
6. more talkative
7. most considerate
8. most fortunate
9. more interesting
10. more homesick

25.1 Using Adjectives With *More* and *Most* (Page 126)
Practice 2
Exercise 1 Using Adjectives With *More* and *Most*
1. most magnificent
2. more luxurious
3. more modern
4. most sensible
5. most difficult
6. most responsible
7. most interesting
8. more attractive
9. more colorful
10. most thoughtful

Exercise 2 More Practice Using Adjectives With *More* and *Most*
1. more comfortable
2. most exciting
3. most incredible
4. more famous
5. most outrageous
6. more enthusiastic
7. more convincing
8. most eventful
9. most delicious
10. more interesting

Writing Application
Using Adjectives with *More* and *Most*
(Two sample sentences are given.)
1. Andrew is more thoughtful than Tom.
2. The silk dress is the most expensive of all.

25.1 Using Adverbs to Compare (Page 127)
Practice 1
Exercise 1 Forming the Positive, Comparative, and Superlative Degrees of Adverbs
1. slowly, most slowly
2. longer, longest
3. quietly, most quietly
4. carefully, more carefully
5. more willingly, most willingly
6. loudly, more loudly
7. easily, most easily
8. recently, more recently
9. more completely, most completely
10. more often, most often

Exercise 2 More Work With Positive, Comparative, and Superlative Adverbs
(Samples are given.)
1. We ride cautiously on busy streets.
2. I behaved more selfishly than my younger sister.
3. You spoke more bluntly than you should have.
4. I hit the nail hardest.

25.1 Using Adverbs to Compare (Page 128)
Practice 2
Exercise 1 Forming the Comparative and Superlative Degrees of Adverbs
1. more plainly/most plainly
2. lower/lowest
3. more safely/most safely
4. more recently/most recently
5. more quickly/most quickly
6. deeper/deepest
7. more nearly/most nearly
8. livelier/liveliest

9. more hastily/most hastily
10. more definitely/most definitely

Exercise 2 More Work With the Comparative and Superlative Degrees of Adverbs
1. more softly/most softly
2. more silently/most silently
3. longer/longest
4. more briefly/most briefly
5. more suddenly/most suddenly
6. harder/hardest
7. more firmly/most firmly
8. shorter/shortest
9. more carefully/most carefully
10. more distantly/most distantly

Writing Application
Using Adverbs to Compare Actions
(A sample paragraph is given.)

Luke runs faster than the other players on the team. Tom pitches best. Only Joe plays ball more skillfully than Luke or Tom.

25.1 Avoiding Double Comparisons (Page 129)
Practice 1
Exercise 1 Avoiding Double Comparisons
1. crispest
2. curlier
3. richest
4. wider
5. more often
6. longest
7. hardest
8. louder
9. gentlest
10. sleepiest

Exercise 2 More Work Correcting Double Comparisons
1. shorter
2. handiest
3. dullest
4. bigger
5. cheapest
6. worse
7. hardest
8. most stubborn
9. later
10. better

25.1 Avoiding Double Comparisons (Page 130)
Practice 2
Exercise 1 Avoiding Double Comparisons
1. The planet Venus is closer to us than Neptune is.
2. Here is our newest model.
3. Of all these gems, this is the rarest.
4. (*correct*)
5. We heard the oddest sound before the big storm.
6. My dog is smaller than yours.
7. (*correct*)
8. Robert calculates faster than Alan.
9. The older model still runs well.
10. (*correct*)

Exercise 2 More Practice Correcting Double Comparisons
1. Now that the summer tourist crowd is gone it is quieter.
2. The vegetables sold at the stand here are the freshest.
3. He smiled and acted friendlier than before.

4. Betty worked the hardest during those two weeks.
5. I awoke later than my brother.

25.2 Using *Bad* and *Badly* (Page 131)
Practice 1
Exercise 1   Using *Bad* and *Badly* Correctly
1. badly
2. bad
3. bad
4. badly
5. bad
6. badly
7. badly
8. bad
9. badly
10. bad

Exercise 2   More Work with *Bad* and *Badly*
1. bad
2. badly
3. badly
4. badly
5. bad
6. badly
7. bad
8. bad
9. badly
10. badly

25.2 Using *Bad* and *Badly* (Page 132)
Practice 2
Exercise 1   Using *Bad* and *Badly*
1. bad
2. badly
3. badly
4. bad
5. badly
6. badly
7. badly
8. bad
9. bad
10. badly

Exercise 2   More Practice Using *Bad* and *Badly*
1. bad
2. badly
3. bad
4. bad
5. badly
6. badly
7. badly
8. bad
9. bad
10. badly

Writing Application
Using *Bad* and *Badly* in Sentences
(Two sample sentences are given.)
1. During the snowstorm, driving conditions became *bad*.
2. Lewis speaks *badly* in public.

25.2 Using *Good* and *Well* (Page 133)
Practice 1
Exercise 1   Using *Good* and *Well* Correctly
1. well
2. good
3. well
4. good
5. well
6. good
7. well
8. well
9. well
10. good

Exercise 2   More Practice Using *Good* and *Well*
1. good
2. good
3. well
4. well
5. well
6. good
7. good
8. well
9. well
10. good

25.2 Using *Good* and *Well* (Page 134)
Practice 2
Exercise 1   Using *Good* and *Well*
1. well
2. good
3. well
4. well
5. good
6. good
7. well
8. well
9. good
10. good

Exercise 2   More Work With Using *Good* and *Well*
1. well
2. well
3. good
4. good
5. well
6. well
7. good
8. good
9. good
10. good

Writing Application
Using *Good* and *Well* in Sentences
(Two sample sentences are given.)
1. You look very *good* in blue.
2. Roses grow *well* in this garden.

26.1   Periods (Page 135)
Practice 1
Exercise 1   Using Periods
(The words or letters preceding the period and the period are given here.)
1. St., school.
2. Dr. D. R., teeth.
3. J., now.
4. Sen., arrive.
5. ft., in., feet.
6. Wash., years.
7. Rep., Co., residents.
8. lbs., store.
9. Mar., on.
10. F.

Exercise 2   More Practice Using Periods
(Sample answers are given.)
1. We got 2 in. of rain last night.
2. Put your books under your desks.

3. Ellie asked when the traffic gets back on the freeway.
4. Mrs. J. R. North heads the Communication Committee.
5. Measure 3 pt. of milk into the bowl.

26.1 Periods (Page 136)
Practice 2
Exercise 1   Using Periods
1. Aug. 15, 1769.
2. Pvt. to Corp. to Sgt.
3. nickname.
4. point.
5. warfare.
6. Europe.
7. Apr. ... throne.
8. Waterloo.
9. St. Helena.
10. death.
11. Mr. ... Del.
12. Mrs. ... collection.
13. stamps.
14. Pa.
15. needed.
16. Ave.
17. St. ... stamps.
18. Eng., Fr., and Ger.
19. water.
20. Dr. ... stamp.

Writing Application
Using Periods in a Paragraph
(A sample paragraph is given.)

Mother asked me about the speech I would give at school. I told her about it. "Please listen to my speech," I said.

26.1 Question Marks (Page 137)
Practice 1
Exercise 1   Using Question Marks
(The word preceding the end mark and the end marks are given.)
1. in? track?
2. World?
3. due.
4. me. you?
5. study? When?
6. directions?
7. car. say?
8. dessert? movie?
9. help. when?
10. best?

Exercise 2   More Practice Using Question Marks
(The word preceding the end mark and the end marks are given.)
1. me? busy.
2. it? temperature?
3. window. it?
4. dinner. convenient?
5. school. Where?
6. cast. long?
7. began. answer?
8. door? iron.
9. that. think? said.
10. cards? when?

26.1 Question Marks (Page 138)
Practice 2
Exercise 1   Using Question Marks
1. Jackson?
2. meet? Why?
3. Brasilia. When?
4. Jupiter?
5. comet?
6. tomorrow? Where?
7. representative?
8. Whitman?
9. radium. When?
10. zoo.
11. jump?
12. computers. time?
13. afternoon. Where?
14. library?
15. accepted. one?
16. me? Why?
17. newspaper?
18. class trip? whom?
19. best? Why?
20. problem? How?

Writing Application
Writing Questions
(Sample questions are given.)
1. How old is that antique clock?
2. Where did you buy it? When?

26.1 Exclamation Marks (Page 139)
Practice 1
Exercise 1   Using Exclamation Marks
1. 1 healthy!
2. 3 Hey!
3. 3 Gosh!
4. 2 father!
5. 2 man!
6. 3 Surprise!
7. 1 breathtaking!
8. 2 department!
9. 1 exhausted!
10. 2 bus!

Exercise 2   More Work With Exclamation Marks
(The word preceding the end mark and the correct end mark are given.)
1. us.
2. C
3. C
4. Wow!
5. C
6. Well!
7. car!
8. today.
9. Darn!
10. C

26.1 Exclamation Marks (Page 140)
Practice 2
Exercise 1   Using Exclamation Marks
1. me!
2. mark! Get set! Go!
3. immediately!
4. idea!
5. down!
6. Oh!
7. Hey!
8. Be still!

9. Never!
10. Goodness!

Exercise 2   More Practice Using Exclamation Marks
1. Ah!
2. Look out!
3. Hurray!
4. Wow!
5. once!
6. Super!
7. ball!
8. Impossible!
9. Get out!
10. story!

Writing Application
Using Exclamation Marks to Show Strong Feelings
(Sample answers are given.)
1. Rob: Oh, no! I forgot to go to band practice.
2. Pat: You *should* be upset! You're the band leader!
3. Rob: I was thinking today was Tuesday!

26.2   Commas in Compound Sentences (Page 141)
Practice 1
Exercise 1   Using Commas in Compound Sentences
1. home, for
2. (no commas)
3. now, or
4. today, nor
5. camera, for
6. hours, yet
7. before, so
8. paved, but
9. wanted, and
10. (no commas)

Exercise 2   More Work Using Commas in Compound Sentences
(Sample answers are given.)
1. We tried to make reservations tonight, but the restaurant was booked.
2. I enjoy preparing the salad, and my mother likes to do the desserts.
3. We must get this leak fixed, or the whole basement might flood.
4. I earned money baby-sitting, so I was able to buy the concert tickets.
5. We came out to practice soccer, but the field was too wet.

26.2   Commas in Compound Sentences (Page 142)
Practice 2
Exercise 1   Using Commas in Compound Sentences
1. light, for
2. vote, but
3. explore, or
4. procedure, but
5. club, for
6. week, but
7. shy, so
8. arrived, yet
9. park, or
10. confused, nor

Exercise 2   More Practice Using Commas in Compound Sentences
1. sit, but
2. mongrel, for
3. intelligent, yet
4. outdoors, so

5. picnic, or
6. dogs, and
7. today, or
8. dog, but
9. well, so
10. home, for

Writing Application
Using Commas to Punctuate Compound Sentences
(Two sample sentences are given.)
1. Bob followed all the directions, but he could not build the model plane.
2. We can read for an hour, or we can watch television.

26.2   Commas in a Series (Page 143)
Practice 1
Exercise 1   Using Commas in a Series
1. sniffed, barked, and
2. (no commas)
3. New Hampshire, Vermont, and
4. books, rushed out the door, and
5. trees, shrubs, and
6. peanuts, corn, and
7. buy, rent, or
8. door, down the drive, and
9. addressed, stamped, and
10. (no commas)

Exercise 2   More Work Using Commas in a Series
(Sample answers are given.)
1. the sand, the waves, and the surfers.
2. History, English, and science
3. Aunt Melanie, Uncle Joe, and Cousin Ryan
4. dust, vacuum, and scrub
5. Law and Order, The West Wing, and Providence

26.2   Commas in a Series (Page 144)
Practice 2
Exercise 1   Using Commas With Items in a Series
1. Memphis, Nashville,
2. writer, producer,
3. gasped, cheered,
4. soda, ... hamburgers,
5. June, July,
6. a rug, a bookcase,
7. a dog, a cat, a bird,
8. the potatoes, ... the lemonade,
9. shirt, a sweater,
10. beach, ... a hike,

Exercise 2   More Practice Using Commas With Items in a Series
1. pigeons, sparrows, robins,
2. wrote, folded,
3. waterfront, ... marina,
4. harbors, ... parks,
5. Alex, Patty, Chris,
6. breath, ... eyes,
7. front, ... back,
8. Books, magazines,
9. haircut, ... done,
10. lessons, ... songs,

Writing Application
Writing Sentences with Items in a Series
(Two sample sentences are given.)
1. Kim likes to skate, swim, and bowl.
2. Chad likes to listen to rock, play basketball, and hike.

26.2 Commas With Introductory Words and Phrases (Page 145)

Practice 1

Exercise 1   Recognizing Introductory Words and Phrases

1. With this freeze,
2. To hear the speaker,
3. Joan,
4. During the night,
5. Well,
6. Yes,
7. Calling my friends,
8. True,
9. With your good attitude,
10. Jill,

Exercise 2   Using Commas With Introductory Words and Phrases

1. costumes, we
2. crash, the
3. Shawn, do
4. Well, your
5. town, you
6. delay, the
7. Jason, I'm
8. Yes, I
9. invention, I
10. speech, you

26.2 Commas With Introductory Words and Phrases (Page 146)

Practice 2

Exercise 1   Using Commas with Introductory Words and Phrases

1. Yes,
2. weather,
3. meeting,
4. Oh,
5. podium,
6. Henry,
7. report,
8. book,
9. True,
10. Mexico City,

Exercise 2   More Practice Using Commas With Introductory Words and Phrases

1. Well,
2. team,
3. No,
4. James,
5. time,
6. faults,
7. Yes,
8. Knudsen,
9. table,
10. cousin,

Writing Application

Writing Sentences With Introductory Words and Phrases

(Two sample sentences are given.)

1. In the future, homes will be more efficient.
2. Because of better planning, homes in the future will have more storage space.

26.2 Commas With Interrupting Words and Phrases (Page 147)

Practice 1

Exercise 1   Recognizing Interrupting Words and Phrases

1. , John,
2. , a ten-speed,
3. , our neighbor,
4. , however,
5. , a theme park
6. , Mrs. Talbot,
7. , I think,
8. , a pleated skirt,
9. , Melanie,
10. , in my opinion

Exercise 2   More Work with Interrupting Words and Phrases

1. elk, a large deer,
2. sure, Helen,
3. haircut,
4. right, Dad,
5. grandmother, a native of Ohio,
6. crocodile, not an alligator,
7. reservation, it seems,
8. red,
9. weevils, long-snouted beetles,
10. necessary, Mary,

26.2 Commas With Interrupting Words and Phrases (Page 148)

Practice 2

Exercise 1   Using Commas With Interrupting Words and Phrases

1. dance, Eleanor,
2. Venice, … city,
3. remember, of course,
4. When, Bobby,
5. Walt Disney, … cartoonist,
6. will, I believe,
7. garden, Mrs. Tyler,
8. are, however,
9. Laura, my cousin
10. Please, Phil,

Exercise 2   More Practice Using Commas with Interrupting Words and Phrases

1. Lee, … pitcher,
2. book, Natalie,
3. Morris, … writer,
4. packed, John,
5. fans, no doubt,
6. Listen, Matt,
7. Poe, … tales,
8. ideas, nevertheless,
9. bridge, … Gate,
10. will, … sure,

Writing Application

Using Interrupting Words and Phrases in Sentences

(Two samples sentences are given.)

1. True, stamp collecting can be expensive.
2. Crossword puzzles, a popular pastime, amuse many people.

26.2 Commas in Letters (Page 149)

Practice 1

Exercise 1   Using Commas in Letters

1. Knoxville, June 12,
2. yours,

3. friend,
4. Mobile, October 19,
5. Alberti,
6. Martin,
7. Wichita, January 13,
8. truly,
9. Dad,
10. Pittsburg, August 9,

Exercise 2   More Work Using Commas in Letters
(Sample answers are given.)
1. 193 Fisher Avenue … Des Moines, Iowa 50309 … June 29, 2001
2. Dear Mrs. Handelmann,
3. With love,
4. 6120 Sinoloa Drive … Norfolk, Virginia 23510 … November 14, 2001
5. Dear Mrs. Brasher,

26.2   Commas in Letters (Page 150)
Practice 2
Exercise 1   Using Commas in Letters
1. Pearl River, New York 10965
   December 7, 2000
2. Dear Ellen,
3. Your friend,
4. Fondly,
5. Dear Uncle Ted,
6. Danbury, Connecticut 06810
   June 10, 2001
7. My dear Michelle,
8. Bye, for now
9. Dallas, Texas 75240
   January 9, 2003
10. Love,

Exercise 2   More Practice Using Commas in Letters
1. Phoenix, Arizona 85029
   August 3, 2001
2. Yours truly,
3. Plainview, New York 11803
   March 28, 2002
4. Dear Mr. Tyler,
5. Sincerely,
6. Dear Melanie,
7. My dear Aunt Jo,
8. With love,
9. Your nephew,
10. Dear George,

Writing Application
Using Commas in a Letter
(A sample letter is given.)

22 Mayberry Lane
Morris, Alaska 05505
Dear Cousin Mary,
   How was your vacation? I would love to hear about your trip. Please write soon.
Love,
Jill

26.2   Commas in Numbers (Page 151)
Practice 1
Exercise 1   Using Commas in Numbers
1. 1009
2. diagrams 7, 8, and 9
3. 4,500
4. 2788
5. 24,901.55
6. (415) 952–5555
7. 2002
8. pages 64, 65, and 66
9. 27,878,400
10. 4,145

Exercise 2   More Work Using Commas With Numbers
(Sample answers are given.)
1. $98,700.00
2. 34521
3. 105,670
4. (245) 555–3679
5. 1,600

26.2   Commas in Numbers (Page 152)
Practice 1
Exercise 1   Using Commas in Numbers
1. 2,750
2. correct
3. 12,161
4. correct
5. correct
6. 43,560
7. 3,707,000
8. correct
9. 20,320
10. $40,948,900

Exercise 2   More Practice Using Commas in Numbers
1. correct
2. 450,000
3. 22, 23,
4. 42,515,800
5. 92,900,000
6. correct
7. 22,834
8. 64,186,300
9. correct
10. 1,350

Writing Application
Using Large Numbers in Sentences
(A sample paragraph is given.)
   The story was about a planet 33,000,000 miles from Earth. It was discovered 1,001 years ago. It is 12,650 miles in diameter and has a circumference of 42,389 miles. The highest mountain is 38,249 feet high.

26.3   Semicolons (Page 153)
Practice 1
Exercise 1   Using Semicolons
1. vacuumed; my
2. rolled; the
3. wet; it
4. given; the
5. gently; I
6. wheat, it
7. night; no
8. win; they
9. food; I
10. boring; give

Exercise 2   More Practice Using Semicolons
(Sample answers are given.)
1. I love sports; I hate work.
2. My mother wants me to baby-sit; I want to go to the amusement park.
3. I have only six dollars; the tickets cost seven.
4. First we bought the paint; then we chose the wallpaper.

5. High school is different from elementary school; there are lots more activities to get involved in.

26.3 Semicolons (Page 154)
Practice 2
Exercise 1 Using Semicolons
1. ... museum; it is ...
2. ... Revolution; they
3. ... photographer; he
4. ... fascinating; they
5. ... graduation; come
6. ... house; we
7. ... today; it
8. ... desk; it
9. ... bed; the bed
10. ... o'clock; Brett

Exercise 2 More Practice Using Semicolons
1. entertaining; the
2. time; I
3. opinions; let
4. similar; they
5. tonight; an
6. you; you
7. Florida; today
8. player; he
9. mall; we
10. haircut; I

Writing Application
Using Semicolons in Your Own Writing
(Two sample sentences are given.)
1. I went to the library several times; the latest books are on the shelves.
2. My brother and I played baseball; he is learning to pitch.

26.3 Colons (Page 155)
Practice 1
Exercise 1 Using Colons
1. Warning: Keep
2. Kashan:
3. 11:00, 9:00
4. these: spiders
5. no colon
6. magazines: Good
7. Note: These
8. classes: English
9. today: Arden
10. Caution: Roads

Exercise 2 More Work Using Colons
(Sample answers are given.)
1. holidays: Christmas, Thanksgiving, and Valentine's Day
2. 11:00 A.M. to 3:00 P.M.
3. Caution: One-lane road ahead.
4. these: eyes, toes, and legs.
5. girls' names include the following: Jennifer, Sara, and Nicole.

26.3 Colons (Page 156)
Practice 2
Exercise 1 Using Colons
1. month: Edna
2. dates: May
3. these: the
4. 4:30, 6:45
5. Caution: Do
6. times: 1:45, 3:30, and 5:15
7. places: Yellowstone

8. topics: animals
9. following: John
10. Wilson:
11. conclusions:
12. 8:00, 7:00
13. party:
14. Madam:
15. Warning:

Writing Application
Using Colons
(Two sample sentences are given.)
1. At the museum, we saw the works of three painters: Picasso, Rembrandt, and Van Gogh.
2. The string trio included John, Alice, and James.

26.4 Quotation Marks in Direct Quotations (Page 157)
Practice 1
Exercise 1 Using Quotation Marks in Direct Quotations
1. wrote, "One ... tomorrows."
2. "Do ... play?"
3. "What if," my father worried, "I ... keys?"
4. "We ... observatory,"
5. "Papyrus," I wrote in my report, "was ... Egyptians."
6. excitedly, "Here ... parade!"
7. "Is ... easier," I asked, "for ... house?
8. "Do ... recess?"
9. reported, "I ... sharks."
10. suggested, "Imitation ... flattery."

Exercise 2 More Work Using Quotation Marks in Direct Quotations
(Sample answers are given.)
1. "Let's build a fort," my friend said.
2. Our teacher explained, "Your reports must be at least five pages long."
3. "Do you think," I asked, "that I should bring my rain gear?"
4. Our neighbor asked, "Have you had any offers on your house?"
5. "That truck is really noisy!" she shouted.

26.4 Quotation Marks in Direct Quotations (Page 158)
Practice 2
Exercise 1 Using Quotation Marks in Direct Quotations
1. Sam asked, "Do you want to go to the baseball game?"
2. "This movie," Robin said, "is really exciting."
3. "Pick up these puzzle pieces immediately!" Mom ordered.
4. Miss Harris added, "We are going to have to work quickly."
5. "This building is a city landmark," Jeff explained.
6. "Do not," the museum guide warned, "touch the displays."
7. "When can I see your science project?" Steve asked.
8. "Please read me another story," pleaded the child.
9. Captain Lee said, "My next voyage will be to the Bahamas."
10. Simone asked, "Did you just get home?"

Exercise 2 More Practice Using Quotation Marks With Direct Quotations
1. John suggested, "We could drive to Sturbridge for the day."

2. "What activities have been planned?" Emily inquired.
3. Bruce thought, "This Brazilian jazz group is wonderful."
4. "The new schedule," announced Marilyn, "will begin tomorrow.
5. "I can," Stephen volunteered, "come an hour early to help."
6. Michael announced, "I think I'll run for class president."
7. "How," asked Michael's sister, "can I help you campaign?"
8. "I'll need to create several large posters," answered Michael.
9. "Perhaps," suggested Michael's dad, "we can all help."
10. "Let's get started this evening," said Michael's mom.

Writing Application
Writing Sentences With Direct Quotations
(Two sample answers are given.)
1. After her visit to my school, Nancy Drew said, "I can't find any clues to the mystery here."
2. "There are hearty young folk in this school," said Long John Silver.

26.4   Quotation Marks With Other Punctuation (Page 159)
Practice 1
Exercise 1   Using Quotation Marks With Other Punctuation
1. . inside
2. ! inside
3. , inside
4. ? inside
5. ! outside
6. ! inside
7. . inside
8. ? outside
9. , inside
10. ? outside

Exercise 2   Using Quotation Marks With Other Punctuation
1. faster,"
2. car?"
3. reward!"
4. nearsighted,"
5. painting?"
6. again!"
7. present"?
8. almonds,"
9. disaster!"
10. fixed."

26.4   Quotation Marks With Other Punctuation (Page 160)
Practice 2
Exercise 1   Using Quotation Marks With Other Punctuation Marks
1. "Aunt Martha called while you were in school," said Lynn.
2. Marissa volunteered, "I can help you in math."
3. Ruth asked, "Why did you choose that bicycle?"
4. The policeman shouted, "Go back to your houses immediately!"
5. I was thrilled when he said, "You can leave now."
6. Why did Marie say, "Kim should be treasurer"?
7. How did Ira know I wrote, "Ira took the cookies"?

8. Howard muttered, "I can explain why I'm late."
9. Jack wondered, "When did the Johnsons move here?"
10. "Take your time," advised the teacher.

Exercise 2   More Practice Using Quotation Marks With Other Punctuation Marks
1. "Please bring me the evening paper," said Paul.
2. Don't you dare say, "I didn't do it."
3. The detective blurted out, "This case is extraordinary!"
4. Thea inquired, "How much longer will I have to wait?"
5. The waitress asked, "What would you like to order?"
6. "I'd like to be a volunteer tutor," said Patrick.
7. Maureen asked, "What subject would you teach?"
8. "Don't you think I'd be a good reading teacher?" asked Patrick.
9. "Wow!" exclaimed Maureen. "That would be a perfect job for you."
10. Patrick suggested, "You'd be good at it, too, Maureen."

Writing Application
Writing Sentences with Quotation Marks and Other End Marks
(Two sample answers are given.)
1. "Get up early and get things done," says Grandmother Jean.
2. Kate asked her father, "How can anyone smoke with all the warnings?"

26.4   Quotation Marks for Dialogue (Page 161)
Practice 1
Exercise 1   Using Quotation Marks in Dialogue
1. "I ... summer!"
2. "But why?" "I ... weather."
3. "Oh ... flop!"
4. "I'll ... bad," "You're ... it."
5. "You ... embarrassing!"

Exercise 2   Paragraphing Dialogue
"What ... "Unfortunately," ... "Last ... Nicole ... "Now ...

26.4   Quotation Marks for Dialogue (Page 162)
Practice 2
Exercise 1   Using Quotation Marks in Dialogue
"Tomorrow," announced Mom, "is Open School Night. How can I find your classroom?"

"It's on the third floor," I replied. "Walk in the front door, turn left, and go up three flights. The room number is 307."

"Will any of your work be on display?" Mom asked.

"Yes," I said, "our writing folders will be on our desks. The story I wrote about our cat is my best piece of writing."

Mom slowly inquired, "Is there anything I should know before I go?"

"Honestly," I protested, "you don't need to worry."

Exercise 2   More Practice Using Quotation Marks in Dialogue
"Fred, are you busy?" Naomi asked.

"No, why?" replied Fred.

"Well, I'm planning a surprise party for Barbara, and I could use your help."

"What would you like me to do?" asked Fred.

"Two things," answered Naomi. "First, I was hoping you would design the invitations. And second, it would be a real help if you would keep Barbara out of the house while I decorate."

"You can count on me," said Fred.

"Terrific!" said Naomi enthusiastically.

"I am totally," Fred responded, "at your service."

26.4 Underlining and Quotation Marks in Titles (Page 163)
Practice 1
Exercise 1   Using Underlining and Quotation Marks
1. <u>Nite Owl</u>
2. <u>The Secret Garden</u>
3. <u>The Artist's Studio</u>
4. "Blue Moon"
5. <u>The Witness</u>
6. "Bull's Eye!"
7. <u>I Love Lucy</u>
8. <u>Viking I</u>
9. "The Monkey's Paw"
10. <u>Our Town</u>

Exercise 2   More Practice Using Underlining and Quotation Marks
1. underlining
2. quotation marks
3. underlining
4. quotation marks
5. underlining
6. underlining
7. underlining
8. underlining
9. underlining
10. quotation marks

26.5 Underlining and Quotation Marks in Titles (Page 164)
Practice 2
Exercise 1   Using underlining and Quotation Marks
1. <u>My Fair Lady</u>
2. <u>Concorde</u>
3. <u>USA Today</u>
4. <u>The Dream</u>
5. <u>Lizard Music</u>
6. "The Chase"
7. "The Way Out"
8. "Flowers for Algernon"
9. <u>Gone With the Wind</u>
10. <u>Wizard of Earthsea</u>
11. <u>My Side of the Mountain</u>
12. "How Insects Adapt"
13. "How to Say You're Sorry and Mean It"
14. "Love Me Tender"
15. "Beyond the Limits"

Writing Application
Using Titles in Sentences
1. I will never forget <u>Treasure Island</u>.
2. "America the Beautiful" is often played on national holidays.

26.5 Hyphens in Numbers and Words (Page 165)
Practice 1
Exercise 1   Using Hyphens in Numbers and Words
1. C
2. all-star
3. put-upon
4. ex-felon
5. thirty-seven
6. one-third; two-thirds
7. pro-Mexican

8. C
9. second-rate
10. self-winding

Exercise 2   More Practice Using Hyphens
1. all-around
2. C
3. two-thirds
4. mid-March
5. post-Kennedy
6. treasurer-elect
7. best-selling
8. twenty-five
9. self-educated
10. C

26.5 Hyphens in Numbers and Words (Page 166)
Practice 2
Exercise 1   Using Hyphens in Numbers and Words
1. twenty-six
2. all-around
3. correct
4. self-employed
5. one-half
6. senator-elect
7. pro-British
8. self-conscious
9. ex-president
10. correct

Exercise 2   More Practice Using Hyphens in Numbers and Words
1. all-time
2. three-fourths
3. correct
4. correct
5. pre-Reagan

26.5 Hyphens at the Ends of Lines (Page 167)
Practice 1
Exercise 1   Using Hyphens to Divide Words
1. can't be divided
2. mag-ic
3. self-control
4. can't be divided
5. nug-get
6. can't be divided
7. pen-ance
8. can't be divided
9. proj-ect
10. mid-September

Exercise 2   More Practice Hyphenating at the Ends of Lines
1. evict
2. cus|tom
3. Bolivia
4. le|gal
5. noise
6. tasty
7. Grandmother
8. still|ness
9. kept
10. boil|er

11. door|way
12. col|umn
13. (blazed)
14. all-|time
15. pas|sage
16. sce|nic
17. pro-|German
18. main|tain
19. neu|tral
20. (about)

26.5   Hyphens at the Ends of Lines (Page 168)
Practice 2
Exercise 1   Using Hyphens to Divide Words
1. per-form
2. agent
3. group
4. enor-mous
5. hand-book
6. uni-corn
7. con-cern
8. bring
9. over-heard
10. over-due
11. glance
12. dol-phin
13. tic-ket
14. equal-ity
15. open-ended
16. lunch
17. li-on
18. step-son
19. ad-di-tion
20. view

Writing Application
Dividing Words at the Ends of Lines
(Two sample sentences are given.)
1. We like to go mountain biking, but some-times the weather prevents us from going.
2. When the teacher made the assignment, stu-dents were not listening to her directions.

26.5   Apostrophes Used to Show Ownership (Page 169)
Practice 1
Exercise 1   Using Apostrophes to Show Ownership
1. lass's curls
2. birds' nest
3. child's blanket
4. crowd's response
5. doctor's calendar
6. officials' ruling
7. chickens' feed
8. clerk's help
9. Tess's bracelet
10. women's vote

Exercise 2   More Practice Using Apostrophes to Show Ownership
1. sheep's
2. writer's
3. governors'
4. Jenkins'
5. friends'
6. class's
7. lawyer's
8. farmers'

9. men's
10. neighbors'

26.5   Apostrophes Used to Show Ownership (Page 170)
Practice 2
Exercise 1   Using Apostrophes to Show Ownership
1. artist's
2. boss's
3. Sharon's
4. children's
5. rooms'
6. mouse's
7. people's
8. father's
9. Dickens'
10. players'

Exercise 2   More Practice Using Apostrophes to Show Ownership
1. scientist's
2. Hercules'
3. Wallach's
4. women's
5. Bess's
6. youngsters'
7. designers'
8. Doris's
9. musician's
10. mice's

Writing Application
Using Nouns to Show Ownership
(Two sample sentences are given.)
1. landlord's That is the landlord's car.
2. members' The members' contributions support the club.

26.5   Apostrophes in Contractions (Page 171)
Practice 1
Exercise 1   Using Apostrophes in Contractions
1. Who's
2. They'd
3. he'll
4. wouldn't
5. Nancy's
6. wasn't
7. he'd
8. you're
9. shouldn't
10. haven't

Exercise 2   More Practice With Apostrophes in Contractions
1. I would
2. will not
3. you are
4. could not
5. cannot
6. He will
7. George would
8. They are
9. I will
10. would not

26.5   Apostrophes in Contractions (Page 172)
Practice 2
Exercise 1   Using Apostrophes in Contractions
1. He's
2. we'll
3. haven't

4. hasn't
5. They'll
6. Who'll
7. Where's
8. I'm
9. can't
10. aren't

Exercise 2 More Practice Using Apostrophes in Contractions
1. you'll
2. I'd
3. doesn't
4. It's
5. don't
6. you'd
7. I'll
8. couldn't
9. She'll
10. Who's

Writing Application
Using Contractions in a Dialogue
(Sample paragraph is given.)

"I'd like to show you how to paint," said Dad. "It's very easy once you know the steps."

"I'm afraid I'll drip paint all over," replied Ken, "but I'd like to try it." He wasn't sure he'd learn to paint. "It's worth a try," he told himself.

26.5 Avoiding Problems With Apostrophes (Page 173)
Practice 1
Exercise 1 Using Apostrophes Where Necessary
1. It's
2. hers
3. Whose
4. there's
5. ours
6. Your
7. his
8. yours
9. Theirs
10. you're

Exercise 2 More Practice Avoiding Apostrophe Errors
(Sample answers are given.)
1. There's Roger now.
2. Whose wallet is this?
3. You're my best friend.
4. The cat licked its paw.
5. Who's got some extra lunch money?

26.5 Avoiding Problems With Apostrophes (Page 174)
Practice 2
Exercise 1 Using Apostrophes Where Necessary
1. Who's
2. theirs
3. hers
4. It's
5. your
6. who's
7. Ours
8. its
9. there's
10. you're

Exercise 2 More Practice Using Apostrophes Where Necessary
1. its
2. Whose

3. hers
4. Your
5. Theirs

27 Capitals for Sentences and the Word *I* (Page 175)
Practice 1
Exercise 1 Using Capitals to Begin Sentences
1. when, i, i
2. clipper
3. crocodile
4. she, does
5. i, i
6. my, can
7. the, a
8. i, i
9. when, i, i
10. our, a

Exercise 2 More Work With Capital Letters
(Sample answers are given.)
1. Dirk
2. When
3. oranges
4. Spaghetti
5. I
6. What
7. Mary, I
8. car
9. children
10. Airplanes

27 Capitals for Sentences and the Word *I* (Page 176)
Practice 2
Exercise 1 Supplying Capital Letters
1. all
2. there, i
3. i, watch
4. he
5. my, do
6. yes, i, i
7. instead
8. i, that
9. i
10. he

Exercise 2 More Work With Capital Letters
1. a
2. the, did
3. i, i
4. answer
5. i, i
6. they
7. i, i
8. this
9. the, fasten
10. our

Writing Application
Using Capital Letters Correctly
(Two sample sentences are given.)
1. Our summer home is near the ocean.
2. Every day I search for new shells for my collection.

27 Capitals for Names of People and Places (Page 177)
Practice 1
Exercise 1 Using Capital Letters With Specific People and Places
1. britain, falkland, islands
2. death, valley, california
3. robert, e., peary, north, pole
4. galapagos, islands, ecuador
5. john, f., kennedy, richard m., nixon
6. arabian, desert
7. united, states, pennsylvania, avenue
8. sacramento, river, san, francisco, bay
9. mount, st., helens, washington
10. atlantic, ocean

Exercise 2 More Work With Capitalizing Specific Names and Places
(Sample answers are given.)
1. Pacific Ocean
2. 184 Norton Avenue, Austin, Texas 78701
3. Paul Miley Eggers
4. Hawaii and Minnesota
5. Japan
6. the Rocky Mountains
7. Ohio
8. North American
9. Mediterranean
10. New Orleans

27 Capitals for Names of People and Places (Page 178)
Practice 2
Exercise 1 Using Capitals for Names of People and Places
1. madeline spencer, greece
2. great bear lake, canada
3. snake river
4. dr. john s. knickerbocker's
5. hernando cortes, mexico.
6. mount kilimanjaro, africa.
7. victoria c. woodhull
8. j. r. r. tolkien
9. lake george
10. stan laurel, oliver hardy
11. rocky mountains, north america.
12. lake erie
13. west virginia, kentucky
14. europe, danube
15. atlanta, denver
16. africa, lake victoria
17. levi hutchins
18. james l. plimpton
19. harriet tubman
20. charles lindbergh, atlantic

Writing Application
Using the Names of People and Places in Sentences
(Two sample sentences are given.)
1. Albert Einstein made many great discoveries.
2. Maine has a rocky coastline.

27 Capitals for Names of Specific Things (Page 179)
Practice 1
Exercise 1 Using Capitals for the Names of Specific Things
1. mount, rushmore
2. amtrak
3. memorial day, may
4. turkey muslims
5. somalia, somali, arabic
6. concorde
7. sears, tower
8. democratic
9. challenger
10. supreme, court

Exercise 2 More Work Capitalizing Specific Things
1. the spirit of st. louis
2. the medal of honor
3. the republican party
4. the congress
5. father's day
6. bill of rights
7. christians
8. national sewing association
9. the model t
10. June

27 Capitals for Names of Specific Things (Page 180)
Practice 2
Exercise 1 Using Capitals for the Names of Specific Things
1. Constitution
2. Lions Club
3. The Mayas, Aztecs, Mexico
4. English, Spanish, Italian
5. Sears Tower, Chicago, Illinois
6. Nobel Prize
7. Washington's Birthday, February
8. Maine, Mattie
9. We, Carpenter's Hall, Independence Hall
10. Maplewood School, Monday, Saturday
11. Republican Party, Tuesday
12. Golden Kite Award
13. Skylab, American
14. Sunday, Labor Day, Grandparent's Day
15. Treaty of Versailles, Senate

27 Capitals for Titles of People (Page 181)
Practice 1
Exercise 1 Capitalizing Titles of People
1. Congresswoman
2. none
3. Judge
4. Lieutenant
5. Professor

Exercise 2 More Work Capitalizing Titles of People
(Sample answers are given.)
1. Uncle Gabe, can you help me with my bike? Can your uncle help fix the bike?
2. I saw Governor Samuel Benton at a fund-raising dinner. A governor must attend fund-raising dinners.
3. We have hired Attorney Harvey Vann. We have hired an attorney.
4. Doctor Raul Lopez will be the keynote speaker. We have a doctor as the keynote speaker.
5. Mother, thanks for driving last night. I'm thankful my mother could drive last night.

27 Capitals for Titles of People (Page 182)
Practice 2
Exercise 1 Using Capitals for Titles of People
1. captain
2. doctor

3. aunt
4. ambassador
5. cousin
6. grandmother
7. governor
8. rabbi
9. captain
10. mother

Exercise 2   More Practice Capitalizing Titles of People

1. uncle
2. dr.
3. aunt
4. judge smith
5. coach
6. aunt
7. attorney
8. grandpa
9. grandfather
10. cousin

Writing Application
Using Titles of People in Sentences
(Two sample sentences are given.)
1. Doctor Michaels came to dinner.
2. In a few minutes, Uncle Andrew will arrive.

27   Capitals for Titles of Things (Page 183)
Practice 1
Exercise 1   Using Capitals for Titles of Things

1. **S**plash
2. **R**eader's **S**ource
3. **T**he **S**ign of the **B**eaver
4. **S**panish
5. **O**rlando **E**agle
6. "**Y**ou've **G**ot a **F**riend"
7. **F**iddler on the **R**oof
8. **T**he **T**hinker
9. **J**ane **E**yre
10. "**T**he **B**ridge"
11. **T**he **P**easant **D**ance
12. **C**omposition 2
13. "**O**l' **M**an **R**iver"
14. **C**hariots of **F**ire
15. **T**ucson **D**aily **S**tar
16. **C**ollector's **G**uide
17. **T**he **C**at in the **H**at
18. **H**aystacks

19. **O**ur **T**own
20. "**T**rees"

Exercise 2   More Work With Capitalizing Titles of Things

1. **T**hrough the **L**ooking **G**lass
2. **D**enver **S**entinel
3. **C**ats
4. **E**nglish I
5. **T**hat **W**as **T**hen, **T**his **I**s **N**ow
6. **T**he **M**uppets **T**ake **M**anhattan
7. **F**rench, **L**atin
8. (none needed)
9. "**T**he **G**irl **I**s **M**ine"
10. **T**he **B**lue **B**oy

27   Capitals for Titles of Things (Page 184)
Practice 2
Exercise 1   Using Capitals for Titles of Things

1. The Good Earth
2. "Spring Fever"
3. "Sounds of Silence"
4. Mathematics 103
5. Mona Lisa
6. National Geographic
7. The Poseidon Adventure
8. French
9. "The Split Cherry Tree"
10. "The Lady or the Tiger?"
11. the Los Angeles Times
12. Science Digest
13. "The Rain in Spain"
14. Life with Father
15. My Fair Lady
16. Animal Farm
17. The Pearl
18. History 570
19. The Crucible
20. "The Circuit"

Exercise 2   More Practice Using Capital Letters for Titles of Things

1. Algebra II
2. The Way We Were
3. the New York Daily News
4. The Devil and Daniel Webster
5. When the Legends Die
6. "The Most Dangerous Game"
7. Island of the Blue Dolphins
8. "The Fun They Had"
9. Treasure Island
10. "The Road Not Taken"
11. Latin
12. The Sunflowers
13. The Outsiders
14. A Raisin in the Sun

15. "The Base Stealer"
16. The Red Pony
17. A Star is Born
18. Fiddler on the Roof
19. "Mother to Son"
20. Popular Computing

27 Capitals in Letters (Page 185)
Practice 1
Exercise 1   Using Capitals in Letters
1. My dear sister,
2. Camilia Lane, New Orleans, Louisiana
3. Your good friend,
4. Dear Mrs. Dunkin,
5. Vineyard Avenue, Baltimore, Maryland, February
6. Affectionately,
7. Dear Grandma Ethel,
8. My Dear Mr. Larusso,
9. Dunning Way, Akron, Ohio,
10. Sunset Lane, Fort Wayne, Indiana

Exercise 2   More Practice in Using Capitals in Letters
(Sample answers are given.)
1. 217 Canfield Road, Santa Paula, California 93060, January 7, 2001
2. Love always,
3. Dear Mrs. Donlevy,
4. Dear Aunt Linda,
5. Sincerely yours,

27 Capitals in Letters (Page 186)
Practice 2
Exercise 1   Using Capitals in Letters
1. Hollings Drive
   Freeport, Maine
   April
2. Tremont Avenue
   Atlanta, Georgia
   September
3. Dear Uncle Bill,
4. My
5. Sincerely,
6. Affectionately,
7. 43 Tenth Street
   Berkeley, California
   August
8. 225 Highland Street
   Canton, Massachusetts
9. Greetings, Marcia
10. Fondly

Exercise 2   More Practice Using Capitals in Letters
1. 46 Lincoln Avenue
   Hancock, New Hampshire
   February
2. 791 Central Avenue
   Bloomington, Indiana
   August
3. Hello, George
4. Howdy, Mindy
5. Love
6. Yours truly
7. 347 Willow Road
   San Antonio, Texas
   December
8. 86 Kirkland Street
   Portland, Oregon
   June
9. Dear Aunt Karen
10. Your friend

Diagraming Sentences (Page 187)
Practice 1
Exercise 1   Diagraming Declarative and Imperative Sentences

1.
   Snakes | crawl

2.
   (you) | Stop

3.
   Birds | were singing

Exercise 2   Diagraming Interrogative Sentences

1.
   you | Are listening

2.
   he | Has finished

Diagraming Sentences (Page 188)
Practice 2
Exercise 1   Making Sentence Diagrams

1.
   Flowers | grow

2.
   Kenneth | is absent

3.
   it | Is raining

Exercise 2   More Practice Diagraming Sentences

1.
   Kathie | has been swimming

2.
   he | Did forget

3.
   Tornadoes | destroy

© Prentice-Hall, Inc.

Diagraming Phrases (Page 189)
Practice 1
Exercise 1   Diagraming Adjective and Adverb Phrases

1.

2.

3.

Exercise 2   Diagraming Appositive Phrases

1.

2.

Diagraming Phrases (Page 190)
Practice 2
Exercise 1   Diagraming Phrases

1.

2.

3.

Exercise 2   More Practice Diagraming Phrases

1.

2.

3.

Diagraming Compound Sentences (Page 191)
Practice 1
Exercise 1   Diagraming Compound Sentences

1.

2.

3.

5.

Exercise 2   Interpreting Diagrams
1.   We cancelled the picnic, for the weatherman pre-
     dicted rain.

Diagraming Compound Sentences (Page 192)
Practice 2
Exercise 1   Diagraming Compound Sentences

1.

2.

3.

4.